P9-DVU-951

This is a book in the series

STUDIES IN PHYSICS AND CHEMISTRY

Consulting Editors: R. Stevenson and M. A. Whitehead

1 *Stevenson*   **MULTIPLET STRUCTURE OF ATOMS AND MOLECULES**

2 *Smart*   **EFFECTIVE FIELD THEORIES OF MAGNETISM**

3 *Fujita*   **INTRODUCTION TO NON-EQUILIBRIUM QUANTUM STATISTICAL MECHANICS**

4 *Pauncz*   **ALTERNANT MOLECULAR ORBITAL METHOD**

5 *Kyrala*   **THEORETICAL PHYSICS: APPLICATIONS OF VECTORS, MATRICES, TENSORS AND QUATERNIONS**

6 *Shadowitz*   **SPECIAL RELATIVITY**

7 *Fraga and Malli*   **MANY-ELECTRON SYSTEMS: PROPERTIES AND INTERACTIONS**

Additional volumes in preparation

STUDIES IN PHYSICS AND CHEMISTRY

Number 7

MANY-ELECTRON SYSTEMS: PROPERTIES AND INTERACTIONS

by

SERAFIN FRAGA and GULZARI MALLI

MANY-ELECTRON SYSTEMS: PROPERTIES AND INTERACTIONS

SERAFIN FRAGA
Department of Chemistry,
University of Alberta

and

GULZARI MALLI
Department of Chemistry,
Simon Fraser University

1968

W. B. SAUNDERS COMPANY, *Philadelphia, London & Toronto*

W. B. Saunders Company: West Washington Square
Philadelphia, Pa. 19105

12 Dyott Street
London W. C.1

1835 Yonge Street
Toronto 7, Ontario

Many-Electron Systems: Properties and Interactions

To

ROBERT S. MULLIKEN

FOREWORD

This volume will prove invaluable to both the theoretical and the experimental chemist for here are connected, by a rigorous mathematical text, the many aspects of the hamiltonian operator and eigenequation for both free molecules and those subjected to electric and magnetic fields. Thus, topics as apparently distinct as charge densities, magnetic susceptibilities, nuclear quadrupole resonance, and x-ray diffraction are shown to develop logically from the consideration of operators, eigenequations, tensors, and the concepts of perturbation and variation theory. The numerous chemical examples, the tabulated results, and the literature survey at the end of each topic further add to the usefulness of the book.

M. A. WHITEHEAD

PREFACE

"I believe the chemical bond is not so simple
as some people seem to think."

Robert S. Mulliken

The ultimate goal of theoretical chemistry is to obtain knowledge of the
structure, to predict properties, and to understand the nature of the chemical
bond in many-electron systems. In this connection the evaluation of the
energy of the system in question occupies a central position as the most
frequently used criterion of the accuracy of quantum mechanical calculations. The determination of different properties, of interest *per se*,
comes into being in this conjunction, complementing the energy criterion
and helping to overcome the preoccupation it has always had for quantum
theoreticians. This situation can be best understood through the words of
Coulson:*

"It may perhaps be the recognition that this preoccupation with
energy was leading to sterility; or it may be due to the developments of
many types of microwave experiment. But the fact is that attention is now
becoming concentrated much more on the smaller terms in the hamiltonian.
These terms, usually neglected in earlier work, include spin-spin coupling,
spin-orbit interaction, coupling of electron spin and nuclear spin, quadrupole moments, and the influences that result from the coupling of all
these with an applied electric and magnetic field. The most well known
of all effects is the nuclear magnetic chemical screening and there are now
experimental measurements for particular molecules, which provide
excellent tests for any proposed molecular wave function. It is well known
that the ordinary diamagnetic susceptibility provides an estimate of $\langle r^2 \rangle$.
But there are now experimental measurements of many other functions of
position, such as $\langle x^2 \rangle$, $\langle x/r^3 \rangle$, $\langle (x^2 - y^2)/r^3 \rangle$. These measurements are
interesting because they arise from small terms in the hamiltonian. These

---

* C. A. Coulson. Rev. Mod. Phys. *32*, 170 (1960).

small terms are not large enough to cause any serious modifications of the wave function or the energy (this is why they are associated with microwave measurements, where energy differences are minute). But they act as measuring rods, able to be placed within the electronic charge-cloud without affecting it. Further, different members of this series weight the charge cloud in different ways so that, for example, the mean value of r^2 will tend to weight the outer regions of the molecule, but the mean value of x/r^3 will weight those parts of the cloud near the particular origin being used (usually one of the nuclei). In this way we begin to see how it may be possible to test a given wave function for accuracy in one of several chosen respects, rather than, as at present, in just one aspect, its energy."

These have been the considerations in selecting the topic for this text. Its aim, in brief, is to present and discuss the theoretical considerations, within the general field of quantum mechanics, related to the definition and calculation of properties of electronic systems.

The implications of this statement are numerous and have determined the order of presentation and the format of this text. By its very contents, it must necessarily be specialized, in the sense of being concerned exclusively with a very restricted subject. The term "specialized" does not mean, though, that this book is intended solely, or even primarily, for the specialist. On the contrary, it has been our intention, when gathering this material, to provide a basis for the general reader interested in these problems.

The text has been subdivided into two main sections. The first section presents a summary of the fundamental concepts and general treatments in quantum mechanics; the reader familiar with the general theory may omit this section, except for occasional references to the general equations which are presented within. The general reader will find here a useful summary, a knowledge of which is necessary for the understanding of the following chapters. For more details on any of the subjects within this section the reader is referred to the textbooks in the general field of quantum mechanics and the specific references given at the end of each chapter.

The main section of the text consists of a detailed review of most of the properties of electronic systems. It must be pointed out that because of space limitations it has been necessary to omit the interesting subjects related to the interaction of matter with radiation.

The chapters within this section are independent of each other. Care has been exercised to obtain self-contained chapters, while pointing out the possible interdependence between them and the links between the different properties. The main point in deciding this format has been the consideration of those readers interested in a specific subject; on the other hand, the reading of the complete text is not hindered at all by this organization.

This same consideration has led us to decide to present the pertinent references at the end of each chapter. In this connection we would like to mention that, again because of space limitations, it has not been possible, whenever results are quoted for a property evaluated from a given wave function, to present the details of such a function; the reader is advised to consult the original work in these instances. No claim is made here about the completeness of the references, though no efforts have been spared in order not to omit any significant contribution in each field. We would like to apologize for those involuntary omissions that might exist.

S. FRAGA AND G. MALLI

Edmonton, Alberta

ACKNOWLEDGMENTS

We acknowledge the kindness of the following organizations for the use of copyright material:

Academic Press, Inc.; Académie des Sciences (France); The American Institute of Physics; Cambridge University Press; Clarendon Press (Oxford); Commonwealth Scientific and Industrial Research Organization (Australia); Cornell University Press; Dover Publications, Inc.; The Institute of Physics (U.K.); Johann Ambrosius Barth Verlag; Masson et Cie, Editeurs; McGraw-Hill Book Company, Inc.; Munksgaard International Booksellers and Publishers Ltd.; National Academy of Sciences (U.S.A.); National Research Council (Canada); The Physical Society (Japan); The Physical Society (U.K.); Princeton University Press; Research Institute for Fundamental Physics (Japan); Royal Academy of Science (Sweden); The Royal Society (U.K.); Società Italiana di Fisica; Springer Verlag; Taylor & Francis Ltd.; W. H. Freeman & Co.

TABLE OF CONTENTS

CHAPTER 1

OPERATORS AND EIGENEQUATIONS 1

CHAPTER 2

ANGULAR MOMENTUM 11

CHAPTER 3

TENSOR OPERATORS 21

CHAPTER 4

DETERMINATION OF STATE FUNCTIONS:
THE VARIATION METHOD 37

CHAPTER 5

PERTURBATION METHOD 61

CHAPTER 6

ELECTRONIC CHARGE DENSITIES 68

CHAPTER 7

PROPERTIES AND INTERACTIONS 79

CHAPTER 8

ELECTRIC MOMENTS AND POLARIZABILITIES 84

CHAPTER 9

MAGNETIC SUSCEPTIBILITIES 95

CHAPTER 10

NUCLEAR MAGNETIC SHIELDING 107

CHAPTER 11

MAGNETIC DIPOLE AND FERMI CONTACT INTERACTION 115

CHAPTER 12

ELECTRIC FIELD AND ITS GRADIENT 129

CHAPTER 13

ORBIT-ORBIT INTERACTIONS 143

CHAPTER 14

SPIN-ORBIT COUPLING 150

CHAPTER 15

SPIN-SPIN INTERACTION 164

CHAPTER 16

SCATTERING FACTORS 175

APPENDIX

UNITS AND CONSTANTS 187

INDEX 189

Chapter I OPERATORS AND EIGENEQUATIONS

DEFINITIONS

An operator is a formal symbol which defines an operation to be executed on a given function, which is then transformed into another function. This transformation defines the operator.

Operators may be added or multiplied. The addition of operators may be taken in its algebraic sense, but the multiplication is to be understood here as a successive application of (or operation by) the multiplied operators; the convention adopted in the successive application of operators is that of "right to left": One first operates on the function with the operator immediately preceding it, then the next operator acts on the resulting function, etc., and one writes

$$(\mathscr{T}_n \cdots \mathscr{T}_3 \mathscr{T}_2 \mathscr{T}_1 |\Phi\rangle = (\mathscr{T}_n \cdots \mathscr{T}_3 \mathscr{T}_2 |\mathscr{T}_1 \Phi\rangle$$

$$= (\mathscr{T}_n \cdots \mathscr{T}_3 \mathscr{T}_2 |\Phi_1\rangle = (\mathscr{T}_n \cdots \mathscr{T}_3 |\mathscr{T}_2 \Phi_1\rangle = \cdots,$$

where $\mathscr{T}_1, \mathscr{T}_2, \ldots$ are operators (not necessarily identical) and Φ is an arbitrary function.

The "right to left" convention must be adopted in order to avoid the difficulty which arises as a consequence of the noncommutation property in the multiplication of many operators. Two operators, $\mathscr{T}_1$ and $\mathscr{T}_2$, are said to commute when $(\mathscr{T}_1 \mathscr{T}_2 |\Phi\rangle = (\mathscr{T}_2 \mathscr{T}_1 |\Phi\rangle$; they do not commute when the above equality does not hold. In either case one defines $[\mathscr{T}_1 \mathscr{T}_2 - \mathscr{T}_2 \mathscr{T}_1]$, also written as $[\mathscr{T}_1, \mathscr{T}_2]$, as the commutator of the two operators considered. Taking into account that $(\mathscr{T}_1 \mathscr{T}_2)^\dagger = \mathscr{T}_2^\dagger \mathscr{T}_1^\dagger$, one has $[\mathscr{T}_1, \mathscr{T}_2]^\dagger = [\mathscr{T}_2^\dagger, \mathscr{T}_1^\dagger] = -[\mathscr{T}_1^\dagger, \mathscr{T}_2^\dagger]$. (The convention adopted in this text is that Φ^* represents the complex conjugate of Φ, while $\Phi^\dagger$ denotes the hermitian conjugate.)

An operator $\mathcal{T}$ is said to be linear when the condition

$$(\mathcal{T} \, |\Phi_1 c_1 + \Phi_2 c_2\rangle = (\mathcal{T} \, |\Phi_1 c_1\rangle + (\mathcal{T} \, |\Phi_2 c_2\rangle = (\mathcal{T} \, |\Phi_1\rangle c_1 + (\mathcal{T} \, |\Phi_2\rangle c_2$$

is satisfied for any two arbitrary functions Φ_1 and Φ_2, c_1 and c_2 being two nonvanishing, arbitrarily chosen constants.

The hermitian property of an operator is defined by the condition

$$\langle \Phi_1| \, \mathcal{T} \, |\Phi_2\rangle = \langle \Phi_2^*| \, \mathcal{T}^* \, |\Phi_1^*\rangle$$

for any two functions Φ_1 and Φ_2 of the same system.

The equation

$$(\mathcal{T} \, |\Psi\rangle = |\Psi\rangle t \tag{1-1}$$

is the eigenvalue equation (or eigenequation) for the operator $\mathcal{T}$; Ψ is said to be an eigenfunction of $\mathcal{T}$ with eigenvalue t. In the above equation Ψ stands for a general family of functions, each one of them characterized by its own t, the set of t being known as the spectrum (of eigenvalues) of the operator $\mathcal{T}$.

The spectrum is said to be continuous when any value of t is allowed, i.e., satisfies the eigenvalue equation. When, because of secondary conditions imposed on the eigenfunctions, only certain definite eigenvalues can be found, the spectrum is said to be discrete. A mixed spectrum contains discrete and continuous eigenvalues.

Equation (1-1) should be properly written as

$$(\mathcal{T} \, |\Psi_{im}\rangle = |\Psi_{im}\rangle t_i,$$

where the index i labels the different eigenvalues and corresponding eigenfunctions. When, for a value of i, m can take only one value, the corresponding eigenvalue is said to be non-degenerate; but if there are n functions Ψ_{im}, with different values of m corresponding to the same eigenvalue t_i, this eigenvalue is said to be n-fold degenerate.

Considering that the operators corresponding to physical observables are hermitian, the particular properties of this type of operators are reviewed below:

(a) The eigenvalues are real.

(b) Any two eigenfunctions, corresponding to different eigenvalues, are orthogonal to each other.

(c) The degenerate eigenfunctions are not necessarily orthogonal. It is possible, though, to form from them a corresponding number of linear combinations that are mutually orthogonal; in principle, one could form an infinite number of linear combinations, but of those only n will be linearly independent, n being the number of functions in the degenerate set. The new functions are also eigenfunctions of the same operator and with the same eigenvalue.

(d) The linearly independent eigenfunctions belonging to a particular eigenvalue may be chosen in such a way that they form an orthonormal set, completely determined except for a unitary transformation of the functions among themselves. When such an orthonormalization has been carried out for all the eigenfunctions of the operator under consideration, they form an orthonormal set. As a corollary it must be mentioned that the eigenfunctions of a given operator are not necessarily normalized.

COMMON OPERATORS

Tables 1-1 and 1-2 list the common quantum mechanical operators and their symbols. In the following discussion the corresponding mathematical expressions are given for some of them, with the exception of the angular momentum operators, which are discussed in detail in Chapter 2. The transformation from one system of coordinates to another is straightforward. Complete details are given by Margenau and Murphy [7]. Pauling and Wilson [8] present a summary of the most important systems of coordinates, with explicit expressions for the kinetic energy operator. Nevertheless, Table 1-2 presents the common notation for the eigenvalues and quantum numbers associated with various angular momentum operators.

The position vector of an electron i with respect to a given origin, is represented by $\mathbf{r}_i$ (modulus r_i), with components $\mathbf{x}_i$, $\mathbf{y}_i$, and $\mathbf{z}_i$ (with corresponding magnitudes x_i, y_i, and z_i), whereas for a nucleus a it will be denoted by $\mathbf{R}_a$ (modulus R_a). The relative position of an electron i with respect to another electron j or a nucleus a is denoted, respectively, by $\mathbf{r}_{ij}$ (modulus r_{ij}) and $\mathbf{r}_{ia}$ (modulus r_{ia}), defined by the relations $\mathbf{r}_{ij} = \mathbf{r}_i - \mathbf{r}_j$, $\mathbf{r}_{ia} = \mathbf{r}_i - \mathbf{R}_a$. The relative position of a nucleus a with respect to a nucleus b is given by $\mathbf{R}_{ab}$ (modulus R_{ab}), defined similarly by $\mathbf{R}_{ab} = \mathbf{R}_a - \mathbf{R}_b$.

The linear momentum operator $\mathbf{p}$ is defined, for a single particle of mass* m, by $-(i/m)\nabla$, with components $p_x = -(i/m)\partial/\partial x, p_y = -(i/m)\partial/\partial y$, $p_z = -(i/m)\partial/\partial z$; the components of the resultant operator for a set of particles are obtained by algebraic addition of the components of the individual operators.

Under the general designation of energy operators one has to consider a variety of them, namely the kinetic energy operators, the potential energy operators, and the total energy operators. The weak interaction energy operators are not listed in Table 1-1 as there is no common symbol for them.

The kinetic energy operator for a single particle of mass m is defined by

$$\mathscr{T} = -(1/2m)\nabla^2 = -(1/2m)(\partial^2/\partial x^2 + \partial^2/\partial y^2 + \partial^2/\partial z^2),$$

and the resultant operator for many particles is also obtained by algebraic addition of the individual operators.

The potential energy operator cannot be defined in general, as it depends on the characteristics of the system under consideration. For the

---

* Atomic units (Appendix 1) are used consistently throughout this text.

TABLE I-I Operators with a Classical Analogue

DESIGNATION	QUANTITY	OPERATOR
Position[a]	r	$\mathbf{r}$
Linear momentum	p	$\mathbf{p}$
Angular momentum[b]	l	$\mathbf{l}$
Energy		
Kinetic energy	T	$\mathscr{T}$
Scalar potential[c]	V, ϕ	V, ϕ
Vector potential[d]	A	$\mathbf{A}$
Total energy	E	$\mathscr{H}$

Notation: The vector $\mathbf{w}$ (modulus w) has the vector components $\mathbf{w}_x$, $\mathbf{w}_y$, and $\mathbf{w}_z$ (with magnitudes w_x, w_y, and w_z). The vector operator $\mathbf{w}$ has as components the vector operators w_x, w_y, and w_z. The tensor and tensor operator notation is presented in Chapter 3.

a. The vector operator $\mathbf{r}$ is identical to the physical vector r, and both symbols will be used indistinctively. The modulus r can be considered as a scalar operator, and so are the magnitudes r_x, r_y, and r_z of its components.

b. The scalar operator associated with $\mathbf{l}$ is $\ell^2 = \mathbf{l} \cdot \mathbf{l}$. The components of $\mathbf{l}$ are the vector operators l_x, l_y, and l_z, whose magnitudes are the operators ℓ_x, ℓ_y, and ℓ_z, respectively.

c. The symbol V is used to denote internal potentials, whereas ϕ represents the scalar potential associated with an external field.

d. The symbol A is the one usually adopted for vector potentials of external fields.

TABLE I-2 Quantum Numbers and Eigenvalues for Various Many-particle Angular Momentum Operators[a]

DESIGNATION	OPERATOR	QUANTUM NUMBER	EIGENVALUE
Orbital	$\mathscr{L}^2$	L	$L(L+1)$
	$\mathscr{L}_z$	M_L	M_L
Electron spin	$\mathscr{S}^2$	S	$S(S+1)$
	$\mathscr{S}_z$	M_S	M_S
Total electronic	$\mathscr{J}^2$	J	$J(J+1)$
	$\mathscr{J}_z$	M_J	M_J
Nuclear spin	$\mathscr{I}^2$	I	$I(I+1)$
	$\mathscr{I}_z$	M_I	M_I
Total system	$\mathscr{F}^2$	F	$F(F+1)$
	$\mathscr{F}_z$	M_F	M_F

a. The same notation (though in lower case) is used for single-particle angular momentum operators, with the exception of the nuclear spin, for which capital letters are also used. The coupling of angular momenta is discussed in Chapter 2.

systems to be considered here, namely atoms and molecules, the internal potential energy operator is formed by a series of terms, all of them being electrostatic scalar potentials (proportional to the inverse of the separation between the two particles concerned); the general expression for a many-electron, many-nuclei system, including only two-particle interactions, is

$$V = - \sum_{i=1}^{n} \sum_{a=1}^{N} (Z_a/r_{ia}) + \sum_{i=1}^{n} \sum_{j>i} (1/r_{ij}) + \sum_{a=1}^{N} \sum_{b>a} (Z_a Z_b/R_{ab}). \quad (1\text{-}2)$$

The first term in Eq. (1-2) represents the electron-nucleus interaction, the second the electron-electron interaction, and the last one the nucleus-nucleus interaction.

Within the internal potential energy operator one should include the terms corresponding to magnetic interactions, but it is customary to group them independently under the designation of weak interactions.

The total energy operator, i.e., the hamiltonian operator, for a system is defined by the sum of the total (electronic and nuclear) kinetic and potential energy operators, plus the interaction energy operator for external fields (if existing) and the terms corresponding to internal weak interactions.

THE HAMILTONIAN OPERATOR

The time-independent, nonrelativistic hamiltonian operator of a many-electron, many-nuclei system, including electrostatic, external, and magnetic interactions, consists of a series of terms, which are discussed below. In all the following expressions the summations over $i, j, \ldots$ extend over the electrons, whereas the summations over $a, b, \ldots$ correspond to the nuclei in the system.

The hamiltonian operator* consists of the following energy interactions:

(a) Hamiltonian operator for the electronic and nuclear motion and internal electrostatic potential energy terms. It is defined by

$$\mathscr{H}_0 = -\tfrac{1}{2} \sum_{i=1}^{n} \nabla_i^2 - \tfrac{1}{2} \sum_{a=1}^{N} (1/M_a) \nabla_a^2 - \sum_{i=1}^{n} \sum_{a=1}^{N} (Z_a/r_{ia})$$

$$+ \sum_{i=1}^{n} \sum_{j>i} (1/r_{ji}) + \sum_{a=1}^{N} \sum_{b>a} (Z_a Z_b/R_{ba}). \quad (1\text{-}3)$$

The first two terms represent the kinetic energy of the electrons and nuclei, respectively, and the three remaining terms correspond to the electron-nuclei, electron-electron, and nuclei-nuclei electrostatic interactions, respectively; M_a is the mass of nucleus a, with nuclear charge Z_a.

---

* No justification can be given here. Specific discussions on the individual parts of the hamiltonian operator can be found in the references presented in following chapters and general discussions are presented in general texts of quantum mechanics. Mention must be made here, however, of the work of Abragam [1].

(b) Hamiltonian operator for the interaction between the orbital motion of the electrons of the system and an electromagnetic field (E, H) with a vector potential A and a scalar potential ϕ. It is defined by

$$\mathscr{H}_1 = \sum_{j=1}^{n} \{(1/ic)(A_j \cdot \nabla_j) + (1/2c^2)A_j^2 - \phi_j\}, \qquad (1\text{-}4)$$

where A_j and ϕ_j denote the vector and scalar potentials, respectively, acting on electron j, and where A_j represents the modulus of the vector potential A_j.

(c) Hamiltonian operator for the interaction between the electron spins and an electromagnetic field (E, H). It is defined by

$$\mathscr{H}_2 = (1/c) \sum_{i=1}^{n} \{\mathbf{s}_i \cdot (H + (1/2c)[E \times \mathbf{p}_i])\}. \qquad (1\text{-}5)$$

(d) Hamiltonian operator for the orbit-orbit interaction. It is defined by

$$\mathscr{H}_3 = -(1/2c^2) \sum_{i=1}^{n} \sum_{j>i} \{(\mathbf{p}_i \cdot \mathbf{p}_j)/r_{ji} + \tfrac{1}{2}(\mathbf{r}_{ji} \cdot (\mathbf{r}_{ji} \cdot \mathbf{p}_i)\mathbf{p}_j$$
$$+ \mathbf{r}_{ji} \cdot (\mathbf{r}_{ji} \cdot \mathbf{p}_j)\mathbf{p}_i)/r_{ji}^3\}. \qquad (1\text{-}6)$$

(e) Hamiltonian operator for the electron spin-orbit coupling. It is defined by

$$\mathscr{H}_4 = (1/2c^2) \sum_{i=1}^{n} \sum_{a=1}^{N} \mathbf{s}_i \cdot [\mathbf{r}_{ia} \times \mathbf{p}_i] Z_a/r_{ia}^3$$
$$+ (1/c^2) \sum_{i=1}^{n} \sum_{j>i} \{\mathbf{s}_i \cdot [(\mathbf{p}_j - \tfrac{1}{2}\mathbf{p}_i) \times \mathbf{r}_{ji}]\}/r_{ji}^3, \qquad (1\text{-}7)$$

where the first term represents the spin-own orbit coupling, and the second the spin-other orbit coupling.

(f) Hamiltonian operator for the (dipole-dipole) electron spin-electron spin coupling. It is defined by

$$\mathscr{H}_5 = (1/c^2) \sum_{i=1}^{n} \sum_{j>i} \{(\mathbf{s}_i \cdot \mathbf{s}_j)r_{ji}^2 - 3(\mathbf{r}_{ji} \cdot \mathbf{s}_i)(\mathbf{r}_{ji} \cdot \mathbf{s}_j)\}/r_{ji}^5. \qquad (1\text{-}8)$$

(g) Hamiltonian operator for the electron spin-nuclear spin interactions. It is defined by

$$\mathscr{H}_6 = (1/c) \sum_{i=1}^{n} \sum_{a=1}^{N} \{\gamma_a[(\mathbf{s}_i \cdot \mathbf{I}_a)r_{ia}^2 - 3(\mathbf{r}_{ia} \cdot \mathbf{s}_i)(\mathbf{r}_{ia} \cdot \mathbf{I}_a)]/r_{ia}^5$$
$$- (8\pi/3)(\mathbf{s}_i \cdot \mathbf{I}_a)\delta(\mathbf{r}_{ia})\}, \qquad (1\text{-}9)$$

where the first two terms represent the (dipole-dipole) electron spin-nuclear spin coupling and the third term corresponds to the Fermi contact interaction; $\delta(\mathbf{r}_{ia})$ is a three-dimensional Dirac δ-function and γ_a is the nuclear gyromagnetic ratio.

(h) Hamiltonian operator for the interaction between the nuclear spins and an external magnetic field. It is defined by

$$\mathscr{H}_7 = \sum_{a=1}^{N} \gamma_a(\mathbf{I}_a \cdot H). \qquad (1\text{-}10)$$

(i) Hamiltonian operator for the magnetic interaction between the nuclear spins and the orbital motion of the electrons. It is defined by

$$\mathscr{H}_8 = (1/c) \sum_{i=1}^{n} \sum_{a=1}^{N} \gamma_a (\mathbf{I}_a \cdot [\mathbf{p}_i \times \mathbf{r}_{ia}])/r_{ia}^3. \tag{1-11}$$

(j) Hamiltonian operator for the (dipole-dipole) nuclear spin-nuclear spin interactions. It is defined by

$$\mathscr{H}_9 = \sum_{a=1}^{N} \sum_{b>a} \gamma_a \gamma_b \{ (\mathbf{I}_a \cdot \mathbf{I}_b) R_{ab}^2 - 3(\mathbf{R}_{ab} \cdot \mathbf{I}_a)(\mathbf{R}_{ab} \cdot \mathbf{I}_b) \}/R_{ab}^5. \tag{1-12}$$

These terms of the hamiltonian are considered in detail in the following chapters.

THE ENERGY EIGENEQUATION

The most important eigenequations in quantum mechanics are those corresponding to the angular momentum and total energy operators. The angular momentum eigenequations are presented in Chapter 2.

The energy eigenequation, corresponding to the hamiltonian operator considered here, is the time-independent, nonrelativistic equation

$$(\mathscr{H} \, |\Psi_i\rangle = |\Psi_i\rangle E_i,$$

whose eigenfunctions are the state functions, Ψ_i.

The state functions must be well-behaved functions, in the sense that certain restrictions, related to the probability distribution, must be satisfied. For a given function Ψ it is postulated that $\Psi^* \Psi$ represents a probability function, such that the sum of its values over all space must be unity; i.e., $\langle \Psi \, | \, \Psi \rangle = 1$. Therefore the state function must be quadratically integrable, which implies that the function must vanish at infinity and must be single-valued and continuous, with finite second derivatives.

The set of all the eigenfunctions of a given hamiltonian operator forms a complete set in the sense that any arbitrary function can be expanded, with appropriate coefficients, in terms of the functions of the set (including the continuum contribution if it exists, though here such a contribution will be consistently omitted).

The determination of state functions, through the use of the Schrödinger equation, offers insurmountable difficulties. The exact solution of the eigenequation for the hamiltonian operator is not possible. The logical way to determine the approximate solutions consists of using the perturbation method (see Chapter 5), but it is not always possible to have the corresponding zero-order functions, and in such a case one must resort to variation-perturbation treatments. However, in certain cases it is appropriate to employ the variation method (see Chapter 4).

The starting point, in any case, consists of the determination of the eigenfunctions of the zero-order hamiltonian operator $\mathscr{H}_0$. Two main points must be mentioned in this connection: the separation of the electronic and nuclear motions and the existence of singularities.

The Born-Oppenheimer [4] approximation for the separation of the electronic and nuclear motions is based on the disparity of the masses of the electrons and the nuclei. (This approximation cannot be discussed in detail here. The reader is referred to the original work of Born and Oppenheimer or to any general text of quantum mechanics.) The practical consequences of this approximation are that the eigenfunctions Ψ can be approximated by a simple product $\Psi_e \Psi_n$, with Ψ_e and Ψ_n being determined from the eigenequations

$$(\mathscr{H}_e | \Psi_e) = | \Psi_e) E_e,$$
$$(\mathscr{H}_n | \Psi_n) = | \Psi_n) E_n,$$

with

$$\mathscr{H}_e = -\tfrac{1}{2} \sum_{i=1}^{n} \nabla_i^2 - \sum_{i=1}^{n} \sum_{a=1}^{N} (Z_a/r_{ia}) + \sum_{i=1}^{n} \sum_{j>i} (1/r_{ij}),$$

$$\mathscr{H}_n = -\tfrac{1}{2} \sum_{a=1}^{N} \nabla_a^2/M_a + \sum_{a=1}^{N} \sum_{b>a} Z_a Z_b/R_{ab} + E_e.$$

Ψ_e and E_e depend on the configuration considered for the skeleton of the nuclei. On the other hand, the eigenequation for Ψ_n indicates that the nuclei move in an effective potential defined by the electronic energy for the nuclear configuration. The nuclear eigenfunctions will not be considered in this text, and the discussion is centered on the electronic functions and the corrections to them due to the other terms in the hamiltonian operator.

The hamiltonian operator $\mathscr{H}_e$ has singularities for $r_i = 0$ and $r_{ij} = 0$. For the exact function, the ratio $(\mathscr{H}_e | \Psi_e)/| \Psi_e) = E_e$ has a constant value, and the exact function must have a certain type of singularity at those singular points, being a regular function for all the other points. This problem exists also for approximate functions. There can also be higher-order singularities, arising from all the possible combinations of r_i and r_{ij} vanishing simultaneously. (For more details on this problem see the work of Pluvinage [9] and Roothaan and Weiss [10].)

The conditions to be satisfied by the state function to overcome independently the two types of singularities have been determined by Kato [5]. The state function has a cusp at those points, with an average slope,

$$(\partial\overline{\Psi}/\partial r_{ia})_{r_{ia}=0} = -Z_a \Psi(r_i = 0), \qquad (1\text{-}13\text{a})$$

$$(\partial\overline{\Psi}/\partial r_{ij})_{r_{ij}=0} = \tfrac{1}{2}\Psi(r_{ij} = 0), \qquad (1\text{-}13\text{b})$$

which represent, respectively, the coulomb and correlation cusp conditions. (These conditions have also been investigated by Bingel [2, 3] and Steiner [11]. See also Chapter 6.) In Eq. (1-13a) the coordinate system is centered on nucleus a, whereas for Eq. (1-13b) the origin of coordinates is irrelevant. $\overline{\Psi}$ represents an average over a sphere of radius r_i or r_{ij}, respectively; the spheres are centered at nucleus a and at the point defined by $\boldsymbol{r} = \tfrac{1}{2}(\boldsymbol{r_1} + \boldsymbol{r_2})$.

When approximating Ψ by Φ it is also pertinent to investigate the behavior of this approximate function in connection with the singularities. The discussion is restricted here to a many-electron atom, with an electronic hamiltonian (in polar coordinates)

$$\mathcal{H}_e = -\tfrac{1}{2} \sum_i \{(2/r_i)(\partial/\partial r_i) + (\partial^2/\partial r_i^2) + (1/r_i^2 \sin \theta_i)(\partial/\partial \theta_i)(\sin \theta_i\, \partial/\partial \theta_i)$$
$$+ (1/r_i^2 \sin^2 \theta_i)(\partial^2/\partial \phi_i^2) - Z \sum_i (1/r_i) + \sum_{i<j} (1/r_{ij}),$$

and to approximate functions, constructed from antisymmetrized products of one-electron functions. For this type of function the correlation singularities always subsist; they can be overcome only by the use of appropriate correlated functions.

It is then interesting to investigate the behavior of the one-electron functions, which are eigenfunctions of a one-electron operator. The case to be considered here is that in which this operator is formed by the one-electron part of $\mathcal{H}_e$ and a certain scalar potential. Designating the one-electron part of $\mathcal{H}_e$ as $\mathcal{H}'$, one must investigate the conditions to be satisfied by the one-electron function ϕ in order that $\langle \mathcal{H}'\phi \rangle / |\phi\rangle$ be a constant.

Within the expansion method, ϕ_i may be expressed as

$$\phi_i = \sum_p \chi_p c_{pi},$$

where χ_p represents a set of basis functions and c_{pi} are the expansion coefficients. The basis functions are products (excluding the normalization constants) of a radial part, $R_p(r)$, and an angular part, $Y_p(\theta, \phi)$. It is assumed that the radial part has the form $r^{n-1}e^{-\zeta r}$ and that $Y_p(\theta, \phi)$ represents the spherical harmonics; n is the principal quantum number and ζ is the orbital exponent. One obtains, after dividing through by the angular part after the differentiation has been carried out,

$$\tfrac{1}{2}\left\{\left[\sum_p c_p((2/r)(\partial R_p/\partial r) + (\partial^2 R_p/\partial r^2) - (kR_p/r^2))\right]\left[\sum_q c_q R_q\right]^{-1}\right\} + (Z/r) = 0,$$

$$(1\text{-}14)$$

with $k = 0, 2,$ and 6, respectively, for s, p, and d orbitals. In Eq. (1-14) the summations extend over basis functions of the corresponding symmetry designation.

In order that Eq. (1-14) be satisfied, it is necessary that the coefficients of the terms r^{-t} for $t > 1$ vanish identically and that the coefficient of r^{-1}, within the curly brackets, be equal to $-Z$.

For a single basis function, after substituting for R_p, Eq. (1-14) becomes

$$\tfrac{1}{2}\{(1/r^{n-1})[(2/r)((n-1)r^{n-2} - \zeta r^{n-1}) + (n-1)(n-2)r^{n-3}$$
$$- \zeta(n-1)r^{n-2} - \zeta(n-1)r^{n-2} + \zeta^2 r^{n-1}] - (k/r^2)\} + (Z/r),$$

which yields the following solutions, obtained by Malli and Fraga [6]:

$$n = 1, \quad \text{for } k = 0,$$
$$n = 2, \quad \text{for } k = 2,$$
$$n = 3, \quad \text{for } k = 6,$$

with $\zeta = Z/n$.

Therefore, the basis set should include a single $1s$-, $2p$-, and $3d$-type basis function with an orbital exponent Z, $Z/2$, and $Z/3$, respectively. The remaining basis functions in the set should have n values equal to or greater than 3, 4, and 5, respectively. For s-type orbitals a similar condition is found on the basis of an argument involving the electronic density at the nucleus. (See Chapter 6 for more details.)

Regarding the solution of the electronic Schrödinger equation it must be pointed out that it cannot be solved exactly, except for the simplest cases, and approximate methods must be used. There are two distinct cases, depending on whether the aim of the calculation is the determination of functions *per se* or the evaluation of properties other than the energy.

The determination of the electronic state functions is efficiently carried out within the framework of the variation method (Chapter 4), whereas several possibilities exist regarding the determination of physical properties.

Determination of the properties inherent to the system under consideration (such as the electric dipoles) requires only the knowledge of the functions determined on the basis of an energy criterion. The expectation values for the corresponding operator over the electronic state functions can provide a satisfactory approximation to the exact value, though it cannot be said that this type of function must necessarily lead to results for physical properties at the same level of accuracy. This situation can be improved, when working toward the determination of physical properties, by the introduction of subsidiary conditions, related to the corresponding expectation values, in the formulation for the determination of the functions.

Regarding the properties that are related to an energy interaction because of either external interactions (such as external electric or magnetic fields) or internal weak interactions (spin interactions), the corresponding terms are included in the hamiltonian and the calculation is carried out on the basis of an energy criterion, usually by application of perturbation techniques (Chapter 5). In the first of the two cases mentioned, however, variation techniques are also employed. In any case, in perturbation calculations variational functions may be used as zero-order functions.

REFERENCES

1. A. Abragam. Nuovo Cimento (suppl.) *6*, 1015 (1957).
2. W. A. Bingel. Z. Naturforschg. *18a*, 1249 (1963).
3. W. A. Bingel. Theoret. Chim. Acta (Berlin) *5*, 341 (1966).
4. M. Born and J. R. Oppenheimer. Ann. Physik *84*, 457 (1927).
5. T. Kato. Commun. Pure Appl. Math. *10*, 151 (1957).
6. G. Malli and S. Fraga, Can. J. Phys. *44*, 3131 (1966).
7. H. Margenau and G. M. Murphy. "The Mathematics of Physics and Chemistry." D. Van Nostrand Company Inc., Princeton, N.J., 1957.
8. L. Pauling and E. Bright Wilson, Jr. "Introduction to Quantum Mechanics." McGraw-Hill Book Company, Inc., New York, N.Y., 1935.
9. P. Pluvinage. Ann. Phys. *5*, 145 (1950).
10. C. C. J. Roothaan and A. W. Weiss. Rev. Mod. Phys. *32*, 194 (1960).
11. E. Steiner. J. Chem. Phys. *39*, 2365 (1963).

Chapter 2 ANGULAR MOMENTUM

DEFINITIONS

If Ψ describes the state of a physical system in a certain system of cartesian coordinates, after rotation of the coordinates system through a finite angle ϕ about an axis, say z, the state of the physical system is described by a function Ψ''. This function Ψ'' can be obtained from Ψ by the operation of a unitary operator $\mathcal{U}(z, \phi)$,

$$\Psi'' = \mathcal{U}(z, \phi)\Psi.$$

The operator $\mathcal{U}(z, \phi)$ depends upon the parameters of the rotation; in particular, for $\phi = 0$, $\mathcal{U}$ is the identity operator.

If $\mathcal{U}$ is written as

$$\mathcal{U}(z, \phi) = \exp\{-i\mathcal{J}(z, \phi)\},$$

it is evident that the operator $\mathcal{J}(z, \phi)$ must tend to zero with ϕ; for small ϕ one can then write

$$\mathcal{J}(z, \phi) = \phi \mathcal{J}_z,$$

where the subscript z denotes the rotation about the z-axis. Therefore, substituting $\mathcal{J}(z, \phi)$ in the expression of $\mathcal{U}(z, \phi)$ and expanding the exponential, the operator $\mathcal{U}(z, \phi)$ becomes, for small ϕ,

$$\mathcal{U}(z, \phi) = \mathbf{1} - i\phi \mathcal{J}_z,$$

where $\mathbf{1}$ represents the identity operator. Taking into account the unitarity of $\mathcal{U}(z, \phi)$, i.e., $\mathcal{U}^\dagger\mathcal{U} = \mathbf{1}$ (where $\mathcal{U}^\dagger$ is the hermitian conjugate of $\mathcal{U}$), it must be $(\mathbf{1} + i\phi\mathcal{J}_z^\dagger)(\mathbf{1} - i\phi\mathcal{J}_z) = \mathbf{1}$, from which it follows (to first order in ϕ) that $\mathcal{J}_z^\dagger = \mathcal{J}_z$, i.e., $\mathcal{J}_z$ is hermitian.

For small ϕ the change $\delta\Psi$ in Ψ is

$$\delta\Psi = \Psi'' - \Psi = -i\phi\mathcal{J}_z\Psi,$$

which shows that the operator $\phi\mathcal{J}_z$ (times a factor $-i$) produces the change in the original function upon an infinitesimal rotation about the z-axis. The operator $-i\mathcal{J}_z$ is the operator of infinitesimal rotation. The three operators $\mathcal{J}_x$, $\mathcal{J}_y$, and $\mathcal{J}_z$ of infinitesimal rotations about the cartesian axes satisfy the commutation relations

$$[\mathcal{J}_x, \mathcal{J}_y] = i\mathcal{J}_z, \tag{2-1a}$$
$$[\mathcal{J}_y, \mathcal{J}_z] = i\mathcal{J}_x, \tag{2-1b}$$
$$[\mathcal{J}_z, \mathcal{J}_x] = i\mathcal{J}_y. \tag{2-1c}$$

These commutation relations are general conditions satisfied by the components of an arbitrary angular momentum operator. In particular they are satisfied by the orbital angular momentum operator, with components

$$\mathcal{L}_x = -i(y\,\partial/\partial z - z\,\partial/\partial y), \tag{2-2a}$$
$$\mathcal{L}_y = -i(z\,\partial/\partial x - x\,\partial/\partial z), \tag{2-2b}$$
$$\mathcal{L}_z = -i(x\,\partial/\partial y - y\,\partial/\partial x), \tag{2-2c}$$

and by the spin angular momentum operators, with components defined by the Pauli matrices

$$\sigma_x = \begin{pmatrix} 0 & 1 \\ 1 & 0 \end{pmatrix}, \qquad \sigma_y = \begin{pmatrix} 0 & -i \\ i & 0 \end{pmatrix}, \qquad \sigma_z = \begin{pmatrix} 1 & 0 \\ 0 & -1 \end{pmatrix}, \tag{2-3}$$

with $\sigma_x^2 = \sigma_y^2 = \sigma_z^2 = 1$. (Actually it is $\Delta_x = \tfrac{1}{2}\sigma_x$, $\Delta_y = \tfrac{1}{2}\sigma_y$, $\Delta_z = \tfrac{1}{2}\sigma_z$.)

From the projection angular momentum operators $\mathcal{J}_x$, $\mathcal{J}_y$, and $\mathcal{J}_z$ it is possible to define a total angular momentum operator squared $\mathcal{J}^2$ by the expression

$$\mathcal{J}^2 = \mathcal{J}_x^2 + \mathcal{J}_y^2 + \mathcal{J}_z^2, \tag{2-4}$$

where the squares on the right-hand side of the equation indicate the successive application of the corresponding projection operator. For $\mathcal{J}^2$ the situation is different, in the sense that it is not possible to define a total angular momentum operator $\mathcal{J}$; i.e., $\mathcal{J}^2$ is a complete operator, not separable into square root components.

The angular momentum component operators commute with the total angular momentum operator. Because of these commutation properties, it follows that the angular momentum and one of its components (e.g., the z-component) have well-defined values. If we denote by $\Psi(jm)$ a simultaneous eigenfunction of the operators $\mathcal{J}^2$ and $\mathcal{J}_z$, the corresponding eigenequations are

$$(\mathcal{J}^2\,|\Psi(jm)\rangle = |\Psi(jm)\rangle[j(j+1)], \tag{2-5a}$$
$$(\mathcal{J}_z\,|\Psi(jm)\rangle = |\Psi(jm)\rangle\,m; \tag{2-5b}$$

j and m are either both integral or both half-integral, with $|m| \leq j$; for a given j, m can assume $(2j + 1)$ values, from $-j$ to $+j$. j is usually called the angular momentum quantum number and m the angular momentum z-projection quantum number.

It is possible to define two new operators, $\mathscr{J}_+$ and $\mathscr{J}_-$,

$$\mathscr{J}_+ = (\mathscr{J}_-)^\dagger = \mathscr{J}_x + i\mathscr{J}_y, \tag{2-6}$$

for which

$$(\mathscr{J}_\pm|\Psi(jm)\rangle = |\Psi(jm \pm 1)\rangle\,[(j \mp m)(j \pm m + 1)]^{\frac{1}{2}}. \tag{2-7}$$

$\mathscr{J}_+$ and $\mathscr{J}_-$ are called the raising and lowering or shift operators, as they raise and lower by unity the projection quantum number m.

Equations (2-5) and (2-7) determine the standard choice of phases for state functions with different values of m.

COUPLING OF ANGULAR MOMENTA

Very often in quantum-mechanical applications one is faced with the problem of the coupling of angular momenta of two or more systems. Instead of considering the general case of the addition of an arbitrary number of angular momenta, the addition of two and three angular momenta is described here in order to illustrate the method.

Coupling of Two Angular Momenta

Let us consider two systems for which the corresponding angular momentum operators are $\mathbf{J}_1$ and $\mathbf{J}_2$, respectively; these systems are described by the functions $\Psi(\alpha_1 j_1 m_1)$ and $\Psi(\alpha_2 j_2 m_2)$, where α_1 and α_2 are the additional quantum numbers needed to completely describe the independent systems. One is now required to construct the eigenfunctions of the total operator $\mathbf{J} = \mathbf{J}_1 + \mathbf{J}_2$.

As $\mathbf{J}_1$ and $\mathbf{J}_2$ refer to independent systems, they commute with each other. (Two angular momenta operators commute only when they refer either to different particles or to different properties of the same particle.) This implies that the components of $\mathbf{J}$ also obey the general commutation rules for angular momentum operators. Let us denote by $\Psi(\gamma j_1 m_1 j_2 m_2)$ the simultaneous eigenfunctions of the complete set of commuting operators Γ, $\mathscr{J}_1^2, \mathscr{J}_{z_1}, \mathscr{J}_2^2$, and $\mathscr{J}_{z_2}$, where Γ stands for the operators needed to complete the set; $\Psi(\gamma j_1 j_2 JM)$ represents the simultaneous eigenfunctions of the set $\Gamma, \mathscr{J}_1^2, \mathscr{J}_2^2, \mathscr{J}^2$, and $\mathscr{J}_z$. The operators $\mathscr{J}_1^2$ and $\mathscr{J}_2^2$, which belong to both sets, commute with $\mathscr{J}^2$ and $\mathscr{J}_z$, as well as with $\mathscr{J}_{z_1}$ and $\mathscr{J}_{z_2}$, respectively.

Corresponding to the total angular momentum operator $\mathbf{J}$, the projection operator $\mathscr{J}_z$ is given by $\mathscr{J}_z = \mathscr{J}_{z_1} + \mathscr{J}_{z_2}$, from which it follows that $M = m_1 + m_2$. In addition, it can be shown that the possible values of J (i.e., the total angular momentum quantum number of the coupled system) are given by the relation

$$J = j_1 + j_2,\ j_1 + j_2 - 1, \ldots, |j_1 - j_2|$$

and that for each value of J there are $(2J + 1)$ states with $M = J$, $J - 1, \ldots, -J$. That the number of states in the two representations is equal to $(2j_1 + 1)(2j_2 + 1)$ is evident from the relation

$$\sum_J (2J + 1) = (2j_1 + 1)(2j_2 + 1).$$

The eigenfunctions $\Psi(\gamma j_1 j_2 JM)$ are given in terms of the functions $\Psi(\gamma j_1 m_1 j_2 m_2)$ by the unitary transformation

$$\Psi(\gamma j_1 j_2 JM) = \sum_{m_1} \sum_{m_2} \Psi(\gamma j_1 m_1 j_2 m_2)(j_1 m_1 j_2 m_2 \,|\, j_1 j_2 JM),$$

where the expansion coefficients* [sometimes also written as $(j_1 m_1 j_2 m_2 \,|\, JM)$] are independent of γ; $\Psi(\gamma j_1 m_1 j_2 m_2)$ is given by the inverse transformation

$$\Psi(\gamma j_1 m_1 j_2 m_2) = \sum_J \sum_M \Psi(\gamma j_1 j_2 JM)(j_1 j_2 JM \,|\, j_1 m_1 j_2 m_2),$$

with

$$(j_1 j_2 JM \,|\, j_1 m_1 j_2 m_2) = (j_1 m_1 j_2 m_2 \,|\, j_1 j_2 JM).$$

These coefficients, which are real, are designated as vector-coupling, Wigner, or Clebsch-Gordan coefficients. They are unitary matrices of $(2j_1 + 1)(2j_2 + 1)$ dimensions, with their rows and columns labeled by the pairs m_1, m_2 and J, M, respectively.

The Clebsch-Gordan coefficient $(j_1 m_1 j_2 m_2 \,|\, j_1 j_2 JM)$ is given, according to Edmonds [4], by the expression

$$
\begin{aligned}
(j_1 m_1 j_2 m_2 \,|\, j_1 j_2 JM) =\ & \delta(m_1 + m_2, M)[(2J + 1)(j_1 + j_2 - J)!\\
&\times (j_1 - m_1)!(j_2 - m_2)!(J + M)!(J - M)!]^{\frac{1}{2}}\\
&\times [(j_1 + j_2 + J + 1)!(j_1 - j_2 + J)!(j_2 - j_1 + J)!(j_1 + m_1)!\\
&\times (j_2 + m_2)!]^{-\frac{1}{2}}\\
&\times \sum_p \{(-1)^{p+j_1-m_1}(j_1 + m_1 + p)!(j_2 + J - m_1 - p)!\\
&\times [p!(j_1 - m_1 - p)!(J - M - p)!(j_2 - J + m_1 + p)!]^{-1}\}, \qquad (2\text{-}8)
\end{aligned}
$$

where the summation over the positive integer p is terminated when the argument of any factorial becomes negative.

This expression is identical to that of Racah [13], who has also given a more symmetrical and useful form for it. Other derivations of the general formula for the vector-coupling coefficients are given by Wigner [22], who employs group theoretical methods, and by Schwinger [17], who uses operator techniques. Similar expressions have also been given by Van der Waerden [21] and Majumdar [9].

A quantity related to the vector-coupling coefficient is Wigner's 3-*j*

---

* It should be mentioned that in the literature the coefficients of this unitary transformation (also called vector-coupling coefficients) are denoted by different authors with different symbols. In addition, different authors use different phase conventions. The phase convention of Condon and Shortley [3], together with the notation of Edmonds [4], is used here.

symbol, defined by

$$\begin{pmatrix} j_1 & j_2 & j_3 \\ m_1 & m_2 & m_3 \end{pmatrix} = (-1)^{j_1-j_2-m_3}(2j_3 + 1)^{-\frac{1}{2}}(j_1m_1j_2m_2 \,|\, j_1j_2j_3 - m_3). \quad (2\text{-}9)$$

Various symmetry properties of the vector-coupling coefficients and of the 3-j symbols are given in the numerous texts on angular momentum. Only the most common properties are presented here.

An even permutation of the columns of a 3-j symbol leaves its numerical value unchanged, i.e.,

$$\begin{pmatrix} j_1 & j_2 & j_3 \\ m_1 & m_2 & m_3 \end{pmatrix} = \begin{pmatrix} j_2 & j_3 & j_1 \\ m_2 & m_3 & m_1 \end{pmatrix} = \begin{pmatrix} j_3 & j_1 & j_2 \\ m_3 & m_1 & m_2 \end{pmatrix},$$

whereas an odd permutation changes it by $(-1)^{j_1+j_2+j_3}$. This same result is brought about by a change of the signs of all the quantum numbers in the second row,

$$\begin{pmatrix} j_1 & j_2 & j_3 \\ m_1 & m_2 & m_3 \end{pmatrix} = (-1)^{j_1+j_2+j_3} \begin{pmatrix} j_1 & j_2 & j_3 \\ -m_1 & -m_2 & -m_3 \end{pmatrix}.$$

The orthogonality properties of the 3-j symbols are expressed by

$$\sum_{j_3}\sum_{m_3} (2j_3 + 1) \begin{pmatrix} j_1 & j_2 & j_3 \\ m_1 & m_2 & m_3 \end{pmatrix} \begin{pmatrix} j_1 & j_2 & j_3 \\ m_1' & m_2' & m_3 \end{pmatrix} = \delta(m_1, m_1')\,\delta(m_2, m_2'),$$

$$\sum_{m_1}\sum_{m_2} \begin{pmatrix} j_1 & j_2 & j_3 \\ m_1 & m_2 & m_3 \end{pmatrix} \begin{pmatrix} j_1 & j_2 & j_3' \\ m_1 & m_2 & m_3' \end{pmatrix}$$
$$= (2j_3 + 1)^{-1}\,\delta(j_3, j_3')\,\delta(m_3, m_3')\,\Delta(j_1j_2j_3), \quad (2\text{-}10)$$

where $\Delta(j_1j_2j_3) = 1$ if j_1, j_2, and j_3 satisfy the triangular condition, i.e., if $j_1, j_2,$ and j_3 can be the sides of a triangle with an integral perimeter and when the sum of the parameters m_1, m_2, and m_3 is zero. Otherwise $\Delta(j_1j_2j_3)$ is zero.

Another expression for the 3-j symbol has been given by Regge [14],

$$\begin{pmatrix} j_1 & j_2 & j_3 \\ m_1 & m_2 & m_3 \end{pmatrix} = \begin{pmatrix} -j_1+j_2+j_3 & j_1-j_2+j_3 & j_1+j_2-j_3 \\ j_1-m_1 & j_2-m_2 & j_3-m_3 \\ j_1+m_1 & j_2+m_2 & j_3+m_3 \end{pmatrix},$$

where the nine numbers on the right-hand side are positive integers and the sum of the numbers in each column and each row is $(j_1+j_2+j_3)$. From this expression Regge [14] has shown that one can arbitrarily permute the rows or columns, as well as transpose them with respect to the principal diagonal.

Wigner [22] has shown that the Clebsch-Gordan coefficients are related to the representations of the rotation group; the $(2j_1 + 1)(2j_2 + 1)$ functions $\Psi(\gamma j_1 m_1 j_2 m_2)$ form the basis of the Krönecker (direct) product representation

$D_{j_1} \times D_{j_2}$ of the rotation group, and this direct product is reducible, i.e., there exists a matrix S such that

$$S^{-1}(D_{j_1} \times D_{j_2})S = D_{j_1+j_2} + \cdots + D_{|j_1-j_2|}.$$

The state functions of the coupled system form the basis of the reduced representations, and the Clebsch-Gordan coefficients are the elements of the matrix which reduces the direct product of two irreducible representations of the rotation group.

Coupling Schemes for Three Angular Momenta

Let us now consider the coupling of three angular momenta, j_1, j_2, and j_3, to give a resultant angular momentum J. There is more than one possible way of coupling the angular momenta. Three coupling schemes are discussed below:

(a) One can first couple j_1 and j_2 to obtain their resultant, which is denoted J_{12}. J_{12} is then coupled to j_3 to give the resultant J. The state vectors, within this scheme, may be denoted by $\Psi((j_1 j_2)J_{12}, j_3, JM)$.

(b) The angular momenta j_2 and j_3 are coupled to give J_{23}, which is then coupled to j_1 to give again the resultant J. The corresponding state vectors are denoted by $\Psi(j_1, (j_2 j_3)J_{23}, JM)$.

(c) One couples first j_1 and j_3 to give J_{13} and then couples j_2 and J_{13} to give J as before. The state vectors are denoted by $\Psi((j_1 j_3)J_{13}, j_2, JM)$.

The state vectors corresponding to the schemes (a) and (b) can be written using the results of the previous section. (The state vectors are hereafter written in this chapter using the ket notation of Dirac. For example, $\Psi((j_1 j_2)J_{12}, j_3, JM)$ is represented by $|(j_1 j_2)J_{12}, j_3, JM\rangle$.) In the scheme (a) the state vector is

$$|(j_1 j_2)J_{12}, j_3, JM\rangle = \sum_{M_{12}} \sum_{m_3} |(j_1 j_2)J_{12}M_{12}, j_3 m_3\rangle \, (J_{12}M_{12}j_3 m_3 \,|\, J_{12}j_3 JM)$$

$$= \sum_{M_{12}} \sum_{m_1} \sum_{m_2} \sum_{m_3} |j_1 m_1, j_2 m_2, j_3 m_3\rangle \, (J_{12}M_{12}j_3 m_3 \,|\, J_{12}j_3 JM)$$

$$\times (j_1 m_1 j_2 m_2 \,|\, j_1 j_2 J_{12}M_{12}), \quad (2\text{-}11)$$

whereas in the scheme (c) one has

$$|j_1, (j_2 j_3)J_{23}, JM\rangle = \sum_{m_1} \sum_{M_{23}} |j_1 m_1, (j_2 j_3)J_{23}M_{23}\rangle \, (j_1 m_1 J_{23}M_{23} \,|\, j_1 J_{23} JM)$$

$$= \sum_{m_1} \sum_{m_2} \sum_{m_3} \sum_{M_{23}} |j_1 m_1, j_2 m_2, j_3 m_3\rangle \, (j_1 m_1 J_{23}M_{23} \,|\, j_1 J_{23} JM)$$

$$\times (j_2 m_2 j_3 m_3 \,|\, j_2 j_3 J_{23}M_{23}). \quad (2\text{-}12)$$

The unitary transformation that connects the state vectors in these two representations is given by

$$|j_1, (j_2 j_3)J_{23}, JM\rangle$$

$$= \sum_{J_{12}} |(j_1 j_2)J_{12}, j_3, JM\rangle \, ((j_1 j_2)J_{12}, j_3, JM \,|\, j_1, (j_2 j_3)J_{23}, JM). \quad (2\text{-}13)$$

The transformation coefficients are independent of M. Operating with J_+ on both sides of Eq. (2-13), substituting Eqs. (2-11) and (2-12) into Eq. (2-13), and equating the coefficients of $|j_1m_1,j_2m_2,j_3m_3\rangle$, one obtains

$$\sum_{M_{23}}(-1)^{j_2-j_3+M_{23}+j_1-J_{23}+M}[(2J_{23}+1)(2J+1)]^{\frac{1}{2}}$$

$$\times\begin{pmatrix}j_2&j_3&J_{23}\\m_2&m_3&-M_{23}\end{pmatrix}\begin{pmatrix}j_1&J_{23}&J\\m_1&M_{23}&-M\end{pmatrix}$$

$$=\sum_{J_{12}}\sum_{M_{12}}(-1)^{j_1-j_2+M_{12}+J_{12}-j_3+M}$$

$$\times((j_1j_2)J_{12},j_3,J\,|\,j_1,(j_2j_3)J_{23},J)[(2J_{12}+1)(2J+1)]^{\frac{1}{2}}$$

$$\times\begin{pmatrix}j_1&j_2&J_{12}\\m_1&m_2&-M_{12}\end{pmatrix}\begin{pmatrix}J_{12}&j_3&J\\M_{12}&m_3&-M\end{pmatrix}. \quad (2\text{-}14)$$

If one multiplies both sides of Eq. (2-14) by

$$(-1)^{M_{12}'}\begin{pmatrix}j_1&j_2&J_{12}'\\m_1&m_2&-M_{12}'\end{pmatrix}$$

and sums over m_1 and m_2, the right-hand side of Eq. (2-14) becomes, using Eq. (2-10),

$$\sum_{J_{12}}\sum_{M_{12}}(-1)^{j_1-j_2+J_{12}-j_3+M+M_{12}-M_{12}'}((j_1j_2)J_{12},j_3,J\,|\,j_1,(j_2j_3)J_{23},J)$$

$$\times\delta(J_{12},J_{12}')\delta(M_{12},M_{12}')[(2J+1)/(2J_{12}+1)]^{\frac{1}{2}}\begin{pmatrix}J_{12}&j_3&J\\M_{12}&m_3&-M\end{pmatrix}$$

$$=(-1)^{j_1-j_2+J_{12}'-j_3+M}((j_1j_2)J_{12}',j_3,J\,|\,j_1,(j_2j_3)J_{23},J)$$

$$\times[(2J+1)/(2J_{12}'+1)]^{\frac{1}{2}}\begin{pmatrix}J_{12}'&j_3&J\\M_{12}'&m_3&-M\end{pmatrix}. \quad (2\text{-}15)$$

Defining the 6-j symbol by the relation

$$((j_1j_2)J_{12}',j_3,J\,|\,j_1,(j_2j_3)J_{23},J)$$

$$=(-1)^{j_1+j_2+j_3+J}[(2J_{12}'+1)(2J_{23}+1)]^{\frac{1}{2}}\begin{Bmatrix}j_3&J&J_{12}'\\j_1&j_2&J_{23}\end{Bmatrix}, \quad (2\text{-}16)$$

one can write

$$(-1)^{j_1-j_2+J_{12}'-j_3+M-j_1-j_2-j_3-J}[(2J+1)(2J_{23}+1)]^{\frac{1}{2}}$$

$$\times\begin{Bmatrix}j_3&J&J_{12}'\\j_1&j_2&J_{23}\end{Bmatrix}\begin{pmatrix}J_{12}'&j_3&J\\M_{12}'&m_3&-M\end{pmatrix}=\sum_{M_{23}}\sum_{m_1}\sum_{m_2}(-1)^{j_2-j_3+M_{23}+j_1-J_{23}+M-M_{12}'}$$

$$\times[(2J+1)(2J_{23}+1)]^{\frac{1}{2}}$$

$$\times\begin{pmatrix}j_2&j_3&J_{23}\\m_2&m_3&-M_{23}\end{pmatrix}\begin{pmatrix}j_1&J_{23}&J\\m_1&M_{23}&-M\end{pmatrix}\begin{pmatrix}j_1&j_2&J_{12}'\\m_1&m_2&-M_{12}'\end{pmatrix}. \quad (2\text{-}17)$$

If one uses the symmetry properties of the 3-j symbols, and since $M'_{12} = m_1 + m_2$, Eq. (2-17) transforms into

$$\begin{pmatrix} j_3 & J & J'_{12} \\ j_1 & j_2 & J_{23} \end{pmatrix} \begin{pmatrix} J'_{12} & j_3 & J \\ M'_{12} & m_3 & -M \end{pmatrix} = \sum_{m_1} \sum_{m_2} \sum_{M_{23}} (-1)^{j_1+j_2+J_{23}-m_1+m_2+M_{23}}$$

$$\times \begin{pmatrix} j_3 & j_2 & J_{23} \\ m_3 & m_2 & -M_{23} \end{pmatrix} \begin{pmatrix} j_1 & J & J_{23} \\ m_1 & -M & M_{23} \end{pmatrix} \begin{pmatrix} j_1 & j_2 & J'_{12} \\ -m_1 & -m_2 & M'_{12} \end{pmatrix}, \quad (2\text{-}18)$$

which expresses the 6-j symbol as a sum over 3-j symbols. The 6-j symbol is related to the W-function of Racah by the relation

$$\begin{Bmatrix} j_1 & j_2 & j_3 \\ l_1 & l_2 & l_3 \end{Bmatrix} = (-1)^{j_1 + j_2 + l_1 + l_2} W(j_1 j_2 l_2 l_1; j_3 l_3), \quad (2\text{-}19)$$

and it may also be defined by the following relation involving a single summation:

$$\begin{Bmatrix} j_1 & j_2 & j_3 \\ l_1 & l_2 & l_3 \end{Bmatrix} = \Delta(j_1 j_2 j_3)\, \Delta(j_1 l_2 l_3)\, \Delta(l_1 j_2 l_3)\, \Delta(l_1 l_2 l_3)$$

$$\times \sum_p [(-1)^p (p+1)!/(p - j_1 - j_2 - j_3)!(p - j_1 - l_2 - l_3)!$$

$$\times (p - l_1 - j_2 - l_3)!(p - l_1 - l_2 - l_3)!(j_1 + j_2 + l_1 + l_2 - p)!$$

$$\times (j_2 + j_3 + l_2 + l_3 - p)!(j_3 + j_1 + l_3 + l_1 - p)!], \quad (2\text{-}20)$$

where

$$\Delta(abc) = [(a + b - c)!(a - b + c)!(b - a + c)!/(a + b + c + 1)!]^{\frac{1}{2}}$$

and p runs over all those integral values that do not lead to negative arguments in the factorials.

    The various recurrence relations for the 6-j symbols have been given by Biedenharn [2], and their symmetry properties are discussed by Racah [13], Regge [15], Wigner [22], Judd [8], Edmonds [4], and Jahn and Howell [7]. Numerical tables of values of the W-function of Racah have been given by Biedenharn [1], Simon et al. [18], and Obi et al. [10, 11, 12]. The 6-j symbols have been tabulated by Howell [5] and Rotenberg et al. [16].

    The four triangular conditions for the nonvanishing of the 3-j symbols are expressed by the various $\Delta(abc)$ symbols in Eq. (2-20).

Coupling of Four Angular Momenta

An extension of the methods of coupling of three angular momenta to the coupling of four angular momenta leads to the 9-j symbol, defined by the equation

$$((j_1 j_2)J_{12},(j_3 j_4)J_{34},J \mid (j_1 j_3)J_{13},(j_2 j_4)J_{24},J)$$

$$= [(2J_{12}+1)(2J_{34}+1)(2J_{13}+1)(2J_{24}+1)]^{\frac{1}{2}} \begin{Bmatrix} j_1 & j_2 & J_{12} \\ j_3 & j_4 & J_{34} \\ J_{13} & J_{24} & J \end{Bmatrix}. \quad (2\text{-}21)$$

A transformation of great importance in atomic and nuclear spectroscopy connects states in LS and jj coupling. As a matter of fact, the transformation coefficient denoted by $((l_1 l_2)L, (s_1 s_2)S, J \mid (l_1 s_1)j_1, (l_2 s_2)j_2, J)$ is given by the expression

$$((l_1 l_2)L, (s_1 s_2)S, J \mid (l_1 s_1)j_1, (l_2 s_2)j_2, J)$$

$$= [(2L+1)(2S+1)(2j_1+1)(2j_2+1)]^{\frac{1}{2}} \begin{Bmatrix} l_1 & l_2 & L \\ s_1 & s_2 & S \\ j_1 & j_2 & J \end{Bmatrix}. \quad (2\text{-}22)$$

The 9-j symbol can be expressed in terms of 3-j symbols. Detailed expressions are given by Edmonds [4] and Judd [8], who also discuss the symmetry properties of 9-j symbols. Tables of 9-j symbols have been prepared by Smith and Stevenson [20] and Howell [6].

The coupling of five and more angular momenta involves 12-j, 15-j, . . . , etc., symbols.

REFERENCES

1. L. C Biedenharn. "Tables of the Racah Coefficients." Oak Ridge National Laboratory, Physics Division, Report ORNL-1098, April 1952.
2. L. C. Biedenharn. J. Math. and Phys. *31*, 287 (1953).
3. E. U. Condon and G. H. Shortley. "The Theory of Atomic Spectra." The University Press, Cambridge, 1935.
4. A. R. Edmonds. "Angular Momentum in Quantum Mechanics." Princeton University Press, Princeton, N.J., 1957.
5. K. M. Howell. "Revised Tables of 6-j Symbols" (with an introduction by H. A. Jahn and K. M. Howell). Univ. Southampton Research Report 59-1, 1959.
6. K. M. Howell. "Tables of 9-j Symbols." Univ. Southampton Research Report 59-2, 1959.
7. H. A. Jahn and K. M. Howell. Proc. Camb. Phil. Soc. *55*, 338 (1959).
8. B. R. Judd. "Operator Techniques in Atomic Spectroscopy." McGraw-Hill Book Company, Inc., New York, N.Y., 1963.
9. S. D. Majumdar. Prog. Theor . Phys. (Japan) *20*, 798 (1958).
10. S. Obi, T. Ishidzu, H. Horie, S. Yanagawa, Y. Tanabe, and M. Sato. Ann. Tokyo Astron. Obs. *3*, 89 (1953).
11. S. Obi, T. Ishidzu, H. Horie, S. Yanagawa, Y. Tanabe, and M. Sato. Ann. Tokyo Astron. Obs. *4*, 1 (1954).
12. S. Obi, T. Ishidzu, H. Horie, S. Yanagawa, Y. Tanabe, and M. Sato. Ann. Tokyo Astron. Obs. *5*, 75 (1955).
13. G. Racah. Phys. Rev. *62*, 438 (1942).
14. T. Regge. Nuovo Cimento *10*, 544 (1958).
15. T. Regge. Nuovo Cimento *11*, 116 (1959).

16. M. Rotenberg, R. Bivins, N. Metropolis, and J. K. Wooten. "The 3-*j* and 6-*j* Symbols." The Technology Press, M.I.T., Cambridge, Mass., 1959.
17. J. Schwinger. "On Angular Momentum." Nuclear Development Associates, Inc., Report NYO-3071, 26 January 1952.
18. A. Simon, J. H. Vander Sluis, and L. C. Biedenharn. "Tables of Racah Coefficients." Oak Ridge National Laboratory, Physics Division, Report ORNL-1679, March 1954.
19. K. Smith. "Supplement to Table of Wigner's 9-*j* Symbols." Argonne National Laboratory, Report ANL-5860, 1958.
20. K. Smith and J. W. Stevenson. "A Table of Wigner 9-*j* Coefficients." Argonne National Laboratory, Report ANL-5776, 1957.
21. B. L. Van der Waerden. "Die Gruppentheoretische Methode in der Quanten-Mechanik." Springer-Verlag, Berlin, 1932.
22. E. P. Wigner. "Group Theory and Its Applications to the Quantum Mechanics of Atomic Spectra." Academic Press, Inc., New York, N.Y., 1959.

Chapter 3   TENSOR OPERATORS

INTRODUCTION

Quantum mechanical treatments of many-electron problems invariably involve the calculation of matrix elements of certain operators. For example, the matrix for the electrostatic interaction between two electrons depends upon the matrix elements of the spherical harmonics $Y_m^{(l)}(\theta, \phi)$. Here these functions play the role of operators and not of eigenfunctions, although they are eigenfunctions of the angular momentum operators ℓ^2 and ℓ_z. For this reason it is convenient to review these operators. (Only a brief account of tensor operators is presented here. Condon and Shortley [1] have developed in detail the algebra of vector operators and Racah [6] has extended this algebra to tensor operators. Further details are given by Edmonds [3], Rose [9], and Judd [4].)

TENSORS

A vector $\mathbf{v}$ is defined as a set of three quantities that, under a rotation of the frame of reference, undergo the transformation

$$v_i' = \sum_k a_{ik} v_k, \tag{3-1}$$

such that if a point p in space has the coordinates v_i in a σ frame of reference, v_i' are the coordinates of the same point p in space referred to the rotated frame σ'; the coefficients a_{ik} are the elements of a real orthogonal matrix (of determinant $+1$),

$$\sum_k a_{ik} a_{jk} = \delta_{ij},$$

$$\det |a_{ik}| = +1.$$

Similarly one can define a tensor $T^{(r)}$ of rank r (in a three-dimensional space) as a set of 3^r quantities $T_{ij\cdots r}$, if, under a rotation of the type represented by Eq. (3-1), these quantities undergo a linear transformation

$$T'_{ij\cdots r} = \sum_{l,m,n,\ldots} a_{il} a_{jm} a_{kn} \cdots T_{lmn\cdots}. \tag{3-2}$$

Each index may assume independently the values 1, 2, or 3; $T_{lmn\cdots}$ has altogether r indices, and each term in Eq. (3-2) contains a product of r matrix elements a_{il}. A vector, of course, is a tensor of rank one.

Inspection of Eq. (3-2) shows that any linear combination of tensors of a given rank is also a tensor of the same rank. In particular, a linear combination of vectors is a vector.

Tensors, in general, can be built from products of components of vectors.

IRREDUCIBLE TENSORS

Let us consider a tensor $T^{(2)}$ of rank two, which can be built up by forming the nine products of the components of two vectors v and w. Its components are defined by

$$T_{ik} = v_i w_k, \ (i, k = 1, 2, 3).$$

The tensor $T^{(2)}$ can be decomposed into a symmetric and an antisymmetric part, $S^{(2)}$ and $A^{(2)}$ respectively, with components

$$S_{ik} = S_{ki} = \tfrac{1}{2}(T_{ik} + T_{ki}),$$
$$A_{ik} = -A_{ki} = \tfrac{1}{2}(T_{ik} - T_{ki}).$$

The components S_{ik} of the symmetric part of any tensor transform among themselves under rotation. Similarly, the components A_{ik} of the antisymmetric part also transform among themselves. Therefore the decomposition of a tensor into its symmetric and antisymmetric parts has a meaning independent of the frame of reference.

One can consider next whether the symmetric and antisymmetric tensors can be decomposed again in such a way that the new components transform among themselves separately. This decomposition is not possible for the antisymmetric tensor, which has only three independent components. The quantities x_1, x_2, and x_3, defined by the relations

$$x_1 = A_{23} = -A_{32}, \qquad x_2 = A_{31} = -A_{13}, \qquad x_3 = A_{12} = -A_{21},$$

transform like an axial vector, because if one defines an antisymmetric tensor with components $B_{ij} = \zeta_i \eta_j - \zeta_j \eta_i$, then the quantities x_k associated with B_{ij} are the components of the vector product of the vectors ζ and η. Hence, any further condition on the components of the antisymmetric tensor represents a condition on the components of the vector x. However, it must be taken into account that a vector can always be transformed into any other vector of the same length, and therefore it is impossible to find linear combinations of the components of a vector that transform among themselves under rotation. The vector and, therefore, the antisymmetric tensor of rank two are designated as irreducible tensors.

For a symmetric tensor the trace is invariant under rotations, i.e.,

$$\sum_i S'_{ii} = \sum_{i,l,m} a_{il}a_{im}S_{lm} = \sum_{l,m} \delta_{lm}S_{lm} = \sum_m S_{mm}.$$

Therefore it is possible to impose a restriction on the symmetric part of $T^{(2)}$. For example, one can require its trace to vanish. To this end one subtracts one third of the trace from the diagonal elements of the symmetric tensor,

$$S_{ik} = \tfrac{1}{2}(T_{ik} + T_{ki}) - \tfrac{1}{3}\delta_{ik}\sum_m T_{mm}.$$

The general tensor of rank two can then be decomposed into a sum of three irreducible tensors,

$$T_{ik} = S_{ik} + A_{ik} + \tau_{ik}, \tag{3-3}$$

with elements

$$S_{ik} = \tfrac{1}{2}(T_{ik} + T_{ki}) - \tfrac{1}{3}\delta_{ik}\sum_m T_{mm}, \tag{3-4a}$$

$$A_{ik} = \tfrac{1}{2}(T_{ik} - T_{ki}), \tag{3-4b}$$

$$\tau_{ik} = \tfrac{1}{3}\delta_{ik}\sum_m T_{mm}. \tag{3-4c}$$

The single component of the trace, the three independent components of the antisymmetric tensor, and five independent components of the symmetric tensor are completely equivalent to the nine components of the tensor $T^{(2)}$ of rank two. The advantage of this decomposition is that each of the component tensors transforms separately under rotations.

The process of decomposition of a tensor of rank two into its irreducible components can be generalized, in principle, to tensors of higher rank. That is, given a tensor T with a certain number of independent components, one can find a smaller number of linear combinations of these components so that they transform among themselves under any rotation. This process can be continued, independent of the first, so as to obtain a new set of linear combinations such that they also transform among themselves. The totality of such independent linear combinations must equal the original number of independent linear components.

If one can find such linear combinations, the original tensor T is said to be reducible. It can happen, however, that it is impossible to find linear combinations so that they group into two or more sets that transform among themselves; in that case one says that T is an irreducible tensor. Thus, the irreducibility of a tensor is defined with respect to rotations of the frame of reference.

A common example of irreducible tensors is the set of spherical harmonics $Y_m^{(k)}(\theta, \phi)$, because they transform among themselves under rotations. The proof of the irreducibility of the $(2k + 1)$ spherical harmonics of degree k is omitted here, however. Racah [6] has mentioned that each tensor may be decomposed into parts that transform among themselves independently for a rotation of the axes, such that each irreducible part transforms like the spherical harmonics of a definite degree.

SPHERICAL HARMONICS AS TENSORS

Under a rotation of the axes the spherical harmonics transform as

$$Y'^{(k)}_q = DY^{(k)}_q D^\dagger = \sum_p Y^{(k)}_p D^{(k)}_{pq}(\alpha\beta\gamma).$$

Using the modified spherical harmonics

$$C^{(k)}_q = [4\pi/(2k + 1)]^{\frac{1}{2}} Y^{(k)}_q,$$

we see that the product

$$\boldsymbol{C}^{(k)} \cdot \boldsymbol{C}'^{(k)} = \sum_q (-1)^q C^{(k)}_q(\theta, \phi) C^{(k)}_{-q}(\theta', \phi')$$

is invariant under a rotation of the axes. That is, the scalar product must be a function of the angle Θ between the directions (θ, ϕ) and (θ', ϕ'), as it is the only quantity independent of the choice of axes.

If the axes are chosen so that the direction (θ', ϕ') becomes the new z-axis, one has

$$C^{(k)}_q(\theta', \phi') \equiv C^{(k)}_q(0, 0) = \delta(q, 0),$$

$$C^{(k)}_0(\theta, \phi) \equiv P_k(\cos \theta) = P_k(\cos \Theta),$$

and therefore

$$\boldsymbol{C}^{(k)} \cdot \boldsymbol{C}'^{(k)} = \sum_q (-1)^q P_k(\cos \Theta) \, \delta(q, 0) = P_k(\cos \Theta).$$

If $C^{(k)}_q(\theta, \phi)$ and $C^{(k')}_{q'}(\theta, \phi)$ are spherical harmonics of the same angles (θ, ϕ), then

$$\sum_q \sum_{q'} (kqk'q' \,|\, kk'KQ) C^{(k)}_q C^{(k')}_{q'}$$

is a tensor of rank K; $(kqk'q' \,|\, kk'KQ)$ is a Clebsch-Gordan coefficient. Since it is a function of (θ, ϕ) only, it must be proportional to $C^{(K)}_Q(\theta, \phi)$; that is,

$$\sum_q \sum_{q'} (kqk'q' \,|\, kk'KQ) C^{(k)}_q(\theta, \phi) C^{(k')}_{q'} = A_K C^{(K)}_Q(\theta, \phi).$$

In particular, if $\theta = \phi = 0$,

$$\sum_q \sum_{q'} (kqk'q' \,|\, kk'KQ) C^{(k)}_q(0, 0) C^{(k')}_{q'}(0, 0) = A_K C^{(K)}_Q(0, 0),$$

and one has

$$(k0k'0 \,|\, kk'00) = A_k.$$

PRODUCTS OF TENSORS

In cartesian tensor theory the product of two tensors of rank m and n, respectively, yields a tensor of rank $(m + n)$. For example, the nine products $a_i b_j$ of the components of two vectors $\boldsymbol{a}$ and $\boldsymbol{b}$ are the components of a tensor of rank two, which transforms according to the representation $D^{(1)} \times D^{(1)}$ of the rotation group. This direct product can be decomposed into the irreducible representations $D^{(1)}$, $D^{(2)}$, and $D^{(0)}$. If one considers one more vector, $\boldsymbol{c}$, the set of 27 products $a_i b_j c_k$ represents a tensor of rank three, which transforms according to the representation $D^{(1)} \times D^{(1)} \times D^{(1)}$, i.e., $D^{(0)}$, $3D^{(1)}$, $2D^{(2)}$, and $D^{(3)}$; it corresponds to a scalar, three vectors, two tensors of rank two, and one tensor of rank three.

Similarly, if $\boldsymbol{R}^{(k)}$ and $\boldsymbol{S}^{(k')}$ are two irreducible spherical tensors of rank k and k', respectively, the $(2k + 1)(2k' + 1)$ products $R_q^{(k)} S_q^{(k')}$ form a tensor which transforms under the representation $D^{(k)} \times D^{(k')}$. The decomposition of this reducible representation shows that the product corresponds to the irreducible tensors with components

$$[\boldsymbol{R}^{(k)} \boldsymbol{S}^{(k')}]_Q^{(K)} = \sum_q \sum_{q'} (kqk'q' \mid kk'KQ) R_q^{(k)} S_q^{(k')} \tag{3-5}$$

where

$$K = k + k', k + k' - 1, \ldots |k - k'|, Q = q + q'.$$

For $k = k'$ and $K = 0$, it follows from Eq. (3-5) that

$$[\boldsymbol{R}^{(k)} \boldsymbol{S}^{(k)}]_0^{(0)} = \sum_q (kqk - q \mid kk00) R_q^{(k)} S_{-q}^{(k)}$$
$$= (-1)^k (2k + 1)^{-\frac{1}{2}} \sum_q (-1)^{-q} R_q^{(k)} S_{-q}^{(k)}.$$

The scalar product of two tensors is defined by

$$(\boldsymbol{R}^{(k)} \cdot \boldsymbol{S}^{(k)}) = \sum_q (-1)^q R_q^{(k)} S_{-q}^{(k)}, \tag{3-6}$$

and therefore one can write

$$[\boldsymbol{R}^{(k)} \boldsymbol{S}^{(k)}]_0^{(0)} = (-1)^k (2k + 1)^{-\frac{1}{2}} (\boldsymbol{R}^{(k)} \cdot \boldsymbol{S}^{(k)}).$$

The tensor product $[\boldsymbol{R}^{(k)} \boldsymbol{S}^{(k')}]$ is also denoted as $(\boldsymbol{R}^{(k)} \boldsymbol{S}^{(k')})^{(K)}$ if the tensors $\boldsymbol{R}^{(k)}$ and $\boldsymbol{S}^{(k')}$ represent single-particle tensors for the same particle. This convention is used in the remainder of the text.

VECTOR AND TENSOR OPERATORS

Condon and Shortley [1] have developed the algebra of vector operators $\boldsymbol{T}$, which satisfy, with respect to any angular momentum operator $\boldsymbol{J}$, the commutation relations

$$[\mathbf{J}, \mathbf{T}] = [\mathbf{T}, \mathbf{J}] = i\mathbf{T} \times \mathfrak{J}, \qquad (3\text{-}7)$$

where $\mathfrak{J}$ is the unit dyadic $\boldsymbol{ii} + \boldsymbol{jj} + \boldsymbol{kk}$.

Equation (3-7) implies the relations

$$[\mathscr{J}_x, T_x] = [\mathscr{J}_y, T_y] = [\mathscr{J}_z, T_z] = 0,$$
$$[\mathscr{J}_x, T_y] = iT_z, [\mathscr{J}_x, T_z] = -iT_y,$$
$$[\mathscr{J}_y, T_z] = iT_x, [\mathscr{J}_y, T_x] = -iT_z,$$
$$[\mathscr{J}_z, T_x] = iT_y, [\mathscr{J}_z, T_y] = -iT_x.$$

Racah [6] has remarked that Eq. (3-7) is equivalent to the definition of a vector, because the operators $\mathscr{J}_x$, $\mathscr{J}_y$, and $\mathscr{J}_z$ are proportional to the rotation operators (mentioned in Chapter 2), and therefore the commutation law with respect to **J** completely determines the transformation law of each quantity considered under a rotation of the axes. Since Eq. (3-7) holds for the components x, y, and z of a vector, every set of three quantities for which Eq. (3-7) holds transforms as x, y, and z and is thus a vector.

The discussion of tensor properties (namely, the tensor products) presented before applies as well to tensor operators. Other characteristics, such as the hermitian property and the definition of irreducible tensor operators, are presented below. The main point to be discussed, however, is the determination of the matrix elements for tensor operators.

HERMITIAN TENSOR OPERATORS

Taking into account that $\mathscr{J}_\pm^\dagger = \mathscr{J}_\mp$, $\mathscr{J}_0^\dagger = \mathscr{J}_0$ and considering the commutation relations of the spherical components $\mathscr{J}_\lambda$ of **J** with the components of a spherical tensor operator $\mathbf{T}^{(k)}$, one obtains

$$[\mathscr{J}_0, T_q^{(k)\dagger}] = [\mathscr{J}_0^\dagger, T_q^{(k)\dagger}] = [T_q^{(k)}, \mathscr{J}_0]^\dagger = -[\mathscr{J}_0, T_q^{(k)}]^\dagger = -qT_q^{(k)\dagger},$$
$$[\mathscr{J}_\pm, T_q^{(k)\dagger}] = [\mathscr{J}_\mp^\dagger, T_q^{(k)\dagger}] = -[\mathscr{J}_\mp, T_q^{(k)}]^\dagger$$
$$= -[k \pm q + 1)(k \mp q)]^{\frac{1}{2}}T_{q\pm1}^{(k)\dagger}.$$

Hence, if one defines an operator $\mathbf{T}^{(k)}$ by

$$T_q^{(k)} = (-1)^{p-q}T_{-q}^{(k)\dagger}, \qquad (3\text{-}8)$$

then the $(2k + 1)$ components $T_q^{(k)}$ transform as a tensor operator of rank k where p is an arbitrary integral or half-integral number, depending on whether k is integral or half-integral. Equation (3-8) defines a hermitian tensor operator. The choice of phase is arbitrary. In particular, one can choose $p = k$ or $p = 0$. Then the operators that have $p = k + 1$ or $p = 1$, respectively, are called antihermitian. The phase $(-1)^q$ is essential to preserve the correct rotational properties.

The spherical harmonics $Y_m^{(l)}$ and the angular momentum operators $\mathbf{J}$ show this hermitian property with $p = 0$,

$$Y_m^{(l)\dagger} = Y_m^{(l)*} = (-1)^m Y_{-m}^{(l)},$$
$$\mathscr{J}_\lambda^\dagger = (-1)\mathscr{J}_{-\lambda}.$$

IRREDUCIBLE TENSOR OPERATORS

Racah [6] defines an irreducible tensor operator of the degree k as any operator $\mathbf{T}^{(k)}$ whose $(2k+1)$ components $T_q^{(k)}$, $(q = -k, -k+1, \ldots, k)$ satisfy the same commutation rule with respect to $\mathbf{J}$ as the spherical harmonic operators, $Y_q^{(k)}$. The commutation rule is

$$[(\mathscr{J}_x \pm i\mathscr{J}_y), T_q^{(k)}] = [(k \mp q)(k \pm q + 1)]^{\frac{1}{2}} T_{q\pm1}^{(k)},$$
$$[\mathscr{J}_z, T_q^{(k)}] = qT_q^{(k)}.$$

For $k = 1$, i.e. a vector operator, $\mathbf{T}^{(1)}$ obeys Eq. (3-7) if one writes

$$T_1^{(1)} = -(1/\sqrt{2})(T_x + iT_y),$$
$$T_0^{(1)} = T_z,$$
$$T_{-1}^{(1)} = (1/\sqrt{2})(T_x - iT_y).$$

Alternatively, an irreducible tensor operator of rank k is defined as a set of $(2k+1)$ functions $T_q^{(k)}$ which transform under the $(2k+1)$-dimensional representation of the rotation group, i.e.,

$$\mathscr{U}T_q^{(k)}\mathscr{U}^{-1} = \sum_{q'} T_{q'}^{(k)} D_{q'q}^{(k)}(\alpha\beta\gamma),$$

where the operator $\mathscr{U} = \exp(-i\theta_n\mathscr{J})$ is the rotation operator introduced in Chapter 2. $D_{q'q}^{(k)}$ are the matrix elements of $\mathscr{U}$ in the kq representation and $\alpha\beta\gamma$ are the Euler angles that describe the rotation. As $D^{(k)}$ is irreducible, so is the tensor $\mathbf{T}^{(k)}$. Only irreducible tensors of integral rank appear in physical applications; otherwise, transitions would take place between bosons (integral spin) and fermions (half-integral spin).

MATRIX ELEMENTS OF TENSOR OPERATORS

It was mentioned before that a number of physical interactions can be expressed in terms of irreducible tensor operators. In particular, the electrostatic interaction between two electrons depends upon the matrix of spherical harmonics, considered as irreducible tensor operators. It is necessary, therefore, to evaluate the matrix elements of irreducible tensors, since they appear in all those processes whenever states of definite angular momentum are involved.

Using the fact that $\mathbf{J} \cdot \mathbf{T}$ is diagonal with respect* to j and m and that $\mathbf{J}$ is diagonal with respect to α, Condon and Shortley [1] define the matrix element of $\mathbf{T}$ joining the states $\alpha j m$ and $\alpha' j m'$ as

$$(\alpha j m| \, \mathbf{T} \, |\alpha' j m') = [j(j+1)]^{-1}(\alpha j m| \, \mathbf{J} \, |\alpha j m')(\alpha j m'| \, \mathbf{J} \cdot \mathbf{T} \, |\alpha' j m').$$

When angular momentum is conserved, the state vectors are eigenfunctions of $\mathscr{J}^2$ and $\mathscr{J}_z$, and the matrix elements of a tensor operator have a simple geometrical dependence on the magnetic quantum numbers. Let us consider, for example, the matrix element $(\alpha j m| \, T_q^{(k)} \, |\alpha' j' m')$ of the component $T_q^{(k)}$ of a tensor of rank k.

The state vector $T_q^{(k)} \, |\alpha' j' m')$ transforms according to the representation $D^{(k)} \times D^{(j')}$ of the rotation group. This representation can be reduced to its irreducible components by forming the vectors $|\beta K Q)$ with angular momentum (K, Q),

$$|\beta K Q) = \sum_{q m'} T_q^{(k)} \, |\alpha' j' m')(k q j' m' \, | \, k j' K Q).$$

Taking the matrix element with $(\alpha j m|$, one obtains

$$(\alpha j m \, | \, \beta K Q) = \sum_{q m'} (k q j' m' \, | \, k j' K Q)(\alpha j m| \, T_q^{(k)} \, |\alpha' j' m').$$

Multiplying by $[(k q j' m' \, | \, k j' K Q)]^\dagger$ and summing over $K Q$, one obtains

$$\sum_{K Q} (k q j' m' \, | \, k j' K Q) \sum_{q m'} (k j' K Q \, | \, k q j' m')(\alpha j m| \, T_q^{(k)} \, |\alpha' j' m')$$
$$= \sum_{K Q} (\alpha j m \, | \, \beta K Q)(k j' K Q \, | \, k q j' m'),$$

$$(\alpha j m| \, T_q^{(k)} \, |\alpha' j' m') = \sum_{K Q} (\alpha j m \, | \, \beta K Q)(k j' K Q \, | \, k q j' m').$$

Taking into account that

$$(\alpha j m \, | \, \beta K Q) = \delta_{j K} \delta_{m Q}$$

one first has

$$(\alpha j m| \, T_q^{(k)} \, |\alpha' j' m') = (k j' j m \, | \, k q j' m')(\alpha j m \, | \, \beta j m),$$

and, finally,

$$(\alpha j m| \, T_q^{(k)} \, |\alpha' j' m') = (-1)^{2k}(j' k j m \, | \, j' m' k q)(\alpha j| \, |\mathbf{T}^{(k)}| \, |\alpha' j'), \qquad (3\text{-}9)$$

where $(\alpha j| \, |\mathbf{T}^{(k)}| \, |\alpha' j')$ is the reduced matrix element of $\mathbf{T}^{(k)}$. Inverting this equation one obtains

$$(\alpha j| \, |\mathbf{T}^{(k)}| \, |\alpha' j') = (-1)^{2k} \sum_{q m'} (j' k j m \, | \, j' m' k q)(\alpha j m| \, T_q^{(k)} \, |\alpha' j' m'), \qquad (3\text{-}10)$$

which constitutes the analogue of the scalar contraction of vectors.

The integration over three spherical harmonics represents the prototype

---

* In general, j and m are used for single-particle systems, whereas J and M denote many-particle systems. When such a distinction is not needed, j and m are used indistinctively to denote the general system under consideration.

of such matrix elements. One has, in general,

$$(lm|\ \mathbf{Y}_M^{(L)}\ |l'm') = \int\ \mathbf{Y}_m^{(l)*}(\theta,\ \phi)\mathbf{Y}_M^{(L)}(\theta,\ \phi)\mathbf{Y}_{m'}^{(l')}(\theta\ \phi,)\ d\Omega.$$

Combining the last two harmonics, one first obtains

$$\mathbf{Y}_M^{(L)}\mathbf{Y}_{m'}^{(l')} = \sum_{kq}\mathbf{Y}_q^{(k)}(\theta,\ \phi)\,(l'Lkq\,|\,l'm'LM)$$
$$\times\ (l'Lk0\,|\,l'0L0)[(2l'+1)(2L+1)/4\pi(2k+1)]^{\frac{1}{2}}.$$

Taking into account the orthonormality properties of the spherical harmonics, one sees that the integral will vanish unless $k = l$ and $q = m$, and therefore

$$(lm|\ \mathbf{Y}_M^{(L)}\ |l'm') = (l'Llm\,|\,l'm'LM)(l|\ |\mathbf{Y}^{(L)}|\ |l'),$$

in which the reduced matrix element is defined by

$$(l|\ |\mathbf{Y}^{(L)}|\ |l') = [(2l'+1)(2L+1)/4\pi(2l+1)]^{\frac{1}{2}}(l'Ll0\,|\,l'0L0). \quad (3\text{-}11)$$

For a hermitian tensor operator $\mathbf{T}^{(k)}$ one has

$$(jm|\ \mathbf{T}_q^{(k)}\ |j'm') = (-1)^{p-q}(jm|\ \mathbf{T}_{-q}^{(k)\dagger}\ |j'm') = (-1)^{p-q}(j'm'|\ \mathbf{T}_{-q}^{(k)}\ |jm)^*,$$

or, in terms of reduced matrix elements,

$$(2j+1)^{\frac{1}{2}}(j|\ |\mathbf{T}^{(k)}|\ |j') = (-1)^{j-j'-p}(2j'+1)^{\frac{1}{2}}(j'|\ |\mathbf{T}^{(k)}|\ |j)^*. \quad (3\text{-}12)$$

The unit tensor operator of rank r is defined as the tensor $\mathbf{u}^{(r)}$, whose reduced matrix elements are given by

$$(\alpha j|\ |\mathbf{u}^{(r)}|\ |\alpha'j') = \delta_{\alpha\alpha'}\delta_{jj'}.$$

These operators act on the coordinates of a single particle.

WIGNER-ECKART THEOREM

The most important theorem regarding the matrix elements of irreducible tensor operators is that by Wigner [10] and Eckart [2]. It is important because it displays explicitly how the matrix elements of an irreducible tensor operator depend upon the projection quantum numbers. Furthermore, the theorem embodies the important conservation laws of angular momentum.

It is thus possible to separate those features of a physical process that depend entirely upon the geometry of the system from those that depend on the detailed physical description.

The Wigner-Eckart theorem states that the Clebsch-Gordan coefficient $(jmLM\,|\,jLj'm')$ contains entirely the dependence of the matrix element $(j'm'|\ \mathbf{T}_M^{(L)}\ |jm)$ on the projection quantum numbers. The reduced matrix element, $(j'|\ |\mathbf{T}^{(L)}|\ |j)$, of the set of tensor operators $\mathbf{T}_M^{(L)}$ is independent of

M, m, and m'. The Clebsch-Gordan coefficient vanishes, of course, unless $m' = M + m$ and unless $|j - j'| \leq L \leq j + j'$, and thus the conservation of angular momentum is contained in these relations.

MATRIX ELEMENTS OF TENSOR OPERATOR PRODUCTS

Let us consider a tensor operator $\mathbf{T}^{(K)}$ that is the tensor product of two tensor operators $\mathbf{R}^{(k)}$ and $\mathbf{S}^{(k')}$ of rank k and k', respectively. Its components are defined by

$$T_Q^{(K)} = (\mathbf{R}^{(k)}\mathbf{S}^{(k')})_Q^{(K)} = \sum_q R_q^{(k)} S_{Q-q}^{(k')}(kqk'Q - q \mid kk'KQ). \quad (3\text{-}13)$$

The reduced matrix of the composite tensor operator $\mathbf{T}^{(K)}$ may be evaluated in terms of the matrices of the tensor operators $\mathbf{R}^{(k)}$ and $\mathbf{S}^{(k')}$, using Eq. (3-13) and introducing intermediate states between the two tensor operators. One can write

$$(j| |\mathbf{T}^{(K)}| |j') = \sum_Q (j'Kjm \mid j'm - QKQ)(jm| T_Q^{(K)} |j'm - Q)$$

$$= \sum_{Qqj''} (j'Kjm \mid j'm - QKQ)(kqkQ - q \mid kk'KQ)$$

$$\times (jm| R_q^{(k)} |j''m - Q)(j''m - q| S_{Q-q}^{(k')} |j'm - Q)$$

$$= \sum_{j''} (-1)^{K-k-k'}[(2j'' + 1)(2K + 1)]^{\frac{1}{2}}$$

$$\times W(jj'kk'; \; Kj'')(j| |\mathbf{R}^{(k)}| |j'')(j''| |\mathbf{S}^{(k')}| |j'). \quad (3\text{-}14)$$

The function W expresses the coupling of three angular momentum vectors, giving the coupling scheme like $[(kk')K, j'; j]$ in terms of the coupling $[k, (k'j')j''; j]$; that is, it represents the transformation coefficient between these two schemes.

When $K = 0$, Eq. (3-13) defines the scalar product of two tensors,

$$\mathbf{R}^{(k)} \cdot \mathbf{S}^{(k)} = (-1)^k (2k + 1)^{\frac{1}{2}} \mathbf{T}^{(0)}, \quad (3\text{-}15)$$

and Eq. (3-14) reduces to

$$(j| |\mathbf{R}^{(k)} \cdot \mathbf{S}^{(k)}| |j) = \sum_{j'} (-1)^{-j+j'}[(2j' + 1)/(2j + 1)]^{\frac{1}{2}}$$

$$\times (j| |\mathbf{R}^{(k)}| |j')(j'| |\mathbf{S}^{(k)}| |j), \quad (3\text{-}16)$$

after the value of the Racah function is substituted. If $\mathbf{R}^{(k)} = \mathbf{S}^{(k)}$ and they are hermitian, then taking into account Eq. (3-12) one can then write

$$(j| |\mathbf{R}^{(k)} \cdot \mathbf{S}^{(k)}| |j) = \sum_{j'} |(j| |\mathbf{R}^{(k)}| |j')|^2. \quad (3\text{-}17)$$

MATRIX ELEMENTS OF TENSOR OPERATORS FOR COMPOSITE SYSTEMS

Let us consider a composite system consisting of two parts with angular momenta j_1 and j_2, their resultant angular momentum being J, and a tensor operator* $\mathbf{T}^{(k)}(1)$ that acts only on the first part of the system. The coupled state vectors are given by application of the formula for the coupling of two angular momenta,† and the reduced matrix of $\mathbf{T}^{(k)}(1)$ is found by expanding the coupled state vectors,

$$(j_1 j_2 J \| \mathbf{T}^{(k)}(1) \| j_1' j_2' J') = \sum_q (J'kJM \mid J'M - qkq)(j_1 j_2 JM \mid \mathbf{T}_q^{(k)}(1)$$

$$\times \mid j_1' j_2' J'M - q) = \sum_{qm} (J'kJM \mid J'M - qkq)(j_1 m j_2 M - m \mid j_1 j_2 JM)$$

$$\times (j_1' m - q j_2' M - m \mid j_1' j_2' J'M - q)$$

$$\times (j_1' m - qkq \mid j_1' k j_1 m)(j_1 \| \mathbf{T}^{(k)}(1) \| j_1') \, \delta(j_2, j_2') = (-1)^{(J+j_1'-k-j_2)}[(2J'+1)$$

$$\times (2j_1 + 1)]^{\frac{1}{2}} W(j_1 j_1' JJ'; \ k j_2)(j_1 \| \mathbf{T}^{(k)}(1) \| j_1') \, \delta(j_2, j_2'). \quad (3\text{-}18)$$

An example will illustrate the applications of Eq. (3-18). Let us consider a particle with orbital as well as spin angular momentum and an operator that acts upon only the orbital part. The spherical harmonic $C_M^{(L)}$ is such an operator. The total angular momentum j of the particle is made up of orbital l and spin s, and thus in the lsj representation

$$(lsj \| \mathbf{C}^{(L)} \| l'sj') = (-1)^{j-L-s+l'}[(2l+1)(2j'+1)]^{\frac{1}{2}}$$
$$\times W(ll'jj'; \ Ls)(l \| \mathbf{C}^{(L)} \| l'). \quad (3\text{-}19)$$

In particular, if $s = \frac{1}{2}$, as is the case for an electron, and if $(l + l' + L)$ is even, then Eq. (3-19) simplifies to

$$(l\tfrac{1}{2}j \| \mathbf{C}^{(L)} \| l'\tfrac{1}{2}j') = (-1)^{j'-\frac{1}{2}+L}(2j'+1)^{\frac{1}{2}} \begin{pmatrix} j & j' & L \\ \frac{1}{2} & -\frac{1}{2} & 0 \end{pmatrix}, \quad (3\text{-}20)$$

which is independent of l and l'. In general, one may have to evaluate the matrix element of the product of the tensor operators $\mathbf{R}$ and $\mathbf{S}$ such that $\mathbf{R}$ acts on part 1 and $\mathbf{S}$ acts on part 2 of the composite system. The matrix of such an operator can be written in terms of the matrices of the two parts, as in Eq. (3-18). Such a matrix element in general involves a 6-j symbol. However, a simple but important example of such a matrix element is that

---

* Hereafter the notation $\mathbf{T}^{(k)}(n)$ represents a tensor operator that acts on the n-th component of the system.

† That is, $\mid j_1 j_2 JM) \sum_{m_1 m_2} \mid j_1 m_1 j_2 m_2)(j_1 m_1 j_2 m_2 \mid j_1 j_2 JM)$.

of the scalar product of tensor operators $\mathbf{C}^{(k)}$,

$$(l_1 l_2 L | \, \mathbf{C}^{(k)}(1) \cdot \mathbf{C}^{(k)}(2) \, | \, l_1' l_2' L') = (-1)^{L+k} [(2l_1 + 1)(2l_2 + 1)(2l_1' + 1)$$

$$\times (2l_2' + 1)]^{\frac{1}{2}} \, W(l_1 l_1' l_2 l_2'; \, kL) \begin{pmatrix} k & l_1 & l_1' \\ 0 & 0 & 0 \end{pmatrix} \begin{pmatrix} k & l_2 & l_2' \\ 0 & 0 & 0 \end{pmatrix} \delta_{LL'}. \quad (3\text{-}21)$$

SELECTION RULES

Application of the Wigner-Eckart theorem to the matrix element $(j'm' | \, T_q^{(k)} \, | jm)$ shows that it vanishes unless $m' = q + m$ and the triangular conditions $|j' - j| \le k \le j' + j$ are satisfied. For $k = 0$ one must then have $j = j'$ and $m = m'$ and the corresponding Clebsch-Gordan coefficient is unity. This shows that the matrix element of a scalar is independent of the magnetic quantum number and is identical to the reduced matrix element,

$$(j'm' | \, \mathbf{T}^{(0)} \, | jm) = (j' | \, |\mathbf{T}^{(0)}| \, | j)) \delta_{jj'} \delta_{mm'}. \quad (3\text{-}22)$$

The spherical harmonic integral, Eq. (3-11), also contains the parity selection rule for the spatial part of a single particle matrix element: $l + l' + L$ must be even; otherwise $(l'Ll0 \, | \, l'0L0)$ is zero.

COEFFICIENTS OF FRACTIONAL PARENTAGE

The determination of the symmmetric and antisymmetric eigenfunctions of the angular momentum operators $\mathscr{S}^2$ and $\mathscr{L}^2$ for a configuration l^2, with two equivalent electrons, does not offer any difficulty. In fact, the antisymmetric eigenfunctions, allowed by the Pauli exclusion principle, correspond to $L + S$ even and are the normalized eigenfunctions of the allowed states of l^2.

If one adds now a third equivalent electron (with the same value of l) to the allowed states of l^2, one obtains functions that are antisymmetric, in general, only with respect to the first two electrons but not with respect to the third one. Using the coupling of three angular momenta (discussed in Chapter 2), one obtains

$$\Psi(l^2(S'L')lSL) = \sum_{S''L''} \Psi(l, \, ll(S''L''), \, SL)(l, \, ll(S''L''), \, SL \, | \, l^2(S'L')lSL), \quad (3\text{-}23)$$

where the transformation matrix is related to the Racah coefficient. In Eq. (3-23), however, the summation extends over all the values of $S''L''$, allowed as well as forbidden, and therefore $\Psi(l^2(S'L')lSL)$ is not an eigenstate of l^3.

It is possible to find, however, a linear combination such that the coefficients of the transformation subsist only for the allowed values of

$S''L''$. That is, one can obtain eigenstates of l^3 as linear combinations of $\Psi(l^2(S'L')lSL)$. One can write such a linear combination as

$$\Psi(l^3\alpha SL) = \sum_{S'L'} \Psi(l^2(S'L')lSL)(l^2(S'L')lSL \mid \}l^3\alpha SL), \qquad (3\text{-}24)$$

where $(l^2(S'L')lSL \mid \}l^3\alpha SL)$ are the "coefficients of fractional parentage" (hereafter abbreviated as CFP). These coefficients must satisfy the equations

$$\sum_{S'L'} (l, ll(S''L''), SL \mid l^2(S'L')lSL)(l^2(S'L')lSL \mid \}l^3\alpha SL) = 0, \qquad (3\text{-}25)$$

for $S'' + L''$ odd.

The relations, represented by Eq. (3-25), are necessary and sufficient to determine the CFP of l^3, since an eigenfunction that is antisymmetric with respect to electrons 1 and 2 and also antisymmetric with regard to electrons 2 and 3 is automatically antisymmetric with respect to all three electrons. The number of allowed terms in l^3 is, of course, equal to the number of independent nonvanishing solutions of Eq. (3-25) for a given value of SL; if there is more than one allowed term, the different terms can be distinguished by an index α.

This method for three equivalent particles can be extended to a configuration l^n of n equivalent electrons if the CFP of l^{n-1} are known, for in that case one can write*

$$\Psi(l^n\alpha SL) = \sum_{\alpha'S'L'} \Psi(l^{n-1}(\alpha'S'L')lSL)(l^{n-1}(\alpha'S'L')lSL \mid \}l^n\alpha SL)$$
$$= \sum \Psi(l^{n-2}(\alpha''S''L'')l(S'L')lSL)(l^{n-2}(\alpha''S''L'')lS'L' \mid \}l^{n-1}\alpha'S'L') \qquad (3\text{-}26)$$
$$\times (l^{n-1}(\alpha'S'L')lSL \mid \}l^n\alpha SL).$$

Therefore the CFP $(l^{n-1}(\alpha'S'L')lSL \mid \}l^n\alpha SL)$ must satisfy the system of equations

$$\sum_{\alpha'S'L'} (S''L'', ll(S'''L'''), SL \mid S''L''l(S'L')lSL)$$

$$(l^{n-2}(\alpha''S''L'')lS'L' \mid \}l^{n-1}\alpha'S'L')(l^{n-1}(\alpha'S'L')lSL \mid \}l^n\alpha SL) = 0 \qquad (3\text{-}27)$$

(for $S''' + L'''$ odd). It should be mentioned that the matrix

$$(l^{n-1}(\alpha'S'L')lSL \mid \}l^n\alpha SL)$$

is a rectangular matrix that is a part of a unitary matrix, as its columns do not exhaust all the states of l^{n-1}, but only those which are allowed in l^n.

The hermitian conjugate of this matrix is

$$(l^n\alpha SL\{\mid l^{n-1}(\alpha'S'L')lSL) = [(l^{n-1}(\alpha'S'L')lSL \mid \}l^n\alpha SL)]^*, \qquad (3\text{-}28)$$

and therefore it satisfies the relation

$$\sum_{\alpha'S'L'} (l^n\alpha SL\{\mid l^{n-1}(\alpha'S'L')lSL)(l^{n-1}(\alpha'S'L')lSL \mid \}l^n\alpha''SL) = \delta_{\alpha\alpha''}. \qquad (3\text{-}29)$$

---

* The summation in the last term of this equation extends over $\alpha'S'L'\alpha''S''L''$. It has been omitted for simplicity.

However, in calculations involving symmetrical operators one may formally treat the matrix $(l^{n-1}(\alpha'S'L')lSL \mid \}l^n\alpha SL)$ as a unitary matrix, since symmetrical operators do not have matrix elements between states of different symmetry, and therefore the sum over the neglected states vanishes.

Racah [8] has given the CFP of the terms of the p^n and d^n configurations, and Nielson and Nutter [5] have obtained the CFP for f^n configurations. For further details on CFP of f^n configurations the reader is referred to the pioneering work of Racah [7] who has obtained important simplifications in their calculations with the help of theory of continuous groups.

MATRIX ELEMENTS OF MANY-PARTICLE TENSOR OPERATORS

In most quantum-mechanical applications to many-electron systems one is often interested in evaluating the matrix elements between n-electron functions for the hamiltonian operator $\mathscr{H}$, which consists of a sum of single-particle and two-particle operators

$$\mathscr{H} = \mathbf{F} + \mathbf{G} = \sum_{i=1}^{n} \mathbf{f}(i) + \sum_{i>j} \mathbf{g}(j, i).$$

The evaluation of the matrix elements of operators of the types $\mathbf{F}$ and $\mathbf{G}$ can be described briefly here. Let us suppose that the system is described by the total angular momentum quantum number J and its z-component M. Using the results of the CFP, one can write the function for n-particles as a sum of products, in which each product consists of an antisymmetric function for $n - 1$ particles times a function for the n-th particle,

$$|\alpha(n), JM) = \sum_{\alpha_p, J_p, a, j} |\alpha_p(n - 1)J_p, aj; \ JM)(\alpha_p(n - 1)J_p, aj \mid \}\alpha(n)J),$$

$$(3\text{-}30)$$

where

$$|\alpha_p(n - 1)J_p, aj; \ JM) = \sum_{m} |\alpha_p(n - 1)J_pM - m) \ |ajm)_n$$

$$\times (J_pM - mjm \mid J_pjJM),$$

and $(\alpha_p(n - 1)J_p, aj \mid \}\alpha(n)J)$ is the CFP, and α, α_p, and a are any additional quantum numbers necessary to specify the states. The parent states $|\alpha_pJ_pM_p)$ are orthonormal and fully antisymmetric in the first $(n - 1)$ particles, and the n-th particle occupies the state $|ajm)_n$. Therefore the individual terms in Eq. (3-30) are not fully antisymmetric in all n particles, but their sum weighted by the CFP must be. In fact the CFP describe how the state $|\alpha JM)$ may be built from its parent states obtained by the removal of one particle.

The expansion of the type given in Eq. (3-30) is of great importance when the many-particle wavefunction $|\alpha JM)$ represents a single independent particle configuration in which each particle has a set of quantum numbers

(αj) independent of the others, such that when all are suitably vector coupled they give the correct total angular momentum J. Configurations involving a number of equivalent fermions, that is, all having the same quantum numbers, have been studied in great detail. Since the n equivalent particles are indistinguishable, the matrix element of the one-body operator $\mathbf{F}$ must be n times that of $\mathbf{f}(i)$. Let us now suppose that $\mathbf{F}$ is a tensor operator of rank k, $\mathbf{F}^{(k)}$. If we take into account that the single particle tensor operator $\mathbf{f}^{(k)}(i)$ acts upon only the i-th particle, the reduced matrix element of $\mathbf{F}^{(k)}$ is

$$(\alpha(n)J| \,|\mathbf{F}^{(k)}| \,|\alpha'(n)J') = n \sum (-1)^{J_p+k-J-j'}[(2J' + 1)(2j + 1)]^{\frac{1}{2}}$$
$$\times \; W(jj'JJ'; \; kJ_p)(\alpha(n)J\{ \,|\, \alpha_p(n-1)J_p, \alpha j) \quad (3\text{-}31)$$
$$\times \; (\alpha_p(n-1)J_p, a'j' \,|\, \}\alpha'(n)J')(\alpha j| \,|\mathbf{f}^{(k)}| \,|a'j'),$$

where the summation in Eq. (3-31) runs over α_p, J_p, a, a', j, and j'. However, because of the orthogonality of the parent functions, only the parent states common to $|\alpha(n)JM)$ and $|\alpha'(n)J'M)$ contribute. For n equivalent particles, all with angular momentum j, the sum over j and j' reduces to one term only

$$(\alpha(j^n)J| \,|\mathbf{F}^{(k)}| \,|\alpha'(j^n)J') = n(\alpha j| \,|\mathbf{f}^{(k)}| \,|\alpha j) \sum_{\alpha_p J_p} (-1)^{J_p+k-J-j'}[(2J' + 1)$$
$$\times \; (2j + 1)^{\frac{1}{2}} \, W(jjJJ'; \; kJ_p)(\alpha J\{ \,|\, \alpha_p J_p, \alpha j)(\alpha_p J_p, \alpha j \,|\, \}\alpha'J'). \quad (3\text{-}32)$$

If $\mathbf{F}^{(k)}$ is a scalar, that is, if $k = 0$, then Eq. (3-32) reduces to

$$(\alpha(j^n)J| \,|\mathbf{F}^{(0)}| \,|\alpha(j^n)J') = n(\alpha j| \,|\mathbf{f}^{(0)}| \,|\alpha j)\delta_{\alpha\alpha'}\delta_{JJ'}.$$

For configurations of equivalent particles, the ratio of the matrix elements of two one-body operators, $\mathbf{F}^{(k)}$ and $\mathbf{S}^{(k)}$, is equal to the ratio of the corresponding single particle matrix elements,

$$\frac{(\alpha(j^n)J| \,|\mathbf{F}^{(k)}| \,|\alpha'(j^n)J')}{(\alpha(j^n)J| \,|\mathbf{S}^{(k)}| \,|\alpha'(j^n)J')} = \frac{(\alpha j| \,|\mathbf{f}^{(k)}| \,|\alpha j)}{(\alpha j| \,|\mathbf{s}^{(k)}| \,|\alpha j)}.$$

For a vector operator, $\mathbf{V}^{(1)}$, one may take $\mathbf{S}^{(1)}$ to be $\mathbf{J}$,

$$(\alpha(j^n)J| \,|\mathbf{V}^{(1)}| \,|\alpha'(j^n)J') = [J(J + 1)/j(j + 1)]^{\frac{1}{2}}(\alpha j| \,|\mathbf{V}^{(1)}| \,|\alpha j)\delta_{\alpha\alpha'}\delta_{JJ'}.$$

The matrix elements of the two-body operator $\mathbf{G}$ are evaluated similarly, with the difference that one must apply the CFP expansion twice to remove the n-th and $(n-1)$-th particles. The matrix element of $\mathbf{G}$ is then equal to the matrix of the two particle operator $\mathbf{g}(j, i)$ times the number of pairs $(n/2)(n-1)$. In this case again, only those parent states common to the $(n-2)$- and n-particle states contribute to the matrix of $\mathbf{G}$. This means that for a system of independent particles the configurations for the two states can differ at most in two sets of single particle quantum numbers if the matrix element is not to vanish.

The above discussion shows how the CFP can simplify the evaluation of matrix elements of many-particle tensor operators; further details may be found in Judd [4].

REFERENCES

1. E. U. Condon and G. H. Shortley. "The Theory of Atomic Spectra." The University Press, Cambridge, 1935.
2. C. Eckart. Rev. Mod. Phys. *2*, 305 (1930).
3. A. R. Edmonds. "Angular Momentum in Quantum Mechanics." Princeton University Press, Princeton, N.J., 1957.
4. B. R. Judd. "Operator Techniques in Atomic Spectroscopy." McGraw-Hill Book Company, Inc., New York, N.Y., 1963.
5. C. W. Neilson and P. B. Nutter. Bull. Am. Phys. Soc. *7*, 80 (1962).
6. G. Racah. Phys. Rev. *62*, 438 (1942).
7. G. Racah. Phys. Rev. *63*, 367 (1943).
8. G. Racah. Phys. Rev. *76*, 1352 (1949).
9. M. E. Rose. "Elementary Theory of Angular Momentum." John Wiley & Sons, Inc., New York, N.Y., 1957.
10. E. P. Wigner. "Group Theory and Its Applications to the Quantum Mechanics of Atomic Spectra." Academic Press, Inc., New York, N.Y., 1959.

Chapter 4 DETERMINATION OF STATE FUNCTIONS: THE VARIATION METHOD

VARIATIONAL PRINCIPLE

A function Φ, which constitutes an approximation to one of the eigenfunctions Ψ_i of a given hamiltonian operator $\mathscr{H}$, is of such a form that it can transform, under proper variation, into Ψ_i. The corresponding expectation value over the hamiltonian operator, $\langle\Phi|\mathscr{H}|\Phi\rangle/\langle\Phi|\Phi\rangle$, represents an approximation to E_i, the eigenvalue corresponding to Ψ_i. In particular, it is $E = E_j$ when $\Phi = \Psi_i$.

When an arbitrary infinitesimal, nonvanishing variation $\delta\Phi$ is given to Φ, which is then transformed into $(\Phi + \delta\Phi)$, the corresponding expectation value over $\mathscr{H}$ becomes

$$(E + \delta E)\langle\Phi + \delta\Phi \,|\, \Phi + \delta\Phi\rangle = \langle\Phi + \delta\Phi|\,\mathscr{H}\,|\Phi + \delta\Phi\rangle.$$

Assuming that Φ is normalized, this equation reduces to

$$\delta E\langle\Phi + \delta\Phi \,|\, \Phi + \delta\Phi\rangle = 2\langle\delta\Phi|\,\mathscr{H} - E\,|\Phi\rangle + \langle\delta\Phi|\,\mathscr{H} - E\,|\delta\Phi\rangle,$$

if the functions Φ and $\delta\Phi$ are real. The assumption is made here without any loss of generality. If Φ is an eigenfunction of $\mathscr{H}$, that is, $\Phi = \Psi_i$, then $E = E_i$ and

$$\delta E\langle\Phi + \delta\Phi \,|\, \Phi + \delta\Phi\rangle = \langle\delta\Phi|\,\mathscr{H} - E\,|\delta\Phi\rangle, \qquad (4\text{-}1)$$

which shows that if Φ is an approximation to Ψ_i, then E constitutes a better approximation to E_i than Φ is to Ψ_i.

It has been assumed that Φ can transform, under a proper variation, into Ψ_i, but this condition is not always satisfied. In a general case, the variational principle defines the existence of an upper bound for the ground state of the system considered. If one expands the function Φ in terms of the complete set of functions Ψ_i, one obtains

$$\delta E \langle \Phi + \delta\Phi \mid \Phi + \delta\Phi \rangle = \sum_k \sum_l \langle \Psi_k c_k \mid \mathscr{H} - E_i \mid \Psi_l c_l \rangle$$

$$= \sum_k c_k^* (E_k - E_i) c_k \geq 0.$$

This condition only holds for the ground state, and therefore there is no possibility, by using the variational principle in this simple form, of obtaining an upper bound for the excited states.

There are two different approaches to overcome this difficulty. The simplest method is based on the fact that the eigenfunctions of the hamiltonian operator must form an orthogonal set, with the assumption being made that the approximate solutions should also be orthogonal to each other.

Given the expectation value $E_i = \langle \Phi_i | \mathscr{H} | \Phi_i \rangle$ and assuming Φ_i to be normalized, the necessary (though not sufficient) condition for E to be stationary is that $\delta E = 0$ for any nonzero, infinitesimal variation $\delta\Phi$. One obtains then

$$\delta E_i = \langle \delta\Phi_i | \mathscr{H} | \Phi_i \rangle + \langle \Phi_i | \mathscr{H} | \delta\Phi_i \rangle = 0. \tag{4-2}$$

The infinitesimal variations must be such that the resulting functions remain orthonormalized. The original orthonormality conditions

$$\tfrac{1}{2} \langle \Phi_i \mid \Phi_j \rangle + \tfrac{1}{2} \langle \Phi_j \mid \Phi_i \rangle = \delta_{ij}$$

transform, under the variation, into

$$\langle \delta\Phi_i \mid \Phi_j \rangle + \langle \Phi_i \mid \delta\Phi_j \rangle = 0. \tag{4-3}$$

The solution of Eq. (4-2), under the subsidiary conditions represented by Eq (4-3), is achieved by their coupling through the corresponding lagrangian multipliers, E_{ij}. The resultant equation is

$$\langle \delta\Phi_i | \mathscr{H} | \Phi_i \rangle - \sum_j E_{ji} | \Phi_j \rangle + \langle \delta\Phi_i^* | \mathscr{H} | \Phi_i^* \rangle - \sum_j E_{ij} | \Phi_j^* \rangle = 0,$$

where the summations extend over all the states that are approximated. This equation can be separated into two equivalent equations, one for $\delta\Phi_i$ and another for its complex conjugate $\delta\Phi_i^*$. The equation

$$\langle \delta\Phi_i | \mathscr{H} | \Phi_i \rangle - \sum_j E_{ji} | \Phi_j \rangle = 0$$

leads, for a nonvanishing $\delta\Phi_i$, to the condition

$$(\mathscr{H} | \Phi_i \rangle = \sum_j | \Phi_j \rangle E_{ji}. \tag{4-4}$$

For the exact functions, the cross terms $E_{ji} (j \neq i)$ vanish identically and Eq. (4-4) transforms into the original eigenvalue equation. In any other case it is necessary to eliminate them in order to transform Eq. (4-4) into a pseudoeigenvalue equation.

If we take into account that

$$E_{ji} = \langle \Phi_j | \mathscr{H} | \Phi_i \rangle,$$

Eq. (4-4) transforms into

$$(\mathscr{H} | \Phi_i \rangle - \sum_j |\Phi_j\rangle \langle \Phi_j| \mathscr{H} |\Phi_i\rangle + |\Phi_i\rangle \langle \Phi_i| \mathscr{H} |\Phi_i\rangle = |\Phi_i\rangle \langle \Phi_i| \mathscr{H} |\Phi_i\rangle. \tag{4-5}$$

When one defines a coupling operator $\mathscr{R}$ (both linear and hermitian) by

$$\mathscr{R} = \sum_k (\mathscr{H} | \Phi_k\rangle \langle \Phi_k| - \tfrac{1}{2} \sum_k \sum_1 |\Phi_k\rangle \langle \Phi_k| \mathscr{H} |\Phi_l\rangle \langle \Phi_l| + \sum_k |\Phi_k\rangle$$

$$\times \langle \Phi_k| \mathscr{H} |\Phi_k\rangle \langle \Phi_k| - \tfrac{1}{2} \sum_k \sum_l |\Phi_l\rangle \langle \Phi_l| \mathscr{H} |\Phi_k\rangle \langle \Phi_k| + \sum_k |\Phi_k\rangle \langle \Phi_k| \mathscr{H}),$$

Eq. (4-5) becomes

$$(\mathscr{R} | \Phi_i \rangle = |\Phi_i\rangle E_{ii},$$

which can be solved   The solutions of this pseudoeigenvalue equation are orthogonal.

Pluvinage [81] indicates that this procedure can be carried out by parts. That is, one first determines the approximate solution for the ground state. Then one determines the function for the first excited state under the condition that it will minimize the energy while being orthogonal to the ground state function, and so on.

The alternate approach is based on a generalized variation princple, developed by Weinstein [117] and MacDonald [60], which permits the determination of upper and lower bounds to the eigenvalues of any state. For a function Φ, which consitutes an approximation to one of the eigenfunctions of $\mathscr{H}$, one can define the function

$$\Delta_p^r = \langle (\mathscr{H} - E)^r \Phi \mid (\mathscr{H} - E)^{p-r} \Phi \rangle, \tag{4-6}$$

where p and r are integers $(0 \leq r \leq p)$ and E is an arbitrary constant. The value of Δ_p^r is independent of r.

Applying a variation to Δ_p^0 with respect to Φ, with the usual constraints, leads to

$$\Delta_p^0 \geq (E_i - E)^p,$$

which can be generalized to

$$\Delta_p^r \geq (E_i - E)^p,$$

where E_i is the discrete eigenvalue of $\mathscr{H}$ that gives a minimum for $(E_i - E)^p$ for the chosen value of E.

The extremals of Δ_p^r with respect to E are given by

$$(\delta \Delta_p^r / \delta E) \geq -p(E_i - E)^{p-1} = -p\Delta_{p-1}^r = 0,$$

which is satisfied (for $r = 0$) when $p = 2$, if the constant E is defined by $E = \langle \Phi| \mathscr{H} |\Phi\rangle$, in which case

$$(\Delta_2^0)^{\frac{1}{2}} \geq E_i - E,$$

and therefore

$$(\Delta_2^0)^{\frac{1}{2}} + E \geq E_i \geq E - (\Delta_2^0)^{\frac{1}{2}}. \tag{4-7}$$

The use of these equations within the framework of the variational method imply the optimization of Φ in such a way that Δ_2^0 becomes a minimum. One obtains upper and lower bounds for the energy.

GENERAL VARIATION TREATMENTS

The variational principle can be applied in various ways. The trial function, in any case, must contain a number of variables parameters to be determined.

The general approach implies the use of an analytical function, which can transform under proper variation, into the exact function. An alternate procedure consists of constructing the function out of arbitrary functions of given analytical form but with undetermined parameters.

The common approach involves the expansion of Φ in terms of arbitrary functions, completely determined. The problem reduces to the determination of the corresponding expansion coefficients. This is the method inherent in the self-consistent field theory (see next section) and in the configuration interaction method.

The formulation of configuration interaction is straightforward. If we write

$$|\Phi\rangle = \sum_i |\Phi_i\rangle C_i,$$

the energy expectation value becomes

$$E = \langle\Phi|\,\mathscr{H}\,|\Phi\rangle/\langle\Phi\,|\Phi\,\rangle = \left(\sum_i \sum_j C_i^* H_{ij} C_j\right) \Big/ \left(\sum_i \sum_j C_i^* S_{ij} C_j\right),$$

with

$$H_{ij} = \langle\Phi_i|\,\mathscr{H}\,|\Phi_j\rangle,\ S_{ij} = \langle\Phi_i\,|\,\Phi_j\rangle.$$

For real expansion coefficients, the minimization condition leads to a set of linear equations

$$\sum_i (H_{ij} - ES_{ij})C_j = 0,$$

which have a nontrivial solution only when the secular determinant vanishes,

$$|H_{ij} - ES_{ij}| = 0.$$

The solution of the secular equation yields the energy roots, which are used to determine all the expansion coefficients but one, which is found on the basis that the function be normalized.

For orthonormalized basis functions the secular equation reduces to

$$|H_{ij} - ES_{ij}\delta_{ij}| = 0. \tag{4-8}$$

The corresponding matrix formulation, with solution by diagonalization, is immediate.

SELF-CONSISTENT FIELD THEORY WITHOUT PERTURBATION

In the orbital approximation the variation of the energy expectation value is determined for the independent variations of the orbitals.

Every electron is described by a spin-orbital. If we use an electronic hamiltonian operator, free of magnetic interactions, the spin-orbitals are approximated by the product

$$\psi_i^{\lambda\gamma}(\rho) \equiv \psi_i^{\lambda\gamma}(x_\rho, y_\rho, z_\rho; s_\rho) = \phi_i^{\lambda\gamma}(x_\rho, y_\rho, z_\rho)\eta_i(s_\rho) \equiv \phi_i^{\lambda\gamma}(\rho)\eta_i(\rho),$$

where $\psi_i^{\lambda\gamma}$ is the spin-orbital, $\phi_i^{\lambda\gamma}$ is the orbital, dependent only on the spatial coordinates of the electron, and η_i is the spin function (either α or β). $\lambda\gamma$ stands for the symmetry designation of the orbital under consideration: λ represents the species and γ the subspecies, that is, λ refers to the irreducible representation for which the orbital serves as functional basis and γ labels the individual members of the set of degenerate orbitals which together transform according to the representation λ. The subscript i is an ordering index, which distinguishes nondegenerate orbital sets of the same symmetry designation.

The total electronic function must be antisymmetric under the exchange of any two electrons. When formed from one-electron orbitals, antisymmetrized functions are constructed from Slater determinants, defined in terms of the corresponding occupied spin-orbitals, with the condition that no two of such occupied spin-orbitals will be identical. If such a condition is not satisfied, the determinant vanishes identically.

Only one determinant is needed for the closed-shell case and for the highest multiplicity case of an open-shell system. For open-shell systems a linear combination of Slater determinants is required for the function to correspond to the symmetry and multiplicity of the state under consideration. Alternatively the use of a single determinant function as a basis for the definition of the Hartree-Fock limit (see p. 46) has also been proposed. Such a distinction in the formulation is secondary, in the sense that only a difference in the numerical value of the Hartree-Fock limit is involved and that a limit does not have any physical meaning, its significance being limited to the independent particle approximation. It is convenient, however, to use functions that although representing only an approximation to the exact function, bear a correspondence to the state under consideration.

The orbitals used to construct the function must be linearly independent, though not necessarily orthonormal. One can always find the best set of linearly independent orbitals, which minimize the energy, and then carry out an orthonormalization. The only change in the function under such a transformation is the introduction of a constant factor: the energy remains unchanged. It is no restriction, therefore, to assume that the orbitals form an orthonormal set, and this assumption will be implicit hereafter.

The total function need not be normalized, although it will assumed to be so unless specified otherwise. In the general unrestricted case, using a function not necessarily normalized, two different approaches are possible. One, designated as a total-energy variational procedure, leads to total energy eigenvalues (see Roothaan and Weiss [95]). The other (using orbitals not necessarily orthonormal) is equivalent to the formulation for normalized functions. Because in the latter case the energy expression is simpler, the corresponding formulation is presented here. The orbital variational procedure for the unnormalized case constitutes the foundation of the constrained self-consistent field procedure, leading to optimized functions under a modified energy criterion, as discussed later in this chapter.

Regarding the energy expression, that is, the energy expectation value over the total electronic time-, and spin-independent hamiltonian operator, it is convenient to define first the integrals and operators used.

The two-electron operators (both linear and hermitian) corresponding to those integrals are represented by $\mathscr{J}_m^{\mu\delta}$ and $\mathscr{K}_m^{\mu\delta}$ and by $\mathscr{L}_m^{\mu\delta}$ and $\mathscr{M}_m^{\mu\delta}$, designated as coulomb and exchange operators of the first and second kinds, respectively. They are defined by how they operate on an arbitrary one-electron function ϕ,

$$(\mathscr{J}_m^{\mu\delta}\,|\phi\rangle = \left\{ \int \phi_m^{\mu\delta*}(2)\phi_m^{\mu\delta}(2)\,(1/r_{12})\,d\tau_2 \right\} \phi(1), \qquad (4\text{-}9a)$$

$$(\mathscr{K}_m^{\mu\delta}\,|\phi\rangle = \left\{ \int \phi_m^{\mu\delta*}(2)\phi(2)\,(1/r_{12})\,d\tau_2 \right\} \phi_m^{\mu\delta}(1), \qquad (4\text{-}9b)$$

$$(\mathscr{L}_m^{\mu\delta}\,|\phi\rangle = \left\{ \int \phi_m^{\mu\delta*}(2)\phi_m^{\mu\delta*}(2)\,(1/r_{12})\,d\tau_2 \right\} \phi^*(1), \qquad (4\text{-}9c)$$

$$(\mathscr{M}_m^{\mu\delta}\,|\phi\rangle = \left\{ \int \phi_m^{\mu\delta*}(2)\phi^*(2)\,(1/r_{12})\,d\tau_2 \right\} \phi_m^{\mu\delta*}(1). \qquad (4\text{-}9d)$$

The one- and two-electron integrals corresponding to $\mathscr{H}'$ and the preceding operators, respectively, are

$$H_{ii}^{\lambda\gamma} = \langle\phi_i^{\lambda\gamma}|\,\mathscr{H}'\,|\phi_i^{\lambda\gamma}\rangle, \qquad (4\text{-}10a)$$

$$J_{im}^{\lambda\gamma,\mu\delta} = \langle\phi_i^{\lambda\gamma}|\,\mathscr{J}_m^{\mu\delta}\,|\phi_i^{\lambda\gamma}\rangle = \langle\phi_i^{\lambda\gamma}\phi_i^{\lambda\gamma}\,|\,\phi_m^{\mu\delta}\phi_m^{\mu\delta}\rangle = \langle\phi_m^{\mu\delta}\phi_m^{\mu\delta}\,|\,\phi_i^{\lambda\gamma}\phi_i^{\lambda\gamma}\rangle$$
$$= \langle\phi_m^{\mu\delta}|\,\mathscr{J}_i^{\lambda\gamma}\,|\phi_m^{\mu\delta}\rangle = J_{mi}^{\mu\delta,\lambda\gamma}, \qquad (4\text{-}10b)$$

$$K_{im}^{\lambda\gamma,\mu\delta} = \langle\phi_i^{\lambda\gamma}|\,\mathscr{K}_m^{\mu\delta}\,|\phi_i^{\lambda\gamma}\rangle = \langle\phi_i^{\lambda\gamma}\phi_m^{\mu\delta}\,|\,\phi_m^{\mu\delta}\phi_i^{\lambda\gamma}\rangle = \langle\phi_m^{\mu\delta}\phi_i^{\lambda\gamma}\,|\,\phi_i^{\lambda\gamma}\phi_m^{\mu\delta}\rangle$$
$$= \langle\phi_m^{\mu\delta}|\,\mathscr{K}_i^{\lambda\gamma}\,|\phi_m^{\mu\delta}\rangle = K_{mi}^{\mu\delta,\lambda\gamma}, \qquad (4\text{-}10c)$$

$$L_{im}^{\lambda\gamma,\mu\delta} = \langle\phi_i^{\lambda\gamma}|\,\mathscr{L}_m^{\mu\delta}\,|\phi_i^{\lambda\gamma}\rangle = \langle\phi_i^{\lambda\gamma}\phi_i^{\lambda\gamma*}\,|\,\phi_m^{\mu\delta}\phi_m^{\mu\delta*}\rangle = \langle\phi_m^{\mu\delta}\phi_m^{\mu\delta*}\,|\,\phi_i^{\lambda\gamma}\phi_i^{\lambda\gamma*}\rangle$$
$$= \langle\phi_m^{\mu\delta}|\,\mathscr{L}_i^{\lambda\gamma}\,|\phi_m^{\mu\delta}\rangle = L_{mi}^{\mu\delta,\lambda\gamma}, \qquad (4\text{-}10d)$$

$$M_{im}^{\lambda\gamma,\mu\delta} = \langle\phi_i^{\lambda\gamma}|\,\mathscr{M}_m^{\mu\delta}\,|\phi_i^{\lambda\gamma}\rangle = \langle\phi_i^{\lambda\gamma}\phi_m^{\mu\delta*}\,|\,\phi_m^{\mu\delta}\phi_i^{\lambda\gamma*}\rangle = \langle\phi_m^{\mu\delta}\phi_i^{\lambda\gamma*}\,|\,\phi_i^{\lambda\gamma}\phi_m^{\mu\delta*}\rangle$$
$$= \langle\phi_m^{\mu\delta}|\,\mathscr{M}_i^{\lambda\gamma}\,|\phi_m^{\mu\delta}\rangle = M_{mi}^{\mu\delta,\lambda\gamma}; \qquad (4\text{-}10e)$$

$H_{ii}^{\lambda\gamma}$ is independent of the subspecies γ, and the two-electron integrals are equal to their complex conjugates.

For the state under consideration, all degenerate functions are taken into account. The energy expression is the average of the energies corresponding to all those functions. One can write, toward the variation of the energy corresponding to the variation of orbitals of symmetry designation $\lambda\gamma$,

$$E = 2\sum_i f_i^\lambda H_{ii}^{\lambda\gamma} + \sum_i \sum_j f_i^\lambda f_j^\lambda I_{ij}^{\lambda\gamma,\lambda\gamma} + 2\sum_i \sum_m \sum_\mu \sum_{\delta\neq\gamma} f_i^\lambda f_m^\mu I_{im}^{\lambda\gamma,\mu\delta} + C, \quad (4\text{-}11)$$

where C contains all the terms not involving orbitals of symmetry designation $\lambda\gamma$. The i and j summations extend over all the occupied orbitals of symmetry designation $\lambda\gamma$, and the m summation extends over all the occupied orbitals of symmetry designation $\mu\delta$; for $\mu = \lambda$, the index δ cannot represent γ. f represents the fractional occupancy of the shell under consideration, as indicated by the corresponding super- and subscript, with a maximum value of 1 for a closed shell.

$I_{ij}^{\lambda\gamma,\lambda\gamma}$ and $I_{im}^{\lambda\gamma,\mu\delta}$ represent combinations of two-electron integrals. In general, such combinations are of the form

$$I_{im}^{\lambda\gamma,\mu\delta} = 2a_{im}^{\lambda\gamma,\mu\delta}J_{im}^{\lambda\gamma,\mu\delta} - b_{im}^{\lambda\gamma,\mu\delta}K_{im}^{\lambda\gamma,\mu\delta} + 2p_{im}^{\lambda\gamma,\mu\delta}L_{im}^{\lambda\gamma,\mu\delta} - q_{im}^{\lambda\gamma,\mu\delta}M_{im}^{\lambda\gamma,\mu\delta}, \quad (4\text{-}12)$$

where a, b, p, and q are constants, which depend upon the occupancy of the orbitals involved and can differ for the different states of the same configuration. Birss and Fraga [5] discuss the form of this linear combination and Laidlaw [53] has investigated the symmetry dependence of the parameters.

The problem to be considered now is the determination of the best set of orthonormal orbitals, under an energy criterion, via the variational principle. The method to be discussed here in this connection is the self-consistent field procedure.

The self-consistent field (SCF) theory was first developed by Hartree [46] and Fock [27–29] for closed-shell configurations and those configurations that differ from a closed shell by a single spin-orbital. The formulation was later extended to other open-shell configurations by Shortley [99] and Hartree and Hartree [48].

However the formulation of the analytical SCF procedure for closed-shell configurations, introduced by Roothaan [89], constitutes the basis for all developments in this field. This formalism is used here for the discussion of the generalized SCF theory. The energy has a stationary value when its variation under a variation of the orbitals is zero. Because the energy expression is obtained for orthonormal orbitals, it is necessary that they remain orthonormal during the variational process. In order to achieve this condition, the orthonormalization constraints must be introduced into the variational problem. Orthogonality conditions between orbitals of different symmetry are always satisfied and do not have to be included. Taking into account the constraints defined by the expressions

$$\langle \phi_i^{\lambda\gamma} \mid \phi_k^{\lambda\gamma} \rangle = \delta_{ik},$$

one defines the corresponding lagrangian multipliers $-2\varepsilon_{ki}^{\lambda\gamma}$ and forms the new energy function as

$$E' = E - 2 \sum_i \sum_k \{\langle\phi_i^{\lambda\gamma}| \phi_k^{\lambda\gamma}\rangle + \langle\phi_i^{\lambda\gamma} |\phi\rangle\}\varepsilon_{ki}^{\lambda\gamma}.$$

The necessary, though not sufficient, condition that E will have a stationary value reduces to $\delta E' = 0$ when the orbitals undergo an arbitrary, infinitesimal variation, with no other constraints. One can then write

$$\delta E' = \sum_i \langle\delta\phi_i^{\lambda\gamma}| f_i^\lambda \mathscr{H}' + \sum_j f_i^\lambda f_j^\lambda \mathscr{I}_j^{\lambda\gamma} + \sum_m \sum_\mu \sum_{\delta\neq\gamma} f_i^\lambda f_m^\mu \mathscr{I}_m^{\mu\delta})\phi_i^{\lambda\gamma} - \sum_k \varepsilon_{ki}^{\lambda\gamma} |\phi_k^{\lambda\gamma}\rangle$$

$$+ \sum_i \langle\delta\phi_i^{\lambda\gamma*}| f_i^\lambda \mathscr{H}'^* + \sum_j f_i^\lambda f_j^\lambda \mathscr{I}_j^{\lambda\gamma*} + \sum_m \sum_\mu \sum_{\delta\neq\gamma} f_i^\lambda f_m^\mu \mathscr{I}_m^{\mu\delta*})\phi_i^{\lambda\gamma*}$$

$$- \sum_k \varepsilon_{ik}^{\lambda\gamma} |\phi_k^{\lambda\gamma}\rangle = 0. \quad (4\text{-}13)$$

Equation (4-13) should now hold for any infinitesimal variations, $\delta\phi_i$ and $\delta\phi_i^*$, with suitable values for the lagrangian multipliers. Therefore, one can write the two parts of the above equation independently and obtain

$$(f_i^\lambda \mathscr{H}' + \sum_j f_i^\lambda f_j^\lambda \mathscr{I}_j^{\lambda\gamma} + \sum_m \sum_\mu \sum_{\delta\neq\gamma} f_i^\lambda f_m^\mu \mathscr{I}_m^{\mu\delta} |\phi_i^{\lambda\gamma}\rangle = \sum_k |\phi_k^{\lambda\gamma}\rangle \varepsilon_{ki}^{\lambda\gamma}, \quad (4\text{-}14a)$$

$$(f_i^\lambda \mathscr{H}'^* + \sum_j f_i^\lambda f_j^\lambda \mathscr{I}_j^{\lambda\gamma*} + \sum_m \sum_\mu \sum_{\delta\neq\gamma} f_i^\lambda f_m^\mu \mathscr{I}_m^{\mu\delta*} |\phi_i^{\lambda\gamma*}\rangle = \sum_k |\phi_k^{\lambda\gamma*}\rangle \varepsilon_{ik}^{\lambda\gamma}.$$

$$(4\text{-}14b)$$

Subtracting the complex conjugate of Eq. (4-14b) from Eq. (4-14a), we get

$$\sum_k |\phi_k^{\lambda\gamma}\rangle (\varepsilon_{ki}^{\lambda\gamma} - \varepsilon_{ik}^{\lambda\gamma*}) = 0,$$

which shows that the lagrangian multipliers are the elements of a hermitian matrix. Equations (4-14a) and (4-14b) are then equivalent and it is sufficient to use only one of them, for example Eq. (4-14a), which can be written in contracted form as

$$(\mathscr{F}_i^{\lambda\gamma} |\phi_i^{\lambda\gamma}\rangle = \sum_k |\phi_k^{\lambda\gamma}\rangle \varepsilon_{ki}^{\lambda\gamma}. \quad (4\text{-}15)$$

There is one such SCF equation for each occupied orbital of a symmetry designation $\lambda\gamma$ (and similarly for every symmetry designation $\mu\delta$).

In the case of systems with only closed shells, all the parameters are independent of the symmetry designation and or orbital labeling. The values are $f = 1$, $a = b = 1$, and $p = q = 0$. Therefore all the operators $\mathscr{F}$ become identical. Roothaan [89] has proved that a unitary transformation, which leaves $\mathscr{F}$ unchanged, can be used to diagonalize the lagrangian multiplier matrix. Equation (4-15) is then transformed into a pseudo-eigenvalue equation

$$(\mathscr{F} |\phi_i\rangle = |\phi_i\rangle \varepsilon_{ii}, \quad (4\text{-}16)$$

which can be diagonalized.

For open-shell systems a unitary transformation cannot be used to eliminate the off-diagonal lagrangian multipliers. Efforts to overcome this difficulty have led to various formulations. Nesbet [73] introduced approximations in the SCF equations in order to transform them into a pseudo-eigenvalue form. Lefebvre [55] proposed an SCF method with direct solution in the expansion approximation, obviating the need for pseudo-eigenvalue equations. Roothaan [90] extended his original formulation to configurations with one open shell, solving the problem of the off-diagonal lagrangian multipliers through the use of coupling operators, and Huzinaga [50] applied this formulation to systems with two open shells of different symmetry.

Finally Huzinaga [51] developed a generalized SCF theory, reducing the problem to a number of small SCF steps. Birss and Fraga [5], through the use of a general coupling operator, obtained a simpler formulation which can be applied to any electronic configuration without any restriction in the number or symmetry of the open shells.

Taking into account that

$$\varepsilon_{ji}^{\lambda\gamma} = \langle \phi_j^{\lambda\gamma} | \mathscr{F}_i^{\lambda\gamma} | \phi_i^{\lambda\gamma} \rangle,$$

we can rearrange Eq. (4-15) as

$$(\mathscr{F}_i^{\lambda\gamma} | \phi_i^{\lambda\gamma}\rangle - \sum_k |\phi_k^{\lambda\gamma}\rangle \langle \phi_k^{\lambda\gamma}| \mathscr{F}_i^{\lambda\gamma} |\phi_i^{\lambda\gamma}\rangle + |\phi_i^{\lambda\gamma}\rangle \langle \phi_i^{\lambda\gamma}| \mathscr{F}_i^{\lambda\gamma} |\phi_i^{\lambda\gamma}\rangle$$
$$= |\phi_i^{\lambda\gamma}\rangle \langle \phi_i^{\lambda\gamma}| \mathscr{F}_i^{\lambda\gamma} |\phi_i^{\lambda\gamma}\rangle. \quad (4\text{-}17)$$

Birss and Fraga [5] defined a coupling operator (both linear and hermitian)

$$\mathscr{R}^{\lambda\gamma} = \sum_k |\phi_k^{\lambda\gamma}\rangle \langle \phi_k^{\lambda\gamma}| \mathscr{F}_k^{\lambda\gamma}) - \sum_k \sum_l |\phi_k^{\lambda\gamma}\rangle \langle \phi_k^{\lambda\gamma}| \mathscr{F}_i^{\lambda\gamma} |\phi_l^{\lambda\gamma}\rangle \langle \phi_l^{\lambda\gamma}|$$
$$+ \sum_k |\phi_k^{\lambda\gamma}\rangle \langle \phi_k^{\lambda\gamma}| \mathscr{F}_k^{\lambda\gamma} |\phi_k^{\lambda\gamma}\rangle \langle \phi_k^{\lambda\gamma}| - \sum_k \sum_l |\phi_l^{\lambda\gamma}\rangle \langle \phi_l^{\lambda\gamma}| \mathscr{F}_l^{\lambda\gamma} |\phi_k^{\lambda\gamma}\rangle \langle \phi_k^{\lambda\gamma}|$$
$$+ \sum_k (\mathscr{F}_k^{\lambda\gamma} |\phi_k^{\lambda\gamma}\rangle \langle \phi_k^{\lambda\gamma}|$$

and therefore Eq. (4-17) becomes

$$(\mathscr{R}^{\lambda\gamma} |\phi_i^{\lambda\gamma}\rangle = |\phi_i^{\lambda\gamma}\rangle \varepsilon_{ii}^{\lambda\gamma}, \quad (4\text{-}18)$$

with a single distinct equation for each symmetry designation.

The solution of these pseudoeigenvalue equations is carried out, usually in matrix form, by trial and error. (The matrix formulation of Eq. (4-18) is given by Fraga and Birss [34].) A trial set of orbitals is chosen, the operators are evaluated, and the eigenvalue equations are solved for improved forms of the orbitals. These functions, or some others suggested by them, are now used in repetition of the process, which is continued until self-consistency has been reached.

Unoccupied (virtual) orbitals may also be determined. This is the case when the (closed-shell) operator $\mathscr{F}$ is used. But whether $\mathscr{F}$ has any eigenfunctions aside from the ones corresponding to the occupied orbitals is a question that depends on the system under consideration. (See, in particular, the discussion given by Roothaan [89] in this connection.) The same argument can be applied to the operator $\mathscr{R}$, with the difference that, because of its definition, the eigenvalues corresponding to the unoccupied orbitals are all identically zero.

The eigenvalues (diagonal lagrangian multipliers) of $\mathscr{F}$ are designated as orbital energies. In the case of $\mathscr{R}$, the orbital energies are defined from the eigenvalues by the relation

$$\eta_{ii}^{\lambda\gamma} = \varepsilon_{ii}^{\lambda\gamma}/f_i^\gamma.$$

The correspondence between the orbital energies and the ionization potentials has been discussed in detail by Roothaan [89], Laidlaw and Birss [54], and Birss and Laidlaw [7].

The total energy is expressed by

$$E = \sum_i \sum_\lambda \sum_\gamma f_i^\lambda \{\eta_{ii}^{\lambda\gamma} + H_{ii}^{\lambda\gamma}\}. \tag{4-19}$$

The energy limit that can be reached in SCF calculations is known as the Hartree-Fock limit. Lower energies can be obtained only by the introduction of other techniques, some of which can also be formulated in a self-consistent manner. (See for example, the work of Fraga [31] and Veillard [113].)

Because the effective fields, which act on the electrons in open-shell configurations, are spin-dependent, as pointed out by Hartree and Hartree [48], the possibility of considering the closed shells as pseudo-open shells has been discussed by Berthier [2], Pople and Nesbet [85], and Pratt [87]. It constitutes the basis of the so-called unrestricted Hartree-Fock (UHF) method. The loss of symmetry, inherent in the UHF method, can be avoided by the use of a projected UHF procedure (PUHF). (Sachs [96] discusses both methods in detail and Löwdin [56, 57] has also dealt with this problem.)

The SCF theory has also been applied to excited states by Fraga and Birss [35]. (The corresponding matrix formulation is given by Birss and Fraga [6].) This procedure is based on the generalized variational procedure, described at the beginning of this chapter. Because of the singularities occurring, the formulation is applied to the variation of Δ_2^1 better than to Δ_2^0. This SCF method is valid for both excited and lowest states, without any restriction in the number or symmetry of the open shells, and yields lower and upper bounds. Fraga [32, 33] has reformulated it for the determination of optimized virtual orbitals.

Other developments and additional formulations cannot be discussed here,* but we should mention the simplified formulations of Gombás [43] and Simonetta and Gianinetti [100] and the work of Gilbert [42] and Schmeising and Miller [98] on localized orbitals. An alternate formulation for positive ions has also been proposed by Fraga, Malli, and Valdemoro [38], and Huzinaga [52] has developed an SCF theory for geminals.

---

* Berthier [3] and Löwdin [58] have provided detailed reviews.

Mention must also be made of the SCF Hückel theory, developed by McWeeny [71] and of the so-called Pariser-Parr-Pople method for unsaturated compounds. This is an SCF method with a series of simplifying approximations. This method is based on the work of Pariser and Parr [78, 79], Pariser [75–77], Parr and Pariser [80], Pople [82–84], Brickstock and Pople [10], and Pople and Schofield [86]. Ohno [74] has reviewed this formulation and Weltin, Weber, and Heilbronner [118] have developed a simplified formalism.

RELATIVISTIC SELF-CONSISTENT FIELD THEORY

The self-consistent field formalism just presented suffers from the defects inherent in the nonrelativistic theory of quantum mechanics. It neglects the relativistic effects, and the use of the spin functions is purely formal. In relativistic theory, instead, as developed by Dirac [25] for a single electron, the electron spin is built into the theory at the outset.

Unfortunately, it is not easy to generalize the Dirac theory to many-electron systems and the corresponding exact formulation for such systems does not exist. Breit [9], in order to extend the theory to two electrons, had to approximate the electron-electron interaction; however, this formulation is not Lorentz invariant. Brown [11] rederived the electron-electron interaction as a modification of the Breit [9] interaction for electron pairs. Grant [44] developed his relativistic SCF theory,* using the modified Breit interaction for electron pairs, for (Slater) determinantal functions of Dirac spinors.

Relativistic Theory for a Single Electron

The Dirac equation for a stationary state of an electron in a central field potential $V(r)$ is

$$i(\partial u/\partial t) = \{c\alpha(\mu) \cdot \mathbf{p}(\mu) + \beta c^2 - V(r)\}u, \qquad (4\text{-}20)$$

where u is a four-component spinor; α and β are defined by

$$\alpha = \begin{pmatrix} 0 & \sigma^p \\ \sigma^p & 0 \end{pmatrix}, \beta = \begin{pmatrix} I & 0 \\ 0 & -I \end{pmatrix},$$

where I is the unit matrix of order 2 and σ^p represents any of the three Pauli spin matrices.

Bethe and Salpeter [4] have discussed in detail the angular momentum classification of the eigenfunctions of Eq. (4-20). It is apparent that $\mathbf{1}$ is no

---

* Some work has also been done on the relativistic SCF theory by Malli and Roothaan [65], and Synek [103].

longer a constant of the motion. Instead, $\mathbf{j} = \mathbf{1} + \frac{1}{2}\mathbf{\sigma}^D$ is now a constant of of the motion; $\mathbf{\sigma}^D$ being the Dirac spin matrix defined by

$$\mathbf{\sigma} = \begin{pmatrix} \mathbf{\sigma}^D & 0 \\ 0 & \mathbf{\sigma}^D \end{pmatrix}.$$

Considering the simultaneous eigenfunctions $\psi_{k,m}$ of the operators ℓ^2 $\mathit{\Delta}^2$, j^2, and j_z (where $\mathbf{j} = \mathbf{1} + \mathbf{s}$ and $\mathbf{s} = \frac{1}{2}\mathbf{\sigma}^D$), defined by the eigenequations

$$(\ell^2 |\psi_{k,m}\rangle = |\psi_{k,m}\rangle\, l(l+1), \tag{4-21a}$$

$$(\mathit{\Delta}^2 |\psi_{k,m}\rangle = |\psi_{k,m}\rangle\, \tfrac{3}{4}, \tag{4-21b}$$

$$(\mathit{j}^2 |\psi_{k,m}\rangle = |\psi_{k,m}\rangle\, j(j+1), \tag{4-21c}$$

$$(\mathit{j}_z |\psi_{k,m}\rangle = |\psi_{k,m}\rangle\, m, \tag{4-21d}$$

with $k = -(j + \frac{1}{2})a$, $l = j - \frac{1}{2}a$, and $a = \pm 1$, we can show that

$$\psi_{k,m} = \sum_{\sigma = \pm\frac{1}{2}} C(l\tfrac{1}{2}j;\ m-\sigma, \sigma) \mathrm{Y}^{(l)}_{m-\sigma}\, \Phi^\sigma_{\frac{1}{2}}, \tag{4-22}$$

where $C(l\frac{1}{2}j;\ m-\sigma, \sigma)$ is a Clebsch-Gordan coefficient related to the 3-j symbol by the relation

$$C(ll'L;\ m, m') = (-1)^{l-l'+m+m'}(2L+1)^{\frac{1}{2}} \begin{pmatrix} l & l' & L \\ m & m' & -(m+m') \end{pmatrix};$$

$\mathrm{Y}^{(l)}_{m-\sigma}$ is a spherical harmonic and $\Phi^\sigma_{\frac{1}{2}}$ is a two-component spinor function, namely

$$\Phi^{\frac{1}{2}}_{\frac{1}{2}} = \begin{pmatrix} 1 \\ 0 \end{pmatrix}, \quad \Phi^{-\frac{1}{2}}_{\frac{1}{2}} = \begin{pmatrix} 0 \\ 1 \end{pmatrix}.$$

It can be proved (see Bethe and Salpeter [4]) that the four-component function

$$\psi = \begin{pmatrix} i\psi_{-k,m}\ f(\mathrm{r}) \\ \psi_{k,m}\ g(\mathrm{r}) \end{pmatrix}$$

is an eigenfunction of j^2, $\mathit{\Delta}^2$, j_z, and $\mathbf{k} = \mathbf{\beta}(1 + \mathbf{\sigma}^D \cdot \mathbf{1})$. Titchmarsh [112] has shown that these eigenfunctions form a complete set in the sense that four arbitrary functions can be simultaneously expanded in terms of them.

Many-electron Relativistic Theory

The relativistic self-consistent field (RSCF) theory for many-electron atomic systems can be developed in an analogous manner to the nonrelativistic theory.

The usual approximation is made in which each electron is supposed to be in a stationary state in the field of the nucleus and in an average field due to the remaining electrons; each stationary state is described by four quantum numbers, corresponding to the four degrees of freedom of the electron. Adopting the central field approximation, the one-electron spinor function just discussed above can be used, taking n, j, m, and a as the four quantum numbers of the electron. The principal quantum number n is related to the number of nodes in the radial function by $n = n_r + |k|$. Denoting by l and $\bar{l}$, respectively, two groups of functions corresponding to the same value of j but having $a = \pm 1$ and $l = j \pm \frac{1}{2}$, one can obtain the following sets of values:

	s	$\bar{\text{p}}$	p	$\bar{\text{d}}$	d	$\bar{\text{f}}$	f
l	0	1	1	2	2	3	3
j	$\frac{1}{2}$	$\frac{1}{2}$	$\frac{3}{2}$	$\frac{3}{2}$	$\frac{5}{2}$	$\frac{5}{2}$	$\frac{7}{2}$
a	$+1$	-1	$+1$	-1	$+1$	-1	$+1$
$k = -(j + \frac{1}{2})a$	-1	$+1$	-2	$+2$	-3	$+3$	-4

The number of linearly independent functions in an (nl) or $(n\bar{l})$ group is equal to $(2j + 1)$.

The relativistic hamiltonian operator for many-electron systems cannot be written down exactly. The variation of mass with velocity and the spin-orbit coupling for an electron are taken into consideration by the Dirac hamiltonian operator given in Eq. (4-20). The interaction between pairs of electrons can be approximated by the Breit-Brown formula,

$$g(\rho\tau) = [1 - \boldsymbol{\alpha}(\rho) \cdot \boldsymbol{\alpha}(\tau)]/r_{\rho\tau},$$

which takes into account the electrostatic and magnetic interaction but neglects the retardation effects. $r_{\rho\tau}$ is the distance between electrons ρ and τ. The total hamiltonian operator $\mathscr{H}$ for an N-electron atom, with atomic number Z, can then be written as the sum of N Dirac hamiltonian operators plus the Breit-Brown interaction for all the distinct pairs of electrons, that is,

$$\mathscr{H} = \sum_{\rho=1}^{N} [c\boldsymbol{\alpha}(\rho) \cdot \mathbf{p}(\rho) + \boldsymbol{\beta}(\rho)c^2 - Z/r_\rho] + \sum_{\rho<\tau} g(\rho\tau) = \sum_{\rho=1}^{N} \mathscr{H}'_\rho$$

$$+ \sum_{\rho<\tau} g(\rho\tau). \quad (4\text{-}23)$$

The total function Ψ for the atom (for the closed-shell case) can be assumed to consist of an antisymmetrized product of one-electron central field functions ψ_{njm}. For normalized one-electron spinors, in which case the total function is normalized, the energy expectation value is

$$E' = \sum_k H(k) + \sum_{k,l} [J(k, l) - K(k, l)], \quad (4\text{-}24)$$

where k and l denote the one-electron quantum numbers (n_k, j_k, m_k, a_k) and (n_l, j_l, m_l, a_l) corresponding to the one-electron spinor functions ψ_k and ψ_l, respectively. The sum over k includes all the occupied one-electron states, and the sum over k and l extends over all the distinct pairs of occupied one-electron states.

The integrals $H(k)$, $J(k, l)$, and $K(k, l)$ are defined by the expressions

$$H(k) = \langle \psi_k | \, \mathcal{H}' \, | \psi_k \rangle = \int \psi_k^*(\rho) \mathcal{H}'_\rho \psi_k(\rho) \, dv_\rho,$$

$$J(k, l) = \langle \psi_k \psi_k | \, \mathcal{g} \, | \psi_l \psi_l \rangle = \iint \psi_k^*(\rho) \psi_k(\rho) g(\rho\tau) \psi_l^*(\tau) \psi_l(\tau) \, dv_\rho \, dv_\tau,$$

$$K(k, l) = \langle \psi_k \psi_l | \, \mathcal{g} \, | \psi_l \psi_k \rangle = \iint \psi_k^*(\rho) \psi_l(\rho) g(\rho\tau) \psi_l^*(\tau) \psi_k(\tau) \, dv_\rho \, dv_\tau.$$

The evaluation of the matrix elements of $g(\rho\tau)$ is simplified if one considers the electrostatic and magnetic interactions separately. Grant has developed expressions for these matrix elements using the tensor analysis of Racah.

The matrix elements for the electrostatic interaction term $(1/r_{\rho\tau})$ are

$$J^E(k, l) = \langle \psi_k | \, \mathcal{J}_l^E \, | \psi_k \rangle = \langle \psi_l | \, \mathcal{J}_k^E \, | \psi_l \rangle,$$
$$K^E(k, l) = \langle \psi_k | \, \mathcal{K}_l^E \, | \psi_k \rangle = \langle \psi_l | \, \mathcal{K}_k^E \, | \psi_l \rangle,$$

where the coulomb and exchange operators $\mathcal{J}^E$ and $\mathcal{K}^E$, respectively, are defined, as in the nonrelativistic formulation, by how they operate on an arbitrary one-electron spinor function.

The term $1/r_{12}$ can be expanded, in tensor form, as

$$1/r_{12} = \sum_{k=0}^{\infty} (r_<^k/r_>^{k+1})(\mathbf{C}^{(k)}(1) \cdot \mathbf{C}^{(k)}(2)), \qquad (4\text{-}25)$$

where $r_>$ and $r_<$ are the greater and lesser of r_1 and r_2, respectively; $\mathbf{C}^{(k)}$ is a tensor operator of rank k, with components

$$C_q^{(k)} = [4\pi/(2k+1)]^{\frac{1}{2}} Y_q^{(k)}$$

and with q taking the values $-k, \dots, k$. It can then be shown that

$$J^E(A, B) = \sum_k a^k (j_A m_A; \, j_B m_B) F_k^E(A, B), \qquad (4\text{-}26a)$$

$$K^E(A, B) = \sum_k b^k (j_A m_A; \, j_B m_B) G_k^E(A, B), \qquad (4\text{-}26b)$$

where

$$F_k^E(A, B) = \int_0^\infty \int_0^\infty [P_A^2(1) + Q_A^2(1)][P_B^2(2) + Q_B^2(2)](r_<^k/r_>^{k+1}) \, dr_1 \, dr_2,$$

$$G_k^E(A, B) = \int_0^\infty \int_0^\infty [P_A(1)P_B(1) + Q_A(1)Q_B(1)][P_A(2)P_B(2)$$
$$+ Q_A(2)Q_B(2)](r_<^k/r_>^{k+1}) \, dr_1 \, dr_2,$$

where P and Q are the radial functions. The expansion coefficients* are defined by

$$a^k(j_A m_A; \, j_B m_B) = d^k(j_A m_A; \, j_A m_A) d^k(j_B m_B; \, j_B m_B),$$
$$b^k(j_A m_A; \, j_B m_B) = [d^k(j_A m_A; \, j_B m_B)]^2,$$

---

* Grant [45] has tabulated a^k and b^k for electrons with j up to 5/2.

with

$$d^k(jm;\ j'm') = (-1)^{m+\frac{1}{2}}\{[(2j+1)(2j'+1)]^{\frac{1}{2}}/(2k+1)\}$$

$$C(jj'k;\ \tfrac{1}{2},\ -\tfrac{1}{2})C(jj'k;\ -m, m'),$$

$C(jj'k;\ m, m')$ being a Clebsch-Gordan coefficient. The functions P and Q are defined by the relations $P = gr$ and $Q = fr$. In the summation in Eq. (4-26a) k takes the values $0, 2, 4, \ldots, min\ (2j_A - 1, 2j_B - 1)$, whereas in Eq. (4-26b) k goes from $|j_A - j_B|$ to $(j_A + j_B)$, with the restriction that $(j_A + j_B + k)$ is even if $a_A \neq a_B$ and odd if $a_A = a_B$.

The magnetic interaction operator $(\boldsymbol{\alpha}(1) \cdot \boldsymbol{\alpha}(2))/r_{12}$ can be written in terms of the products of tensor operators $\boldsymbol{\sigma}(1) \cdot \boldsymbol{\sigma}(2)$ and $\mathbf{C}^{(k)}(1) \cdot \mathbf{C}^{(k)}(2)$. Grant [44] has obtained for the corresponding matrix elements the expressions

$$J^M(A, B) = \sum_k f^k(j_A m_A;\ j_B m_B) F_k^M(A, B), \qquad (4\text{-}27a)$$

$$K^M(A, B) = \sum_{kJ\gamma} g^k(j_A m_A;\ j_B m_B;\ J\gamma) G_k^K(A, B;\ \gamma). \qquad (4\text{-}27b)$$

In the summation in Eq. (4-27a) k can take the values $1, 3, \ldots, min\ (2j_A, 2j_B)$, whereas in Eq. (4-27b) k is limited by $max\ [\{j - j' + \frac{1}{2}(a + a')\beta\},$ $(J - 1)] \leq k \leq min\ [\{j + j' + \frac{1}{2}(a - a')\beta\}, (J + 1)]$, with $j + j' + k$ being even if $a = a'$ and odd if $a \neq a'$. The values of J are limited by $|j - j'| \leq J \leq j + j'$.

In Eqs. (4-27a) and (4-27b),

$$F_k^M(A, B) = \int_0^\infty \int_0^\infty [P_A(1)Q_A(1)][P_B(2)Q_B(2)](r_<^k/r_>^{k+1})\ dr_1\ dr_2,$$

$$G_k^M(A, B;\ 1) = \int_0^\infty \int_0^\infty [P_A(1)Q_B(1)][P_A(2)Q_B(2)](r_<^k/r_>^{k+1})\ dr_1\ dr_2,$$

$$G_k^M(A, B;\ 0) = \int_0^\infty \int_0^\infty [P_A(1)Q_B(1)][Q_A(2)P_B(2)](r_<^k/r_>^{k+1})\ dr_1\ dr_2,$$

$$G_k^M(A, B;\ -1) = \int_0^\infty \int_0^\infty [Q_A(1)P_B(1)][Q_A(2)P_B(2)](r_<^k/r_>^{k+1})\ dr_1\ dr_2,$$

and

$$f^k(j_A m_A;\ j_B m_B) = 8C(j_A k j_A;\ -m_A, 0)C(j_B k j_B;\ -m_B, 0)$$

$$\times\ e_1^k(j_A a_A;\ j_A a_A;\ k)\ e_1^k(j_B a_B;\ j_B a_B;\ k),$$

$$g^k(j_A m_A;\ j_B m_B;\ J\gamma) = 2[C(j_B J j_A;\ -m_B, -m_A + m_B)]^2$$

$$\times \sum_{\beta\beta'} \delta[\gamma, (\beta + \beta')/2](-1)^{(\beta-\beta')/2}\ e_\beta^k(j_B a_B;\ j_A a_A;\ J)\ e_{\beta'}^k(j_B a_B;\ j_A a_A;\ J).$$

The coefficients $e^k_\beta(ja; j'a'; J)$ are defined* by

$$e^k_\beta(ja; j'a'; J) = [3(2J+1)(2j+1)]^{\frac{1}{2}}(j + \tfrac{1}{2}a\beta|\,|\mathbf{C}^{(k)}|\,|j' - \tfrac{1}{2}a'\beta)$$

$$X \begin{pmatrix} j + \tfrac{1}{2}a\beta & \tfrac{1}{2} & j \\ j - \tfrac{1}{2}a'\beta & \tfrac{1}{2} & j' \\ k & 1 & J \end{pmatrix}.$$

The reduced matrix elements of $\mathbf{C}^{(k)}$ can be evaluated using the formulation of Racah, and the X coefficients are defined by Fano and Racah [26].

The energy expectation value for configurations of closed shells can then be written as

$$E' = E^E + E^M,$$

with

$$E^E = \sum_A \left\{ q_A H(\mathrm{A}) + \tfrac{1}{2}q_A(q_A - 1)F^E_0(A, A) - \sum_{k>0}(1/4)q^2_A \Gamma_{j_Akj_A}F^E_k(A, A) \right.$$

$$\left. + \sum_{B \neq A}' [q_A q_B F^E_0(A, A) - \sum_k \tfrac{1}{2}q_A q_B \Gamma_{j_Akj_B}G^E_k(A, B)] \right\}, \quad (4\text{-}28a)$$

$$E^M = \sum_A \left\{ (\tfrac{1}{4})q^2_A \sum_{\substack{J,k \\ (\mathrm{odd})}} \Gamma_{j_Akj_A}(J)F^M_k(A, A) + \sum_{B \neq A} \sum_{\substack{J,k \\ (\mathrm{odd})}} \tfrac{1}{2}q_A q_B \right.$$

$$\left. \times \sum_\gamma \Gamma^{a_Aa_B}_{j_Akj_B}(J; \gamma)G^M_k(A, B; \gamma) \right\}. \quad (4\text{-}28b)$$

The prime on the summation over B implies that the pairs of groups A and B are to be counted only once; q_A and q_B represent the maximum number of electrons in the shell of angular momentum j_A.

The various coefficients† in Eqs. (4-28a) and (4-28b) are

$$\Gamma_{j_Akj_B} = [2/(j_A + 1)][C(j_Bkj_A; \tfrac{1}{2}, 0)]^2, \quad (4\text{-}29a)$$

$$\Gamma_{j_Akj_A}(J) = [16/(2j_A + 1)][e^k_1(j_Aa_A; j_Aa_A; J)]^2, \quad (4\text{-}29b)$$

$$\Gamma^{a_Aa_B}_{j_Akj_B}(J; \gamma) = [4/(2j_B + 1)]\sum_{\beta\beta'}(-1)^{(\beta-\beta')/2}\delta[\gamma, (\beta + \beta')/2]$$

$$\times e^k_\beta(j_Ba_B; j_Aa_A; J)e^k_{\beta'}(j_Ba_B; j_Aa_A; J). \quad (4\text{-}29c)$$

In Eq. (4-29b) k and J are both odd integers.

Hartree-Fock Equations for Closed-shell Configurations

Applying a variational treatment to the expectation value E' for a closed-shell configuration, Grant [44] has derived the following equations for the radial

---

* Grant [45] has tabulated the coefficients e^k for values of j and j' up to 3/2; these tables have been extended by Cooper [23, 24].

† These coefficients have been listed by Grant [45] and Cooper [23, 24] for values of J up to 3.

functions P_A and Q_A:

$$(dP_A/dr) + (K_A P_A/r)[2c + (1/c)(Y^E(A;\ r)/r - \varepsilon_{AA})]Q_A - Y^M(A;\ r)P_A/r$$
$$- W_Q(A;\ r) + V_p(A;\ r) - \sum_{B \neq A} (1/c)\varepsilon_{AB}\delta(j_A, j_B)\delta(a_A, a_B)Q_B = 0,$$

$$(4\text{-}30a)$$

$$(dQ_A/dr) - (K_A Q_A/r) - (1/c)(Y^E(A;\ r)/r - \varepsilon_{AA})P_A + Y^M(A;\ r)Q_A/rc$$
$$+ W_P(A;\ r) - V_p(A;\ r) + \sum_{B \neq A} (1/c)\varepsilon_{AB}\,\delta(j_A, j_B)\delta(a_A, a_B)P_B = 0,$$

$$(4\text{-}30b)$$

where ε_{AB} and ε_{AA} are the lagrangian multipliers and

$$Y^E(A;\ r) = Y^E(r) + \sum_k \tfrac{1}{2}q_A \Gamma_{j_A k j_A} Y_k^E(A, A;\ r),$$

$$Y^M(A;\ r) = \sum_{kJ} (\tfrac{1}{4})q_A \Gamma_{j_A k j_A}(J) Y_k^M(A, A;\ r),$$

$$Y^E(r) = Z - \sum_A q_{AA} Y_0^E(A, A;\ r),$$

$$W_p(A;\ r) = -(1/rc) \sum_{B \neq A} \sum_k \tfrac{1}{2}q_B \Gamma_{j_A k j_B} Y_k^E(A, B;\ r)P_B(r),$$

$$V_P(A;\ r) = -(1/rc) \sum_{B \neq A} \sum_{kJ} \tfrac{1}{2}q_B [\Gamma_{j_A k j_B}^{a_A a_B}(J;\ -1) Y_k^M(B, A;\ r)$$
$$+ \tfrac{1}{2}\Gamma_{j_A k j_B}^{a_A a_B}(J;\ 0) Y_k^M(A, B;\ r)]P_B(r),$$

$$V_Q(A;\ r) = -(1/rc) \sum_{B \neq A} \sum_{kJ} \tfrac{1}{2}q_B [\Gamma_{j_A k j_B}^{a_A a_B}(J;\ 1) Y_k^M(A, B;\ r)$$
$$+ \tfrac{1}{2}\Gamma_{j_A k j_B}^{a_A a_B}(J;\ 0) Y_k^M(B, A;\ r)]Q_B(r).$$

$$Y_k^E(A, B;\ r) = r \int_0^\infty U_k(r, s)[P_A(s)P_B(s) + Q_A(s)Q_B(s)]\ ds,$$

$$Y_k^M(A, B;\ r) = r \int_0^\infty U_k(r, s)[P_A(s)Q_B(s)]\ ds,$$

$$U_k(r, s) = r^k/s^{k+1}, \qquad \text{if } r < s,$$
$$= s^k/r^{k+1}, \qquad \text{if } r > s.$$

$W_Q(A;\ r)$ is defined by an expression identical to that given for $W_p(A;\ r)$, replacing $P_B(r)$ with $Q_B(r)$.

Mayers [66] has carried out SCF calculations (with exchange), using Eqs. (4-30a) and (4-30b), for neutral Hg and for singly-ionized Hg in the K-shell. The magnetic terms in the SCF equations were not included explicitly, but their effect on the functions is rather small.

Using Mayers' results, Grant has calculated the ionization energy of a single K-electron of Hg. The importance of this quantity lies in the fact that it provides a means of testing the Lamb shift of a tightly bound electron. The value obtained by Grant is 6112 Ry, whereas the experimental value obtained by Saxon [97] is 6107 ± 0.6 Ry. The agreement between these values can be improved by inclusion of the rearrangement energy $\Delta(1s)^{-2}$, defined by the difference $[E(1s)^{-2} - E'(1s)^{-2}]$; $E(1s)^{-2}$ and $E'(1s)^{-2}$ denote all the terms arising from electrons outside the K-shell only for neutral and singly-ionized Hg, respectively.

SELF-CONSISTENT FIELD FORMALISM FOR INTRINSIC PROPERTIES

The expectation values of intrinsic properties are usually calculated from functions determined on the basis of an energy criterion. There is, however, the possibility of their direct determination through constrained variational treatments or by a perturbation approach.

A method, developed by Mukherji and Karplus [72] and later extended by Rasiel and Whitman [88] and Whitman and Carpenter [119], consists of constraining the variational function in order to obtain a preset result for the expectation value of a given operator.

The introduction of an additional constraint determines a sacrifice in energy; that is, a constrained treatment yields an energy higher than an unconstrained calculation. The interest in the constrained method lies in the fact, as pointed out by Byers Brown [13], that perhaps the raising of the energy will be negligible. The calculations carried out on hydrogen fluoride, lithium hydride, and helium by Mukherji and Karplus [72], Rasiel and Whitman [88], and Whitman and Carpenter [119], respectively, justify the use of a constrained method.

Byers Brown [13] has proposed a perturbation formulation, based on the constrained variational method, but Chong and Rasiel [14] have shown, at least for lithium hydride, that the direct solution of the variational approach is preferable to the perturbation treatment.

The constrained variational method, furthermore, can be used as a basis for the development of a modified SCF formalism. This formulation is possible because Fraga and Malli [37] have shown that the orthonormality conditions for the orbitals need not be introduced as subsidiary constraints in the variational treatment. (This result agrees with that obtained by Fraga [30], who reformulated the generalized SCF method without introducing the orthogonality constraints, showing that both formulations are equivalent at self-consistency.) Therefore one can use instead any physical observable as constraint, but the discussion here is restricted to those properties corresponding to one-electron operators. The generalization to two-electron operators does not offer any difficulty.

The alternate constraint, used by Fraga and Birss [36], is that the expectation value for a one-electron operator $\mathscr{P}$,

$$P = \langle\Phi|\,\mathscr{P}\,|\Phi\rangle/\langle\Phi\,|\,\Phi\rangle,$$

shall have a certain desired value. Restricting the discussion to closed-shell systems as a prototype, variation of E and P, coupled by a lagrangian multiplier ω_p, yields

$$\delta E' = 2 \sum_i \langle \delta\phi_i | \mathscr{F} - [E - \sum_k (F_{kk} + H_{kk})] - \omega_p[\mathscr{P} - (P - 2 \sum_k P_{kk})]$$
$$- \sum_j (F_{ji} + \omega_p P_{ji}) |\phi_i\rangle + 2 \sum_i \langle \phi_i | \mathscr{F} - [E - \sum_k (F_{kk} + H_{kk})]$$
$$- \omega_p[\mathscr{P} - (P - 2 \sum_k P_{kk})] - \sum_j (F_{ji} + \omega_p P_{ji}) |\delta\phi_i\rangle,$$

where all the terms have the same meaning as above and

$$P_{ji} = \langle \phi_j | \mathscr{P} | \phi_i \rangle.$$

If we follow the usual procedure, this equation leads to

$$(\mathscr{F} - \omega_p \mathscr{P} - [E - \sum_k (F_{kk} + H_{kk})] + \omega_p[P - 2 \sum_k P_{kk}] |\phi_i\rangle$$
$$= \sum_j |\phi_j\rangle (F_{ji} + \omega_p P_{ji}). \quad (4\text{-}31)$$

The quantity $[E - (F_{kk} + H_{kk})]$ is identically zero since the summation is the expression of the total electronic energy, which is entirely determined by the orbitals. The term $[P - 2 \sum_k P_{kk}]$ must necessarily be given a different treatment.

If no value of P is prechosen, implying the calculation of P from the orbitals, the term is zero and Eq. (4-31) reduces to the normal pseudo-eigenvalue equation for closed-shell systems, with only the energy minimization being operative. If the condition that P shall have a fixed value is imposed, Eq. (4-31) can be written as

$$(\mathscr{T} + \omega_p[P - 2 \sum_k P_{kk}] |\phi_i\rangle = \sum_j |\phi_j\rangle \tau_{ji},$$

with

$$\mathscr{T} = \mathscr{F} - \omega_p \mathscr{P},$$
$$\tau_{ji} = F_{ji} + \omega_p P_{ji}.$$

The unitary transformation which diagonalizes the matrix $\boldsymbol{\tau}$ leaves $\mathscr{F}$, and hence $\mathscr{T}$, invariant so that there exists the pseudoeigenvalue equation

$$(\mathscr{T} + \omega_p[P - 2 \sum_k P_{kk}] |\phi_i\rangle = |\phi_i\rangle \tau_{ii}. \quad (4\text{-}32)$$

If more than one physical property (corresponding to one-electron operators) are to be considered, one requires $\sum_p \omega_p \delta P$ to be added to δE. The equations for this case are analogous to the case of a single constraint.

Because of the presence of the multiplier ω_p the solution of the eigenvalue equation differs from the normal unrestricted SCF. For a given preset value of P there exists a unique value of ω_p. (See for example the discussion given by Bolza [8]. This conclusion is supported by the results of Chong and Rasiel [14].) Restricted self-consistent orbitals which lead to this value of P are not attained until the proper value of ω_p is used. For an arbitrarily chosen set of values of ω_p, one performs the corresponding set of restricted SCF calculations, computing the expectation value of $\mathscr{P}$ for each set of vectors so obtained. From this information a new series of ω_p can be chosen, and the process repeated until one has found that unique value of ω_p that permits self-consistent orbitals giving rise to the chosen value of P.

When more than one physical property is being used as the source of a constraint, the procedure is generalized to include one multiplier associated with each operator $\mathscr{P}$. In this case there may be an impossibility of finding a single set of orbitals that yield, simultaneously, the empirically chosen values of the physical properties. A compromise is then required, and therefore such a general procedure is unlikely to be useful in practice.

HARTREE-FOCK FUNCTIONS

The approximate solution of the Hartree-Fock equations (such as Eqs. (4-16) and (4-18)) can be carried out by numerical methods or by the expansion method, in which case the orbitals are expressed as

$$\phi_i = \sum_p \chi_p c_{pi},$$

where the χ_p are analytical functions.

Various numerical techniques have been developed by Hartree and coworkers,* and functions have been calculated by this method, but the analytical Hartree-Fock procedure offers the advantage of a greater simplicity in the use of the functions for secondary calculations, that is, of physical properties.

Slater [101] proposed the fitting of the Hartree-Fock orbitals by analytical functions,† and Löwdin and Appel [59] have discussed the possibility of executing this fitting by successive approximations.

The direct determination of analytical Hartree-Fock functions can be carried out by two different methods. McWeeny [67–70] has proposed an iteration process using the first-order density matrices, whereas Roothaan [89, 90] uses a direct diagonalization procedure.

Most of the existing analytical Hartree-Fock functions have been determined by the SCF method of Roothaan, which has been discussed with greater emphasis on the practical considerations by Roothaan and Bagus [91]. Roothaan [90], Malli [62], and Malli and Olive [64] have given the coupling coefficients needed in atomic calculations. Clementi [19] has

---

* Complete details are given by Hartree [47]. Some Hartree-Fock functions have been evaluated, using these techniques, by Hartree and Hartree [48], Hartree, Hartree, and Swirles [49], and Froese [39–41].

† These functions, known as Slater orbitals, are the ones commonly used in the expansion method, though gaussian and other functions may also be employed. The discussion in this text is restricted to functions expressed in terms of Slater-type orbitals, abbreviated as STO.

reviewed the situation regarding SCF calculations in atoms and molecules, with additional references to his work.

Analytical Hartree-Fock functions for atoms and their ions have been determined by the following:

(a) Bagus [1]. Excited states of Ne- and A-like ions.

(b) Clementi [15–18, 20]. Ground states and excited states, corresponding to the same configuration as the ground state, of the neutral atoms He to Kr, the negative ions Li$^-$ to Br$^-$, and the isoelectronic series $1s(2)$, ^1S, to $K(2)L(8)M(18)$, ^1S.

(c) Clementi, Roothaan, and Yoshimine [21]. Ground states for the neutral atoms of the first row.

(d) Cohen, Simincic, and Olive [22]. Excited states of Cu and Cu$^+$.

(e) Malli [63]. Ground states and excited states, corresponding to the same configuration as the ground state, of the neutral atoms Na to A.

(f) Roothaan and Kelly [92]. Ground and excited states of N and O and of their ions.

(g) Roothaan, Sachs, and Weiss [93]. Isoelectronic series $1s(2)$, ^1S, $1s(2)2s(1)$, ^2S, and $1s(2)2s(2)$, ^1S.

(h) Roothaan and Synek [94]. Ground states of Mo and Mo$^+$.

(i) Sachs [96]. Ground states of Li, F, F$^-$, Ne, Na$^+$, and Na.

(j) Synek [102, 104, 105]. Ground and excited states of Al, Al$^+$, Cu, Cu$^+$, Cr, Cr$^+$, and Mn^{3+}.

(k) Synek and Rainis [106]. Excited states of Mn^{3+}.

(l) Synek, Rainis, and Peterson [107]. Ground and excited states of Fe^{3+}.

(m) Synek, Rainis, and Roothaan [108]. Ground states of K$^+$, K, and Ca.

(n) Synek and Stungis [109–111]. Ground states of Cr$^+$, Cr^{2+}, Cr^{3+}, Cr^{4+}, Cr^{5+}, Xe and Rn.

(o) Watson [114]. States corresponding to $3d(n)$ configurations in the iron series (Sc to Cu).

(p) Watson and Freeman [115, 116]. Ground states of Al, Si, P, S, Cl, Cl$^-$, Ar, Zn, Ga$^+$, Ga, Ge^{++}, Ge, As, Se, Br, Br$^-$, Kr, and Rb$^+$.

The preceding list is presented for completeness, but it must be pointed out that the most comprehensive work is that of Clementi [20].

There are a large number of Hartree-Fock functions available for molecules. Mention must be made, in particular, of the functions determined* for diatomic molecules (homonuclear and some heteronuclear, including hydrides, fluorides, and oxides) of the first two rows of the periodic system.

---

* These calculations have been carried out at the Laboratory of Molecular Structure and Spectra, Department of Physics, University of Chicago, by P. Cade, J. Greenshields, W. Huo, G. Malli, S. Peyerimhoff, K. D. Sales, A. C. Wahl, and others. Results and details of the calculations have been presented in the successive Technical Reports of that Laboratory, starting in 1964.

REFERENCES

1. P. S. Bagus. Phys. Rev. *139*, A619 (1965).
2. G. Berthier. J. Chim. Phys. *51*, 363 (1954).
3. G. Berthier. Self-Consistent Field Methods for Open-Shell Molecules, *in* "Molecular Orbitals in Chemistry, Physics and Biology," edited by P. O. Löwdin and B. Pullman. Academic Press, Inc., New York, N.Y., 1964.
4. H. A. Bethe and E. E. Salpeter. "Quantum Mechanics of One- and Two-Electron Atoms." Academic Press, Inc., New York, N.Y., 1953.
5. F. W. Birss and S. Fraga. J. Chem. Phys. *38*, 2552 (1963).
6. F. W. Birss and S. Fraga. J. Chem. Phys. *40*, 3212 (1964).
7. F. W. Birss and W. G. Laidlaw. Theoret. Chim. Acta (Berlin) *2*, 186 (1964).
8. O. Bolza. "Lectures on the Calculus of Variations." Dover Publications, Inc., New York, N.Y., 1961.
9. G. Breit. Phys. Rev. *34*, 553 (1929).
10. A. Brickstock and J. A. Pople. Trans. Faraday Soc. *50*, 901 (1954).
11. G. E. Brown. Phil. Mag. *43*, 467 (1952).
12. G. E. Brown and D. F. Mayers. Proc. Roy. Soc. (London) *A251*, 105 (1959).
13. W. Byers Brown. J. Chem. Phys. *44*, 567 (1966).
14. D. P. Chong and Y. Rasiel. J. Chem. Phys. *44*, 1819 (1966).
15. E. Clementi. J. Chem. Phys. *38*, 996 (1963).
16. E. Clementi. J. Chem. Phys. *38*, 1001 (1963).
17. E. Clementi. J. Chem. Phys. *41*, 295 (1964).
18. E. Clementi. J. Chem. Phys. *41*, 303 (1964).
19. E. Clementi. IBM J. Res. Develop. *9*, 2 (1965).
20. E. Clementi. "Tables of Atomic Functions." IBM Corporation, San José, California, 1965.
21. E. Clementi, C. C. J. Roothaan, and M. Yoshimine. Phys. Rev. *127*, 1618 (1962).
22. H. D. Cohen, Z. Simincic, and J. P. Olive. Phys. Rev. *142*, 8 (1966).
23. J. R. A. Cooper. Proc. Phys. Soc. (London) *86*, 529 (1965).
24. J. R. A. Cooper. "Relativistic Electron Interaction Coefficients." National Physical Laboratory, Mathematics Division, Report No. MA53, March 1965.
25. P. A. M. Dirac. Proc. Roy. Soc. (London) *A117*, 610 (1928).
26. U. Fano and G. Racah. "Irreducible Tensorial Sets." Academic Press, Inc., New York, N.Y., 1959.
27. V. Fock. Z. Physik *61*, 126 (1930).
28. V. Fock. Z. Physik *62*, 795 (1930).
29. V. Fock. Z. Phyzik *81*, 195 (1933).
30. S. Fraga. Theoret. Chim. Acta (Berlin) *2*, 403 (1964).
31. S. Fraga. J. Math. Phys. *6*, 18 (1965).
32. S. Fraga. Can. J. Phys. *44*, 303 (1966).
33. S. Fraga. Can. J. Phys. *44*, 307 (1966).
34. S. Fraga and F. W. Birss. J. Chem. Phys. *40*, 3203 (1964).
35. S. Fraga and F. W. Birss. J. Chem. Phys. *40*, 3207 (1964).
36. S. Fraga and F. W. Birss. Theoret. Chim. Acta (Berlin) *5*, 398 (1966).
37. S. Fraga and G. Malli. Theoret. Chim. Acta (Berlin) *5*, 446 (1966).
38. S. Fraga, G. Malli, and C. Valdemoro. Theoret. Chim. Acta (Berlin) *6*, 122 (1966).
39. C. Froese. Can. J. Phys. *41*, 1895 (1963).
40. C. Froese. Phys. Rev. *137*, A1644 (1965).
41. C. Froese. J. Chem. Phys. *45*, 1417 (1966).
42. T. L. Gilbert. Self-Consistent Equations for Localized Orbitals in Polyatomic Systems, *in* "Molecular Orbitals in Chemistry, Physics and Biology," edited by P. O. Löwdin and B. Pullman. Academic Press, Inc., New York, N.Y., 1964.
43. P. Gombás. Theoret. Chim. Acta (Berlin) *5*, 112 (1966).
44. I. P. Grant. Proc. Roy. Soc. (London) *A262*, 555 (1961).
45. I. P. Grant. Proc. Phys. Soc. (London) *86*, 523 (1965).
46. D. R. Hartree. Proc. Camb. Phil. Soc. *24*, 89 (1928).

47. D. R. Hartree. "The Calculation of Atomic Structures." John Wiley & Sons, Inc., New York, N.Y., 1957.
48. D. R. Hartree and W. Hartree. Proc. Roy. Soc. (London) *A154*, 588 (1936).
49. D. R. Hartree, W. Hartree, and B. Swirles. Phil. Trans. Roy. Soc. *238*, 229 (1939).
50. S. Huzinaga. Phys. Rev. *120*, 866 (1960).
51. S. Huzinaga. Phys. Rev. *122*, 131 (1961).
52. S. Huzinaga. IBM Research Paper RJ-292 (1964).
53. W. G. Laidlaw. J. Chem. Phys. *40*, 2040 (1964).
54. W. G. Laidlaw and F. W. Birss. Theoret. Chim. Acta (Berlin) *2*, 181 (1964).
55. R. Lefebvre. J. Chim. Phys. *54*, 168 (1957).
56. P. O. Löwdin. J. Math. Phys. *3*, 1171 (1962).
57. P. O. Löwdin. Quantum Theory Project, special issue for the 1963/64 Winter Institute at the University of Florida.
58. P. O. Löwdin. Molecular Orbitals in the Exact SCF Theory, *in* "Molecular Orbitals in Chemistry, Physics and Biology," edited by P. O. Löwdin and B. Pullman. Academic Press, Inc., New York, N.Y., 1964.
59. P. O. Löwdin and K. Appel. Phys. Rev. *103*, 1746 (1956).
60. J. K. L. MacDonald. Phys. Rev. *46*, 828 (1934).
61. G. Malli. Phys. Rev. *135*, A978 (1964).
62. G. Malli. Can. J. Chem. *44*, 1451 (1966).
63. G. Malli. Can. J. Phys. *44*, 3121 (1966).
64. G. Malli and J. P. Olive. J. Chem. Phys. *43*, 861 (1965).
65. G. Malli and C. C. J. Roothaan. Bull. Am. Phys. Soc. *9*, 101 (1964).
66. D. F. Mayers. Unpublished results.
67. R. McWeeny. Proc. Roy. Soc. (London) *A235*, 496 (1956).
68. R. McWeeny. Proc. Roy. Soc. (London) *A237*, 355 (1956).
69. R. McWeeny. Proc. Roy. Soc. (London) *A241*, 239 (1957).
70. R. McWeeny. Rev. Mod. Phys. *32*, 335 (1960).
71. R. McWeeny. The Self-Consistent Generalization of Hückel Theory, *in* "Molecular Orbitals in Chemistry, Physics and Biology," edited by P. O. Löwdin and B. Pullman. Academic Press, Inc., New York, N.Y., 1964.
72. A. Mukherji and M. J. Karplus. J. Chem. Phys. *38*, 44 (1963).
73. R. K. Nesbet. Proc. Roy. Soc. (London) *A230*, 312 (1955).
74. K. Ohno. Theoret. Chim. Acta (Berlin) *2*, 219 (1964).
75. R. Pariser. J. Chem. Phys. *21*, 568 (1953).
76. R. Pariser. J. Chem. Phys. *24*, 250 (1956).
77. R. Pariser. J. Chem. Phys. *24*, 1112 (1956).
78. R. Pariser and R. G. Parr. J. Chem. Phys. *21*, 466 (1953).
79. R. Pariser and R. G. Parr. J. Chem. Phys. *21*, 767 (1953).
80. R. G. Parr and R. Pariser. J. Chem. Phys. *23*, 711 (1955).
81. P. Pluvinage. "Eléments de Méchanique Quantique." Masson et Cie., Editeurs, Paris, 1955.
82. J. A. Pople. Trans. Faraday Soc. *49*, 1375 (1953).
83. J. A. Pople. Proc. Roy. Soc. (London) *A233*, 233 (1955).
84. J. A. Pople. J. Phys. Chem. *61*, 6 (1957).
85. J. A. Pople and R. K. Nesbet. J. Chem. Phys. *22*, 571 (1954).
86. J. A. Pople and P. Schofield. Proc. Roy. Soc. (London) *A233*, 241 (1955).
87. G. W. Pratt, Jr. Phys. Rev. *102*, 1303 (1956).
88. Y. Rasiel and D. R. Whitman. J. Chem. Phys. *42*, 2124 (1965).
89. C. C. J. Roothaan. Rev. Mod. Phys. *23*, 69 (1951).
90. C. C. J. Roothaan. Rev. Mod. Phys. *32*, 179 (1960).
91. C. C. J. Roothaan and P. S. Bagus. Atomic Self-Consistent Field Calculations by the Expansion Method, *in* "Methods in Computational Physics," vol II. Academic Press, Inc., New York, N.Y., 1963.
92. C. C. J. Roothaan and P. S. Kelly. Phys. Rev. *131*, 1177 (1963).
93. C. C. J. Roothaan, L. M. Sachs, and A. W. Weiss. Rev. Mod. Phys. *32*, 186 (1960).
94. C. C. J. Roothaan and M. Synek. Phys. Rev. *133*, A1263 (1964).
95. C. C. J. Roothaan and A. W. Weiss. Rev. Mod. Phys. *32*, 194 (1960).

96. L. M. Sachs. "A Theoretical Study of Simple Many-Electron Systems." Argonne National Laboratory, Report ANL-6310, 1961.
97. D. Saxon. Ph.D. Thesis. University of Wisconsin, 1954.
98. H. N. Schmeising and R. L. Miller. J. Chem. Phys. *40*, 926 (1964).
99. G. H. Shortley. Phys. Rev. *50*, 1072 (1936).
100. M. Simonetta and E. Gianinetti. The Self-Consistent Field Molecular Orbital Theory: An Elementary Approach, *in* "Molecular Orbitals in Chemistry, Physics and Biology," edited by P. O. Löwdin and B. Pullman. Academic Press, Inc., New York, N.Y., 1964.
101. J. C. Slater. Phys. Rev. *42*, 33 (1932).
102. M. Synek. Phys. Rev. *131*, 1572 (1963).
103. M. Synek. Phys. Rev. *133*, A961 (1964).
104. M. Synek. Phys. Rev. *136*, A1552 (1964).
105. M. Synek. Phys. Rev. *139*, A1049 (1965).
106. M. Synek and A. E. Rainis. Phys. Letters *19*, 205 (1965).
107. M. Synek, A. E. Rainis, and E. A. Peterson. Preprint communication.
108. M. Synek, A. E. Rainis, and C. C. J. Roothaan. Phys. Rev. *141*, A174 (1966).
109. M. Synek and G. E. Stungis. Phys. Rev. *136*, A112 (1964).
110. M. Synek and G. E. Stungis. J. Chem. Phys. *41*, 971 (1964).
111. M. Synek and G. E. Stungis. J. Chem. Phys. *42*, 3068 (1965).
112. E. C. Titchmarsh. Proc. Roy. Soc. (London) *A262*, 489 (1961).
113. A. Veillard. Theoret. Chim. Acta (Berlin) *4*, 22 (1965).
114. R. E. Watson. Phys. Rev. *118*, 1036 (1960).
115. R. E. Watson and A. J. Freeman. Phys. Rev. *123*, 521 (1961).
116. R. E. Watson and A. J. Freeman. Phys. Rev. *124*, 1117 (1961).
117. D. H. Weinstein. Proc. Natl. Acad. Sci. (U.S.) *20*, 529 (1934).
118. E. Weltin, J. P. Weber, and E. Heilbronner. Theoret. Chim. Acta (Berlin) *2*, 114 (1964).
119. D. R. Whitman and R. Carpenter. Bull. Am. Phys. Soc. *9*, 231 (1964).

Chapter 5 PERTURBATION METHOD

GENERAL THEORY

Perturbation theory exists when the hamiltonian operator under consideration may be written as

$$\mathscr{H} = \mathscr{H}^{(0)} + \lambda\mathscr{H}^{(1)}, \tag{5-1}$$

where $\mathscr{H}^{(0)}$, the zero-order hamiltonian operator, leads to a solvable eigenvalue equation, yielding the zero-order functions $\Psi^{(0)}$ and the eigenvalues $E^{(0)}$. $\lambda\mathscr{H}^{(1)}$ is the perturbation that forbids the exact solution of the eigenvalue equation for $\mathscr{H}$, λ being an ordering parameter.

It is pertinent to use a perturbation treatment, in principle, only in those cases in which the contribution to $E^{(0)}$ arising from the perturbation term is small; and therefore it is suitable for the treatment of weak interactions.

The development of the perturbation formalism* requires a consideration of the character of the zero-order solutions, i.e., whether they are degenerate or not. From the practical point of view several possibilities must also be considered. The proper perturbation treatment can be applied only when the zero-order solutions are known, which is not always the case. Not knowing the exact zero-order solutions, the perturbation contributions may be estimated either from approximate solutions to the zero-order functions or by application of a composite treatment (variation-perturbation). In any case, the application of the perturbation theory formulas is carried out by the normal procedure, with truncation of the expansions over the complete set of the unperturbed levels.

Considering the expression of the complete hamiltonian operator $\mathscr{H}$,

---

* General formulations can be found in any text of quantum mechanics. In addition, mention must be made of the work of Byers Brown [4], Dalgarno and Stewart [5], Hirschfelder, Byers Brown, and Epstein [7], Löwdin [10], and Sinanoglu [13].

one can attempt a series expansion, in terms of λ, for both Ψ_n and E_n,

$$|\Psi_n\rangle = \sum_i |\Psi_n^{(i)}\rangle \lambda^i, \tag{5-2a}$$

$$E_n = \sum_i E_n^{(i)} \lambda^i, \tag{5-2b}$$

where $\Psi_n^{(i)}$ and $E_n^{(i)}$ represent the i-th order corrections toward Ψ_n and E_n, respectively.

Substituting these expressions into the perturbed eigenvalue equation, one obtains

$$(\mathcal{H}^{(0)} + \lambda \mathcal{H}^{(1)}|\sum_i \Psi_n^{(i)} \lambda^i\rangle = |\sum_i \Psi_n^{(i)} \lambda^i\rangle \sum_j E_n^{(j)} \lambda^j. \tag{5-3}$$

If we gather the terms with common powers of λ, Eq. (5-3) transforms into

$$\sum_i \lambda^i \left\{ (\mathcal{H}^{(0)}|\Psi_n^{(i)}\rangle + (\mathcal{H}^{(1)}|\Psi_n^{(i-1)}\rangle - \sum_j |\Psi_n^{(i-j)}\rangle E_n^{(j)} \right\} = 0.$$

If this equation is to be valid for all values of λ, it is necessary for the co-efficients of each power of λ to vanish, yielding for the i-th order correction

$$(\mathcal{H}^{(0)}|\Psi_n^{(i)}\rangle + (\mathcal{H}^{(1)}|\Psi_n^{(i-1)}\rangle = \sum_j |\Psi_n^{(i-j)}\rangle E_n^{(j)}, \tag{5-4}$$

and the problem reduces to the determination of the $\Psi_n^{(i)}$ and $E_n^{(i)}$ (except $\Psi_n^{(0)}$ and $E_n^{(0)}$, which at this moment are assumed to be known). Normally it is sufficient to proceed up to the second order, with the understanding that if higher orders are necessary the perturbation treatment loses its meaning. This determination requires a different formulation depending on whether E_n is degenerate or nondegenerate, although this difference is not one of principle but rather of practice.

After the formulation is completed, the ordering parameter λ is absorbed back into the perturbation term.

Treatment for Non-degenerate States

In this case, when λ tends to zero, the perturbed function Ψ_n should transform into $\Psi_n^{(0)}$, and the general formulation introduced before holds. The undetermined functions in the first- and second-order equations can now be expanded in terms of the complete set of orthonormal unperturbed functions Ψ_n,

$$|\Psi_n^{(1)}\rangle = \sum_k |\Psi_k^{(0)}\rangle a_{kn},$$

$$|\Psi_n^{(2)}\rangle = \sum_k |\Psi_k^{(0)}\rangle b_{kn},$$

$$(\mathcal{H}^{(1)}|\Psi_n^{(0)}\rangle = \sum_k |\Psi_k^{(0)}\rangle d_{kn},$$

$$(\mathcal{H}^{(1)}\Psi|_n^{(1)}\rangle = (\mathcal{H}^{(1)}|\sum_k \Psi_k^{(0)} a_{kn}\rangle = \sum_k (\mathcal{H}^{(1)}|\Psi_k^{(0)}\rangle a_{kn} = \sum_k \sum_l |\Psi_l^{(0)}\rangle d_{lk} a_{kn}.$$

The expansion coefficients d_{kn} are defined by

$$d_{kn} = \langle \Psi_k'^{(0)} | \mathcal{H}^{(1)} | \Psi_n'^{(0)} \rangle = H_{kn}^{(1)},$$

so that only the coefficients a_{kn} and b_{kn} remain to be determined.

Substituting into the first- and second-order equations yields, respectively,

$$\sum_k (\mathcal{H}^{(0)} | \Psi_k'^{(0)} \rangle a_{kn} = | \Psi_n'^{(0)} \rangle E_n^{(1)} + \sum_k | \Psi_k'^{(0)} \rangle (a_{kn} E_n^{(0)} - H_{kn}^{(1)}),$$

$$\sum_k (\mathcal{H}^{(0)} | \Psi_k'^{(0)} \rangle b_{kn} = | \Psi_n'^{(0)} \rangle E_n + \sum_k | \Psi_k'^{(0)} \rangle (b_{kn} E_n^{(0)} + a_{kn} E_n^{(1)} - \sum_l a_{kl} a_{ln}).$$

Since the $\Psi_k'^{(0)}$ are independent functions, the coefficients of each $\Psi_k'^{(0)}$ on both sides of both equations must be equal. For $k = n$ one obtains

$$E_n^{(1)} = H_{nn}^{(1)}, \tag{5-5a}$$

$$E_n^{(2)} = \sum_{k \neq n} H_{nk}^{(1)} H_{kn}^{(1)} / (E_n^{(0)} - E_k^{(0)}); \tag{5-5b}$$

and for $k \neq n$ we get

$$a_{kn} = H_{kn}^{(1)} / (E_n^{(0)} - E_k^{(0)}), \tag{5-6a}$$

$$b_{kn} = \sum_{l \neq n} H_{kl}^{(1)} H_{ln}^{(1)} / [(E_n^{(0)} - E_k^{(0)})(E_n^{(0)} - E_l^{(0)})] - H_{nn}^{(1)} H_{kn}^{(1)} / (E_n^{(0)} - E_k^{(0)})^2. \tag{5-6b}$$

The coefficients a_{nn} and b_{nn} are still to be determined. In fact, it can be proved that they must vanish if the resulting function is to be normalized. The same result is obtained by imposing the condition $\langle \Psi_n'^{(0)} | \Psi_n'^{(i)} \rangle = 0$, for $i \neq 0$.

Formulation for Degenerate States

The treatment is identical to the one given for nondegenerate states, except for the difference arising from the fact that when λ tends to zero it cannot be known with certainty into which $\Psi_{np}'^{(0)}$ of the degenerate set Ψ_n will transform.

For a general discussion it is necessary to consider the possibility that in such a case Ψ_n does not transform into any particular $\Psi_{np}'^{(0)}$ but into a linear combination of all the functions of the degenerate set. This is equivalent to replacing $\Psi_n'^{(0)}$ in the preceding formulation by

$$| \Psi_{nq}' \rangle = \sum_n | \Psi_{np}'^{(0)} \rangle c_{pq},$$

with the subindex q labeling the particular function Ψ_{nq}' which is approximated.

When the expansion coefficients c_{pq} are known *a priori*, the nondegenerate formulation applies as presented. Otherwise the problem reduces to the determination of these coefficients. From the first-order equation one obtains in this case, for $k = n$, a set of linear equations

$$\sum_p (H_{np} - E_{np}\delta_{np})c_{pq} = 0,$$

that lead to the corresponding secular equation. The solution of this equation yields the coefficients and the energy values.

FORMULATION FOR SIMULTANEOUS PERTURBATIONS

In the case of more than one perturbation term, the hamiltonian operator may be written as

$$\mathscr{H} = \mathscr{H}^{(0)} + \lambda\mathscr{H}^{(1)} + \lambda^2\mathscr{H}^{(2)} + \cdots, \tag{5-7}$$

where it has been assumed that every $\mathscr{H}^{(j)}$ is smaller than $\mathscr{H}^{(j-1)}$. Proceeding in the manner described in the preceding section, one can obtain the i-th order equation

$$(\mathscr{H}^{(0)}\,|\Psi_n^{(i)}\rangle + \sum_{j=1} (\mathscr{H}^{(j)}\,|\Psi_n^{(i-j)}\rangle = \sum_{j=0} |\Psi_n^{(i-j)}\rangle E_n^{(j)}, \tag{5-8}$$

which transforms into Eq. (5-4) for a single perturbation.

The existence of additional perturbations, as represented by Eq. (5-7), does not produce any change in the first-order corrections. The second-order corrections for nondegenerate states,* obtained by these techniques, include new terms. The second-order energy correction is

$$E_n^{(2)} = H_{nn}^{(2)} + \sum_{k \neq n} H_{nk}^{(1)}H_{kn}^{(1)}/(E_n^{(0)} - E_k^{(0)}), \tag{5-9a}$$

and the expansion coefficients b_{kn} for the second-order correction to the function are given by

$$b_{kn} = \sum_{l \neq n} H_{kl}^{(1)}H_{ln}^{(1)}/[(E_n^{(0)} - E_k^{(0)})(E_n^{(0)} - E_l^{(0)})]$$
$$- H_{nn}^{(1)}H_{kn}^{(1)}/(E_n^{(0)} - E_k^{(0)})^2 - H_{kn}^{(2)}/(E_n^{(0)} - E_k^{(0)}), \tag{5-9b}$$

with

$$H_{kn}^{(2)} = \langle\Psi_k^{(0)}|\,\mathscr{H}^{(2)}\,|\Psi_n^{(0)}\rangle.$$

Higher-order corrections for additional perturbations can be obtained in a similar way.

---

* The reader is referred to the work of Hameka [6] for the formulation for degenerate states.

VARIATION-PERTURBATION METHODS

The difficulties implicit in the summation required for the evaluation of the second-order corrections may be bypassed by the use of a variation-perturbation method. The second-order energy may then be determined from the ground state function. (The formulation presented here is that of Karplus and Kolker [9]. A detailed discussion of variational perturbation methods is presented by Hameka [6], and mention must also be made of the formalism developed by Sinanoglu [12] and of the work of Hylleraas and Undheim [8].)

The first- and second-order equations may be written [see Eq. (5-4)], respectively, as

$$(\mathscr{H}^{(0)} - E^{(0)} |\Psi'^{(1)}\rangle = -(\mathscr{H}^{(1)} - E^{(1)} |\Psi'^{(0)}\rangle, \quad (5\text{-}10a)$$

$$(\mathscr{H}^{(0)} - E^{(0)} |\Psi'^{(2)}\rangle + (\mathscr{H}^{(1)} - E^{(1)} |\Psi'^{(1)}\rangle = E^{(2)}\Psi'^{(0)}. \quad (5\text{-}10b)$$

Multiplying Eq. (5-10b) by $\Psi'^{(0)*}$ and integrating yields

$$E^{(2)} = \langle\Psi'^{(0)}| \; \mathscr{H}^{(1)} - E^{(1)} \; \Psi'^{(1)}\rangle \quad (5\text{-}11a)$$

or, equivalently,

$$E^{(2)} = -\langle\Psi'^{(1)}| \; \mathscr{H}^{(0)} - E^{(0)} |\Psi'^{(1)}\rangle, \quad (5\text{-}11b)$$

when Eq. (5-10a) is taken into account.

Equations (5-11a) and (5-11b) may be used together to define the functional

$$E^{(2)}(\Psi'^{(1)}) = \langle\Psi'^{(1)}| \; \mathscr{H}^{(0)} - E^{(0)} |\Psi'^{(1)}\rangle + \langle\Psi'^{(1)}| \; \mathscr{H}^{(1)} - E^{(1)} |\Psi'^{(0)}\rangle$$
$$+ \langle\Psi'^{(0)}| \; \mathscr{H}^{(1)} - E^{(1)} |\Psi'^{(1)}\rangle, \quad (5\text{-}12)$$

which can serve for the determination of $\Psi'^{(1)}$ and $E^{(2)}$ by application of a variational procedure.

When only approximations to the unperturbed functions are known, Eq. (5-12) cannot be applied. In such a case, a similar formulation leads to

$$E = \langle\Phi^{(0)}| \; \mathscr{H}^{(0)} + \mathscr{H}^{(1)} |\Phi^{(0)}\rangle + \langle\Phi^{(0)}| \; \mathscr{H}^{(1)} - \langle\Phi^{(0)}| \; \mathscr{H}^{(1)} |\Phi^{(0)}\rangle |\Phi^{(1)}\rangle$$
$$+ \langle\Phi^{(1)}| \; \mathscr{H}^{(1)} - \langle\Phi^{(0)}| \; \mathscr{H}^{(1)} |\Phi^{(0)}\rangle |\Phi^{(0)}\rangle + \langle\Phi^{(1)}| \; \mathscr{H}^{(0)}$$
$$- \langle\Phi^{(0)}| \; \mathscr{H}^{(0)} |\Phi^{(0)}\rangle |\Phi^{(1)}\rangle + \langle\Phi^{(0)}| \; \mathscr{H}^{(0)} - \langle\Phi^{(0)}| \; \mathscr{H}^{(0)} |\Phi^{(0)}\rangle |\Phi^{(2)}\rangle$$
$$+ \langle\Phi^{(2)}| \; \mathscr{H}^{(0)} - \langle\Phi^{(0)}| \; \mathscr{H}^{(0)} |\Phi^{(0)}\rangle |\Phi^{(0)}\rangle \quad (5\text{-}13)$$

for the energy to second order.

Different procedures have been proposed in order to avoid the difficulties encountered in the application of Eq. (5-13). Buckingham [3] assumed that the terms involving $\Phi^{(2)}$ are sufficiently small to be neglected. On the other hand, Karplus and Kolker [9] have proposed the introduction of an effective zero-order hamiltonian operator $\mathscr{H}_a^{(0)}$, which has as eigenfunctions the approximate functions $\Phi^{(0)}$. This procedure implies defining an effective potential V_a by

$$(\mathscr{H}_a^{(0)} \,|\Phi^{(0)}\rangle = (\mathscr{T} + V_a^{(0)} \,|\Phi^{(0)}\rangle = |\Phi^{(0)}\rangle \, E^{(0)},$$

or

$$(V_a^{(0)} \,|\Phi^{(0)}\rangle = (E^{(0)} - \mathscr{T} \,|\Phi^{(0)}\rangle. \qquad (5\text{-}14)$$

Equation (5-12) can then be applied using the new effective zero-order hamiltonian operator. For lowest states, the extremal of the function $E^{(2)}(\Psi'^{(1)})$ can be seen to be a minimum. A variational treatment based on Eq. (5-12) yields an upper bound to the approximate second-order energy, the accuracy of the results depending on the functions, $\Phi^{(0)}$, that are used. Dalgarno and Stewart [5] and Schwartz [11] have proposed additional refinements for an improvement of the results, and Karplus and Kolker [9] have presented a detailed formulation for the case when the functions are Hartree-Fock functions.

PERTURBED SELF-CONSISTENT FIELD FORMULATION

The self-consistent field formalism can be adapted to include in the Hartree-Fock operator different types of perturbations. The formulation* is restricted here to a scalar, one-electron perturbing potential λV, for calculations to first-order only.

The discussion is limited to closed-shell systems, and it is assumed that the orthonormal solutions of the unperturbed Hartree-Fock operator

$$(\mathscr{F}^{(0)} \,|\phi_n^{(0)}\rangle = |\phi_n^{(0)}\rangle \, \varepsilon_{nn}^{(0)}$$

are known. The perturbed pseudoeigenvalue equation is

$$(\mathscr{F} \,|\phi_n\rangle = |\phi_n\rangle \, \varepsilon_{nn},$$

with

$$\mathscr{F} = \mathscr{H}' + \sum_p \mathscr{I}_p + \lambda V = \mathscr{H}' + \mathscr{I} + \lambda V,$$

where the operator $\mathscr{I}$ is a function of the perturbed orbitals.

The standard perturbation techniques lead to the i-th order equation

$$(\mathscr{H}' \,|\phi_n^{(i)}\rangle + (V \,|\phi_n^{(i-1)}\rangle + \sum_j (\mathscr{I}^{(i-j)} \,|\phi_n^{(j)}\rangle - \sum_j |\phi_n^{(i-j)}\rangle \, \varepsilon_{nn}^{(j)} = 0;$$

the operator $\mathscr{I}^{(i-j)}$ is defined by a sum of operators $\mathscr{I}_n^{(k,l)}$, given by

$$(\mathscr{I}_n^{(k,l)} \,|\phi_m\rangle = 2\left\{ \int \phi_n^{(k)*}(1)\phi_n^{(l)}(1) \, d\tau_1 \right\}\phi_m(2) - \left\{ \int \phi_n^{(k)*}(1)\phi_m(1) \, d\tau_1 \right\}\phi_n^{(l)}(2),$$

the summation including all the possible combinations of order k and l such that $k + l = i - j$.

---

* This is the formalism developed by Allen [1]. Other treatments are those of Tuan, Epstein, and Hirschfelder [14] and Wyatt and Parr [15]. Amos and Hall [2] have presented a formulation for conjugated systems.

The first-order equation, in particular, becomes

$$(\mathscr{H}' \,|\phi_n^{(1)}\rangle + (V\,|\phi_n^{(0)}\rangle + (\mathscr{I}^{(0,0)}\,|\phi_n^{(1)}\rangle + (\mathscr{I}^{(1,0)} + \mathscr{I}^{(0,1)}\,|\phi_n^{(0)}\rangle$$
$$- |\phi_n^{(1)}\rangle\,\varepsilon_{nn}^{(0)} - |\phi_n^{(0)}\rangle\,\varepsilon_{nn}^{(1)} = 0,$$

which can be used to determine ϕ_n^1 and the corresponding orbital energy correction

$$\varepsilon_{nn}^{(1)} = \langle\phi_n^{(0)}|\,V\,|\phi_n^{(0)}\rangle + \langle\phi_n^{(0)}|\,\mathscr{I}^{(0,0)}\,|\phi_n^{(1)}\rangle + \langle\phi_n^{(0)}|\,\mathscr{I}^{(1,0)} + \mathscr{I}^{(0,1)}|\phi_n^{(0)}\rangle.$$

Additional conditions to be imposed on the perturbed functions, arising from their orthonormalization, are, to second order,

$$\langle\phi_n^{(0)}\,|\,\phi_n^{(1)}\rangle = 0, \quad \langle\phi_n^{(0)}\,|\,\phi_p^{(1)}\rangle = -\langle\phi_n^{(1)}\,|\,\phi_p^{(0)}\rangle = 0,$$

$$2\langle\phi_n^{(0)}\,|\,\phi_n^{(2)}\rangle + \langle\phi_n^{(1)}\,|\,\phi_n^{(1)}\rangle = 0, \quad \langle\phi_n^{(2)}\,|\,\phi_p^{(0)}\rangle + \langle\phi_n^{(0)}\,|\,\phi_p^{(2)}\rangle = -\langle\phi_n^{(1)}\,|\,\phi_p^{(1)}\rangle.$$

The total electronic energy, expanded as

$$E = \sum_i \lambda^i E^{(i)},$$

can be treated in a similar fashion, leading to

$$E^{(1)} = \sum_n \langle\phi_n^{(0)}|\,V\,|\phi_n^{(0)}\rangle,$$

$$E^{(2)} = \text{real part of } \sum_n \langle\phi_n^{(0)}|\,V\,|\phi_n^{(1)}\rangle,$$

this last term being proportional to the dipole polarizability (for a uniform perturbing field).

REFERENCES

1. L. C. Allen. Phys. Rev. *118*, 167 (1960).
2. A. T. Amos and G. G. Hall. Theoret. Chim. Acta (Berlin) *5*, 148 (1966).
3. R. A. Buckingham. Proc. Roy. Soc. (London) *A160*, 94 (1937).
4. W. Byers Brown. J. Chem. Phys. *44*, 567 (1966).
5. A. Dalgarno and A. L. Stewart. Proc. Roy. Soc. (London) *A238*, 269 (1956).
6. H. F. Hameka. "Advanced Quantum Chemistry." Addison-Wesley Publishing Company, Inc., Reading, Mass., 1965.
7. J. O. Hirschfelder, W. Byers Brown, and S. T. Epstein. Recent Developments in Perturbation Theory, *in* "Advances in Quantum Chemistry," vol. I, edited by P. O. Löwdin. Academic Press, Inc., New York, N.Y., 1964.
8. E. A. Hylleraas and B. Undheim. Z. Physik *65*, 759 (1930).
9. M. Karplus and H. J. Kolker. J. Chem. Phys. *38*, 1263 (1963).
10. P. O. Löwdin. "Studies in Perturbation Theory," Reports of the Quantum Chemistry Group, Uppsala University, Uppsala, Sweden, and of the Quantum Theory Project, University of Florida, Gainesville, Fla.
11. C. Schwartz. Ann. Phys. *6*, 170 (1959).
12. O. Sinanoglu. Phys. Rev. *122*, 491 (1961).
13. O. Sinanoglu. Phys. Rev. *122*, 493 (1961).
14. D. F. T. Tuan, S. T. Epstein, and J. O. Hirschfelder. J. Chem. Phys. *44*, 431 (1966).
15. R. E. Wyatt and R. G. Parr. J. Chem. Phys. *41*, 514 (1964).

Chapter 6   ELECTRONIC CHARGE DENSITIES

ELECTRONIC DISTRIBUTIONS

The primary effort in quantum-mechanical calculations is directed, of course, toward the determination of state functions and the corresponding energies. It has already been pointed out that, using the state functions, one can evaluate the physical properties of the system. In the end, the knowledge one has of a system reduces to a series of mathematical expansions (which define the function) and a collection of numerical tables (which at the best provide an overall picture and are sometimes misleading). The general description, in terms of numbers, somehow does not seem to reflect the reality of the system under consideration and does not provide a simple, intuitive picture, which can be useful in many cases.

The gap that exists in this description can be best filled by a knowledge of the electronic densities (to be obtained from the state functions), which ultimately are responsible for the different physical properties of the system.

Different attempts have been made to obtain this representation of the electronic distribution. One could include here (though they do not represent density distributions as such) the typical line plots and radial distributions for atomic or molecular orbitals. The true representations are the density cross sections and the contour diagrams. There is no doubt that for an intuitive picture of the molecular reality (or, at least, of an approximation to it) the latter constitutes the best representation. Related descriptions, however, in terms of numbers, are obtained from the orbital, natural spin-orbital, and natural spin-geminal population analyses.

These representations provide an overall picture of a molecular system, that is, over all the configuration space. In addition, the electronic densities at the nuclei are of importance as they are related to the Fermi contact interaction, which is considered in Chapter 11.

CHARGE DENSITIES AT THE NUCLEI

The charge density distribution in an atom is of general interest in the sense that it is possible to ascribe to different atomic regions a predominant weight towards different physical properties. Particularly important, however, is the charge density itself at the nucleus.

The problem of the singularities in the hamiltonian operator and their bearing on the functions has been considered in Chapter 1. Kato [34] has shown that the eigenfunction Ψ of the spin-independent hamiltonian for an N-electron system must satisfy the condition

$$(\partial \bar{\Psi}/\partial r_n)_{r_n=0} = -Z[\Psi(r_1, r_2, \ldots, r_N)]_{r_n=0}, \tag{6-1}$$

where

$$\bar{\Psi} = (1/4\pi) \int_{w_n} \Psi(r_1, r_2, \ldots, r_N) \, d\omega_n \tag{6-2}$$

represents the average value of Ψ over a sphere of radius r_n (that is, an angular average over the coordinates θ and ϕ of the n-th electron), and Z is the atomic number for the atom under consideration. In the above equations the coordinate system is assumed to be centered on the nucleus under consideration.

This condition implies a corollary, derived by Steiner [77], that relates the charge density and its derivative at the nucleus of an atom. An anti-symmetrized state function, with total electron spin quantum numbers S and M, may be represented by*

$$\Psi_{S,M}(r, \sigma) = (1/f_{S,M})^{\frac{1}{2}} \sum_k \Psi_{S,k}(r) \, \Xi_{S,M,k}(\sigma),$$

where $\Psi_{S,k}(r)$ represents the eigenfunctions (depending only on the spatial coordinates) common to the $(2S + 1)$ functions $\Psi_{S,M}$ and where $\Xi_{S,M,k}(\sigma)$ denotes the appropriate orthonormalized spin functions. The summation extends over the $f_{S,M}$ possible values of k. The factor in front of the summation represents a normalization factor.

The probability density given by $\Psi_{S,M}$ at a given point is defined by

$$\rho(r) = \langle \Psi_{S,M} \,|\, \Psi_{S,M} \rangle = (1/f_{S,M}) \sum_k \rho_k(r) = (1/f_{S,M}) \sum_k \sum_n \rho_k(r_n), \tag{6-3}$$

with

$$\rho_k(r_n) = \langle \Psi_{S,k} \,|\, \Psi_{S,k} \rangle_{r=r_n} \tag{6-4}$$

where the integration is carried out over all the space coordinates other than r_n. The summation over n extends over all the electrons.

If Ψ is one of the eigenfunctions $\Psi_{S,K}$, it follows from Eq. (6-1) that

$$\langle \Psi \,|\, \partial \bar{\Psi}/\partial r_n \rangle_{r_n=0} = -Z\rho_k(0),$$

---

* More details are given by Kotani, Amemiya, Ishiguro, and Kimura [36], and Wigner [80].

where $\rho_k(0)$ is defined as in Eq. (6-4), with $r_n = 0$. Taking into account that $\rho_k(r)$ is real, we see that

$$(\partial\rho_k(r_n)/\partial r_n)_{r_n=0} = 2\langle\Psi \mid \partial\bar{\Psi}/\partial r_n\rangle_{r_n=0},$$

from which one obtains

$$(\partial\rho_k(r_n)/\partial r_n)_{r_n=0} = -2Z\rho_k(0).$$

If we take into account Eq. (6-3), it follows then that

$$(\partial\rho(r)/\partial r)_{r=0} = -2Z\rho(0), \qquad (6\text{-}5)$$

which is valid for any eigenstate of an atomic spin-independent hamiltonian operator.

Within the independent particle approximation the total electronic density is

$$\rho(r) = \sum_i f_i\rho_i(r) = \sum_i f_i\phi_i^*(r)\phi_i(r), \qquad (6\text{-}6)$$

where the summation extends over all the occupied orbitals ϕ_i in the system, f_i being the corresponding occupation numbers.

For the density at the nucleus, only the s-type orbitals must be considered. Within the expansion method (see Malli and Fraga [47]) the electron density and its derivative at the nucleus are

$$\rho_i(0) = \sum_p c_{pi}^2, \qquad (6\text{-}7)$$

$$(\partial\rho_i(r)/\partial r)_{r=0} = -2\sum_q \zeta_q c_{qi}^2 + 2\sum_q\sum_r c_{qi}c_{ri}, \qquad (6\text{-}8)$$

where the summation over q extends only over the $1s$ STO and the summation over r extends only over the $2s$ STO in the s-type basis set; ζ_q denotes the orbital exponent of the q-th $1s$ STO.

If for the expansion of the s-type orbitals one uses only one $1s$ STO, no $2s$ STO, and any other s-type STO with $n \geq 3$, Eqs. (6-7) and (6-8) become

$$\rho_i(0) = c_{1i},$$

$$(\partial\rho_i(r)/\partial r)_{r=0} = -2\zeta c_{1i}^2,$$

and the partial cusp condition

$$(\partial\rho_i(r)/\partial r)_{r=0} = -2Z\rho_i(0)$$

is satisfied if ζ is chosen equal to the atomic number Z of the atom under consideration. Equation (6-5) then becomes

$$(\partial\rho(r)/\partial r)_{r=0} = \sum_i f_i(\partial\rho_i(r)/\partial r)_{r=0} = -2Z\sum_i f_i\rho_i(0) = -2Z\rho(0), \quad (6\text{-}9)$$

which shows that the total cusp condition is satisfied if the partial cusp conditions are satisfied. The conditions imposed on ζ and the type of expansion to be used for s-type orbitals agree with those derived when considering the singularities of the hamiltonian operator in Chapter 1.

Table 6-1 Values for the Electronic Density $\rho(0)$ and Its Derivative $(\partial\rho(r)/\partial r)_{r=0}$ at the Nucleus for s Orbitals in Neutral Atoms[a,b]

ATOM	STATE	$1s$	$2s$	$3s$	TOTAL VALUE	CUSP CONDITION
Na	^2S	785.9	46.8	0.5	833.2	
		-17289.7	-1028.7	-11.6	-18330.0	22.0
Mg	^1S	1025.4	65.5	2.4	1093.3	
		-24609.6	-1572.3	-58.4	-26240.2	24.0
Al	^2P	1309.1	88.4	4.7	1402.2	
		-34035.5	-2298.0	-122.4	-36455.8	26.0
Si	^3P	1640.9	116.1	7.6	1764.6	
		-45945.2	-3249.8	-213.0	-49408.0	28.0
Si	^1D	1640.9	116.1	7.7	1764.7	
		-45946.1	-3250.8	-214.6	-49411.5	28.0
Si	^1S	1640.9	116.1	7.8	1754.8	
		-45946.1	-3251.5	-217.2	-49414.9	28.0
P	^4S	2024.8	149.1	11.2	2185.2	
		-60743.4	-4474.1	-337.2	-65554.7	30.0
P	^2D	2024.8	149.1	11.3	2185.3	
		-60744.6	-4474.1	-339.7	-65558.4	30.0
P	^2P	2024.8	149.2	11.4	2185.4	
		-60744.6	-4475.5	-341.3	-65561.4	30.0
S	^3P	2464.5	187.9	15.8	2668.2	
		-78853.2	-6012.0	-506.1	-85381.3	32.0
S	^1D	2464.5	187.9	15.9	2668.2	
		-78863.2	-6012.0	-507.8	-85383.0	32.0
S	^1S	2464.5	187.9	16.0	2668.3	
		-78863.2	-6011.6	-510.3	-85385.1	32.0
Cl	^2P	2963.7	232.8	21.3	3217.7	
		-100764.2	-7914.6	-724.0	-109402.7	34.0
A	^1S	3526.3	284.0	27.7	3838.0	
		-126945.5	-10224.5	-998.2	-138168.2	36.0

a. Calculated from the Hartree-Fock functions of Malli [46].

b. For each system two rows of values are given; the first one presents the values for $\rho(0)$; those in the second row correspond to $(\partial\rho(r)/\partial r)_{r=0}$. The values under the heading "cusp condition" represent the ratio of the total values $-(\partial\rho(r)/\partial r)_{r=0}$ and $\rho(0)$.

Table 6-1 collects some representative values of the quantities in Eq. (6-9) for the s orbitals of the Hartree-Fock functions of the second row of the periodic system. These results illustrate the application of the conditions mentioned above, which are satisfied by the functions used.

POPULATION ANALYSES

The knowledge of state functions permits one to obtain a statistical insight into the distribution of the atomic electrons in a molecule and also into the various orbitals centered on each atom. The set of results constitutes the population analysis for the system under consideration.

A population analysis can be carried out in different ways, related to each other. The simplest population analysis, attributed to Mulliken [54–57], is expressed in terms of the orbitals (atomic or molecular, though this type of analysis is more useful for molecules) that are used in the construction of the total function. A more complex analysis, in terms of natural spin-orbitals or natural spin-geminals, leads to results in terms of a unique set. These three types of analyses are designated hereafter as molecular orbital, natural spin-orbital, and natural spin-geminal population analyses, respectively.

In the molecular orbital analysis, the concept of population arises from the possible ways of breaking down the electronic distribution associated with a molecular orbital. Given a molecular orbital (assumed to be normalized) $\phi_i = \sum_{r_k} \chi_{r_k} c_{r_k i}$, where the summation extends over all the appropriate basis functions χ_{r_k} and the subindex k labels the different nuclei in the system, the electronic population in this orbital (occupied by N_i electrons) can be expressed as

$$N_i = N_i \sum_{r_k} c_{r_k i}^2 + 2N_i \sum_{\substack{r_k s_l \\ (l > k)}} S_{r_k s_l} c_{r_k i} c_{s_l i}, \qquad (6\text{-}10)$$

assuming that the basis functions χ are normalized; $S_{r_k s_l}$ represents the overlap between two basis functions, χ_{r_k} and χ_{s_l}. The first term in Eq. (6-10) can be considered to represent an atomic population, and the second term constitutes the overlap population. Both types of populations can be broken down in terms of contributions from specific atoms and from given basis functions. The general formulation involves a complete breakdown along these lines.

The atomic populations can be formulated in terms of the partial contributions:

partial gross population in ϕ_i and χ_{r_k}

$$N(i; r_k) = N(i) c_{r_k i} \Big(c_{r_k i} + \sum_{l \neq k} c_{s_l i} S_{r_k s_l} \Big);$$

subtotal gross population in ϕ_i on atom k

$$N(i; k) = \sum_r N(i; r_k);$$

total gross population on atom k

$$N(k) = \sum_i N(i; k) = \sum_r N(r_k);$$

total gross population in ϕ_i

$$N(i) = \sum_{r_k} N(i; r_k) = \sum_k N(i; k) \equiv N_i;$$

total gross population in χ_{r_k}

$$N(r_k) = \sum_i N(i; r_k);$$

total population

$$N = \sum_i N(i) = \sum_{r_k} N(r_k).$$

The overlap populations are:

partial overlap population in ϕ_i between χ_{r_k} and χ_{s_l}

$$n(i; r_k, s_l) = 2N(i)c_{r_k i}c_{s_l i}S_{r_k s_l};$$

subtotal overlap population in ϕ_i between atoms k and l

$$n(i; k, l) = \sum_{r_k}\sum_{s_l} n(i; r_k, s_l);$$

subtotal overlap population between χ_{r_k} and χ_{s_l}

$$n(r_k, s_l) = \sum_i n(i; r_k, s_l);$$

subtotal overlap population between atoms k and l

$$n(k, l) = \sum_{r_k}\sum_{s_l} n(r_k, s_l);$$

subtotal overlap population in ϕ_i

$$n(i) = \sum_{r_k}\sum_{s_l} n(i; r_k, s_l);$$

total overlap population

$$n = \sum_i n(i) = \sum_k\sum_l n(k, l) = \sum_{r_k}\sum_{s_l} n(r_k, s_l).$$

In the case of many-configuration state functions, defined by $\Phi = \sum \Phi_m c_m$, where it is possible to define for each function Φ_m a molecular analysis along the lines considered above, the corresponding analysis for the complete function Φ is expressed by a similar set of equations, derived by Karo [33].

For the atomic populations the set is:

$$N_c(m; r_k) = c_m^2 \sum_i N(i; r_k) = c_m^2 N(r_k),$$

$$N_c(m) = \sum_{r_k} N_c(m; r_k) = \sum_{r_k} c_m^2 N(r_k) = c_m^2 N,$$

$$N_c(r_k) = \sum_m N_c(m; r_k) = \sum_m c_m^2 N(r_k),$$

$$N_c = \sum_m N_c(m) = \sum_{r_k} N_c(r_k) = N \sum_m c_m^2,$$

and for the overlap populations it is:

$$N_c(m; r_k, s_l) = c_m^2 \sum_i n(i; r_k, s_l) = c_m^2 n(r_k, s_l),$$

$$n_c(m) = \sum_{r_k}\sum_{s_l} n_c(m; r_k, s_l) = \sum_{r_k}\sum_{s_l} c_m^2 n(r_k, s_l) = nc_m^2,$$

$$n_c(r_k, s_l) = \sum_m n_c(m; r_k, s_l) = \sum_m c_m^2 n(r_k, s_l),$$

$$n_c = \sum_m n_c(m) = \sum_{r_k}\sum_{s_l} n_c(r_k, s_l) = n \sum_m c_m^2,$$

with a meaning analogous to that of the similar equations for the single-configuration functions; the subscript c denotes configuration interaction.

This type of analysis provides information about the charge transfer (promotion) between the different basis functions (a fact of importance in atoms), it may give a measure of the polarity of the individual molecular orbitals (as compared with the polarity of the system and as determined from the total function), and it describes the source of the bonding power (particularly the covalent bonding, etc.).

Numerical results (in the single- and many-configuration approximations) and their interpretation have been given by Fraga and Ransil [28–30] for simple diatomic molecules of the first row.

The natural functions analysis involves a more complicated formulation but offers the advantage of providing a unique description of the system. No attempt can be made here to present the complete theory,* but rather the discussion will be based on the brief review of Messmer and Fraga [52].

The condition

$$\gamma'^{(n)} = \langle \Phi^* | \gamma_{(n)} | \Phi^* \rangle$$

$$= \langle \gamma_{(n)} \Phi | \Phi \rangle = \binom{N}{n} \int \Phi(1, 2, 3, \ldots, n, n+1, \ldots, N)$$

$$\times \Phi^*(1', 2', 3', \ldots, n', n+1, \ldots, N) \, d\tau_{n+1} \cdots d\tau_N, \qquad (6\text{-}11)$$

defines the n-th order density matrix for an N-electron system, described by a normalized function Φ. The effect of acting with $\gamma_{(n)}$ on Φ is to prime the coordinates of the first n electrons, and the integration is then carried out only over the unprimed coordinates.

The n-th order density matrix $\gamma^{(n)}$ is the kernel of an integral operator $\Gamma^{(n)}$, whose eigenfunctions,

$$(\Gamma^{(n)} | \phi_i^{(n)} \rangle = \int \gamma^{(n)} \phi_i^{(n)}(1', 2', \ldots, n') \, d\tau_1 \, d\tau_2 \ldots d\tau_n = | \phi_i^{(n)} \rangle \lambda_i^{(n)}, \qquad (6\text{-}12)$$

are the natural spin-functions, namely, the natural spin-orbitals NSO ($n = 1$) natural spin-geminals NSG ($n = 2$), etc. For $n = 0$, Eq. (6-12) reduces to an identity, as in this case $\gamma^{(0)} = 1$, and Eq. (6-11) represents the normalization condition.

The definition of NSO and NSG has a meaning only in conjunction with functions that represent an improvement over the single-configuration functions. For a given approximate function Φ there exists a unique set of NSO and NSG, which provides unique population analyses.

A many-configuration function Φ may be written, in terms of the basic

---

* One should mention the work of Bingel [14–18], Davidson [23, 24], Kutzelnigg [37–43], Löwdin [44, 45], McWeeny [48–51], Shull [3, 4, 32, 68–74], Smith [75, 76], and Ter Haar [78], and the contributions of Bardeen *et al.* [12], Blatt [19], Bratoz [20], Carlson and Keller [21], Ebbing [25], Garrod [31], Mizuno [53], and Nakamura [58].

spin-orbitals ϕ_i used in the single-configuration functions, as

$$|\Phi\rangle = \sum_{kl\cdots pq} |\phi_k \phi_l \cdots \phi_p \phi_q\rangle\, c_{kl\cdots pq}$$

$$= \sum_{k<l<\cdots<p<q} |[\phi_k \phi_l \cdots \phi_p \phi_q]\rangle c_{kl\cdots pq},$$

where the sum extends over all the possible Slater determinants that can be constructed from the set $\{\phi_i\}$. The first- and second-order density matrices are then

$$\gamma^{(1)} = \sum_{tu} |[\phi]_t\rangle\, c_t c_u^* \,\langle[\phi_u]| = |[\boldsymbol{\phi}]\rangle\, \boldsymbol{\gamma}^{(1)}\, \langle[\boldsymbol{\phi}]|, \qquad (6\text{-}13a)$$

$$\gamma^{(2)} = \sum_{s<t}\sum_{u<v} |[\phi_s \phi_t]\rangle\, c_{st} c_{uv}^* \,\langle[\phi_u \phi_v]| = \sum_{s<t}\sum_{u<v} |[\omega_{st}]\rangle\, c_{st} c_{uv}^* \,\langle[\omega_{uv}]|$$

$$= |[\boldsymbol{\omega}]\rangle\, \boldsymbol{\gamma}^{(2)}\, \langle[\boldsymbol{\omega}]|. \qquad (6\text{-}13b)$$

The coefficients c_t, c_u, c_{st}, and c_{uv} are obtained from the original coefficients $c_{kl\cdots pq}$. $|[\phi_t]\rangle$ denotes a determinant of order 1 and $|[\omega_{st}]\rangle$ a determinant of order 2, $|[\boldsymbol{\phi}]\rangle$ and $|[\boldsymbol{\omega}]\rangle$ being the corresponding row vectors. The square matrices $\boldsymbol{\gamma}^{(1)}$ and $\boldsymbol{\gamma}^{(2)}$ have elements $c_t c_u^*$ and $c_{st} c_{uv}^*$, respectively, and constitute the matrix representation of the operators $\Gamma^{(1)}$ and $\Gamma^{(2)}$.

The matrix formulation of Eq. (6-12) can now be developed if the NSO and NSG are expanded as linear combinations of the basic spin-orbitals or products of them, respectively. One has

$$|\phi_i^{(1)}\rangle = \sum_t |[\phi_t]\rangle c_{t,i}^{(1)} = |[\boldsymbol{\phi}]\rangle\, \boldsymbol{c}_i^{(1)}, \qquad (6\text{-}14a)$$

$$|\phi_i^{(2)}\rangle = \sum_{s<t} |[\omega_{st}]\rangle c_{st,i}^{(2)} = |[\boldsymbol{\omega}]\rangle\, \boldsymbol{c}_i^{(2)}, \qquad (6\text{-}14b)$$

where $\boldsymbol{c}_i^{(1)}$ and $\boldsymbol{c}_i^{(2)}$ are column vectors whose elements are the corresponding expansion coefficients; in matrix form, Eqs. (6-14a) and (6-14b) are written

$$|\boldsymbol{\phi}^{(1)}\rangle = |[\boldsymbol{\phi}]\rangle\, \mathbf{C}^{(1)},$$

$$|\boldsymbol{\phi}^{(2)}\rangle = |[\boldsymbol{\omega}]\rangle\, \mathbf{C}^{(2)},$$

$\mathbf{C}^{(1)}$ and $\mathbf{C}^{(2)}$ being square matrices, formed by the column vectors $\boldsymbol{c}_i^{(1)}$ and $\boldsymbol{c}_i^{(2)}$, respectively. Equations (6-12) and (6-13) lead then to

$$\langle\boldsymbol{\phi}^{(1)}|\,\gamma^{(1)}\,|\boldsymbol{\phi}^{(1)}\rangle = \mathbf{C}^{(1)\dagger}\,\langle[\boldsymbol{\phi}]|\,\gamma^{(1)}\,|[\boldsymbol{\phi}]\rangle\,\mathbf{C}^{(1)}$$

$$= \mathbf{C}^{(1)\dagger}\,\langle[\boldsymbol{\phi}]\,|\,[\boldsymbol{\phi}]\rangle\,\boldsymbol{\gamma}^{(1)}\,\langle[\boldsymbol{\phi}]\,|\,[\boldsymbol{\phi}]\rangle\,\mathbf{C}^{(1)} = \mathbf{C}^{(1)\dagger}\boldsymbol{\gamma}^{(1)}\mathbf{C}^{(1)} = \boldsymbol{\lambda}^{(1)}$$

for the first-order density matrix. The expansion coefficients and occupation numbers are determined by diagonalization of the matrix $\boldsymbol{\gamma}^{(1)}$. A similar formulation can be given for the second-order density matrix. (The integrals $\langle\phi_i^{(n)}|\,\Gamma^{(n)}\,|\phi_i^{(n)}\rangle$ imply, besides the integrations implicit in the definition of $\gamma^{(n)}$, an integration over the coordinates of $2n$ electrons, the coordinate dependence of the bra-ket parts of the integral being different. The bra part represents an integration over the unprimed coordinates, whereas in the ket part the integration is carried out over the primed coordinates.)

The occupation numbers, for the convention adopted here, must satisfy the normalization condition

$$\sum_i \lambda_i^{(n)} = \binom{N}{n} \quad \text{or} \quad \text{Tr } \gamma^{(n)} = \binom{N}{n}.$$

(A discussion of the different conventions is given by Coleman [22].)

Although the information obtained from a natural function analysis is more complete than that from a molecular orbital analysis, it must be pointed out that the former method is more complicated. A comparison of the merits of both types of analyses can be made from the work carried out on simple systems, with one and two electrons, by Fraga and Ransil [29], Ransil [59], Eliason and Hirschfelder [27], Anex and Shull [4], Shull and Prosser [74], Barnett, Linderberg, and Shull [13], Smith and Fogel [76], and Messmer and Fraga [52]. The two types of analysis are closely related, of course. McWeeny [49] has shown that they differ by a similarity transformation.

PICTORIAL REPRESENTATIONS IN MOLECULES

Though the preceding population analyses can provide, depending on the goodness of the state function on which they are based, a satisfactory description of the electronic density distribution in atoms and molecules, a graphic representation of the total density for each orbital (and, if necessary, for the whole molecule) yields a more intuitive interpretation of the bonding in the molecule under consideration.

Modern computer techniques and programs make it possible, with simultaneous use of very sophisticated auxiliary equipment, to obtain pictorial representations for the electronic densities of individual orbitals and for the molecule. The pictorial contour plots determined by Wahl [79] show how such a representation, when based on an adequate function, can yield a very interesting description regarding chemical bonding, character of the bonding and antibonding orbitals, etc.

In a more detailed representation an attempt can be made to partition the charge density diagrams into binding and antibinding regions. A first approach consists in partitioning the diagram into regions of localized and delocalized charge densities. Of more interest, perhaps, are the so-called bond maps or δ-diagrams, which present the boundaries of the localized charge distributions. These diagrams are representations of the probability charge density difference function δ, introduced by Roux and coworkers [62–66], which is defined as the difference between the total molecular density and the sum of the unperturbed atomic densities. These and other related analyses have been investigated in detail and applied to a series of molecules by Bader and coworkers [5–11], Kern and Karplus [35], Rosenfeld [61], and Ransil and Sinai [60].

Though not related directly to pictorial representations it is necessary to mention the work of Edmiston and Ruedenberg [26] on localized orbitals, because of their usefulness for the understanding of chemical concepts.

REFERENCES

1. R. Ahlrichs, W. Kutzelnigg, and W. A. Bingel. Theoret. Chim. Acta (Berlin) *5*, 289 (1966).
2. R. Ahlrichs, W. Kutzelnigg, and W. A. Bingel. Theoret. Chim. Acta (Berlin) *5*, 305 (1966).
3. T. L. Allen and H. Shull. J. Phys. Chem. *66*, 2281 (1962).
4. B. G. Anex and H. Shull. The Nature of the Two-Electron Chemical Bond. VI. Natural Orbital Analysis for HeH+, *in* "Molecular Orbitals in Chemistry, Physics and Biology," edited by P. O. Löwdin and B. Pullman. Academic Press, Inc., New York, N.Y., 1964.
5. R. F. W. Bader. Can. J. Chem. *41*, 2303 (1963).
6. R. F. W. Bader. J. Am. Chem. Soc. *86*, 5070 (1964).
7. R. F. W. Bader and W. H. Henneker. J. Am. Chem. Soc. *87*, 3063 (1965).
8. R. F. W. Bader and G. A. Jones. Can. J. Chem. *39*, 1253 (1961).
9. R. F. W. Bader and G. A. Jones. Can. J. Chem. *41*, 586 (1963).
10. R. F. W. Bader and G. A. Jones. Can. J. Chem. *41*, 2251 (1963).
11. R. F. W. Bader and G. A. Jones. J. Chem. Phys. *38*, 2791 (1963).
12. J. Bardeen, L. N. Cooper, and J. R. Schrieffer. Phys. Rev. *108*, 1175 (1957).
13. G. P. Barnett, J. Linderberg, and H. Shull. J. Chem. Phys. *43*, S80 (1965).
14. W. A. Bingel. J. Chem. Phys. *32*, 1522 (1960).
15. W. A. Bingel. J. Chem. Phys. *34*, 1066 (1961).
16. W. A. Bingel. J. Chem. Phys. *36*, 2842 (1962).
17. W. A. Bingel. Z. Naturforschg. *18a*, 1249 (1963).
18. W. A. Bingel. Theoret. Chim. Acta (Berlin) *5*, 341 (1966).
19. J. M. Blatt. Prog. Theor. Phys. (Japan) *23*, 447 (1960).
20. S. Bratoz. Compt. Rend. *256*, 5298 (1963).
21. D. C. Carlson and J. M. Keller. Phys. Rev. *121*, 659 (1961).
22. A. J. Coleman. Rev. Mod. Phys. *35*, 668 (1963).
23. E. R. Davidson. J. Chem. Phys. *39*, 875 (1963).
24. E. R. Davidson and L. L. Jones. J. Chem. Phys. *37*, 2966 (1962).
25. D. D. Ebbing and R. C. Henderson. J. Chem. Phys. *42*, 2225 (1965).
26. C. Edmiston and K. Ruedenberg. J. Chem. Phys. *43*, S97 (1965).
27. M. A. Eliason and J. O. Hirschfelder. J. Chem. Phys. *30*, 1397 (1959).
28. S. Fraga and B. J. Ransil. J. Chem. Phys. *34*, 727 (1961).
29. S. Fraga and B. J. Ransil. J. Chem. Phys. *35*, 1967 (1961).
30. S. Fraga and B. J. Ransil. J. Chem. Phys. *36*, 1127 (1962).
31. C. Garrod and J. K. Percus. J. Math. Phys. *5*, 1756 (1964).
32. S. Hagstrom and H. Shull. Rev. Mod. Phys. *35*, 624 (1963).
33. A. M. Karo. J. Chem. Phys. *31*, 182 (1959).
34. T. Kato. Commun. Pure Appl. Math. *10*, 151 (1957).
35. C. W. Kern and M. Karplus. J. Chem. Phys. *40*, 1374 (1964).
36. M. Kotani, A. Amemiya, E. Ishiguro, and T. Kimura. "Tables of Molecular Integrals." Maruzen Co., Ltd., Tokyo, Japan, 1955.
37. W. Kutzelnigg. Z. Naturforschg. *18a*, 1058 (1963).
38. W. Kutzelnigg. Theoret. Chim. Acta (Berlin) *1*, 327 (1963).
39. W. Kutzelnigg. Theoret. Chim. Acta (Berlin) *1*, 343 (1963).
40. W. Kutzelnigg. J. Chem. Phys. *40*, 3640 (1964).
41. W. Kutzelnigg. J. Chem. Phys. *42*, 2795 (1965).
42. W. Kutzelnigg. Theoret. Chim. Acta (Berlin) *3*, 241 (1965).

43. W. Kutzelnigg and V. H. Smith. J. Chem. Phys. *41*, 896 (1964).
44. P. O. Löwdin. Phys. Rev. *97*, 1474 (1955).
45. P. O. Löwdin and H. Shull. Phys. Rev. *101*, 1730 (1956).
46. G. Malli. Can. J. Phys. *44*, 3121 (1966).
47. G. Malli and S. Fraga. Can. J. Phys. *44*, 3131 (1966).
48. R. McWeeny. Proc. Roy. Soc. (London) *A253*, 242 (1959).
49. R. McWeeny. Rev. Mod. Phys. *32*, 335 (1960).
50. R. McWeeny and Y. Mizuno. Proc. Roy. Soc. (London) *A259*, 554 (1961).
51. R. McWeeny and B. Sutcliffe. Proc. Roy. Soc. (London) *A273*, 103 (1963).
52. R. P. Messmer and S. Fraga. Technical Report TC-6704, Division of Theoretical Chemistry, Department of Chemistry, University of Alberta, Edmonton, Alta., 1967.
53. Y. Mizuno and T. Izuyama. Prog. Theor. Phys. (Japan) *18*, 33 (1957).
54. R. S. Mulliken. J. Chem. Phys. *23*, 1833 (1955).
55. R. S. Mulliken. J. Chem. Phys. *23*, 1841 (1955).
56. R. S. Mulliken. J. Chem. Phys. *23*, 2338 (1955).
57. R. S. Mulliken. J. Chem. Phys. *23*, 2343 (1955).
58. K. Nakamura. Prog. Theor. Phys. (Japan) *21*, 713 (1959).
59. B. J. Ransil. J. Chem. Phys. *34*, 2109 (1961).
60. B. J. Ransil and J. Sinai. J. Chem. Phys. *46*, 4050 (1967).
61. J. L. J. Rosenfeld. Acta Chem. Scand. *18*, 1719 (1964).
62. M. Roux. J. Chim. Phys. *55*, 754 (1958).
63. M. Roux. J. Chim. Phys. *57*, 53 (1960).
64. M. Roux, S. Besnainou, and R. Daudel. J. Chim. Phys. *54*, 218 (1956).
65. M. Roux, S. Besnainou, and R. Daudel. J. Chim. Phys. *54*, 939 (1956).
66. M. Roux, M. Cornille, and L. Burnelle. J. Chem. Phys. *37*, 933 (1962).
67. F. Sasaki. Phys. Rev. *138*, B1338 (1965).
68. H. Shull. J. Chem. Phys. *30*, 617 (1959).
69. H. Shull. J. Chem. Phys. *30*, 1405 (1959).
70. H. Shull. J. Am. Chem. Soc. *82*, 1287 (1960).
71. H. Shull. J. Phys. Chem. *66*, 2320 (1962).
72. H. Shull. J. Am. Chem. Soc. *86*, 1469 (1964).
73. H. Shull and P. O. Löwdin. J. Chem. Phys. *30*, 617 (1959).
74. H. Shull and F. Prosser. J. Chem. Phys. *40*, 233 (1964).
75. D. W. Smith. J. Chem. Phys. *43*, S258 (1965).
76. D. W. Smith and S. J. Fogel. J. Chem. Phys. *43*, S91 (1965).
77. E. Steiner. J. Chem. Phys. *39*, 2365 (1963).
78. D. Ter Haar. Rep. Progr. Phys. *24*, 304 (1961).
79. A. C. Wahl. Science *151*, 961 (1966).
80. E. P. Wigner. "Group Theory and Its Applications to the Quantum Mechanics of Atomic Spectra." Academic Press, Inc., New York, N.Y., 1959.

Chapter 7 PROPERTIES AND INTERACTIONS

In the following chapters some of the properties and interactions in many-electron systems are considered individually. The discussion centers on the theoretical formulation, and the possibilities of application of different methods, presented in preceding chapters, are reviewed. At the same time numerical values, evaluated from analytical Hartree-Fock functions, are presented. However, an overall examination and a justification must be given here.

The properties considered here are the electric dipole moment, electric polarizabilities, magnetic susceptibility, nuclear magnetic shielding, and electric field gradient. Only the electric dipole moment is discussed here *per se*. The electric polarizabilities are a consequence of the interaction with an external electric field, and the magnetic susceptibility and the nuclear magnetic shielding arise in the interaction with an external magnetic field. The electric field gradient gives rise to an interaction with the electric nuclear quadrupole moment. The remaining weak interactions, considered here, are the Fermi contact term, octopole, orbit-orbit, spin-orbit, and spin-spin interactions.

What is the reason for the importance of these quantities? The practical application of the principles and methods of quantum mechanics will yield, in due time, accurate numerical values for all physical observables of interest.* At a stage of development of the methods, however, they can be of use as a criterion of accuracy, because of their dependence on different regions of the electronic density distribution for the system under consideration.† This dependence is observed from the different expectation values needed in the corresponding calculations. The scattering factors may

---

* The reader is referred here to the interesting discussion of Walnut [19] on the intractability in *a priori* calculations in complicated systems.

† Karplus, Kuppermann, and Isaacson [12] have proposed the use of functions weighted appropriately according to the one-electron operator under consideration.

be considered a manifestation of the overall electronic distribution, but the diamagnetic susceptibility depends on $\langle r^2 \rangle$, the nuclear magnetic shielding on $\langle r^{-1} \rangle$, and the electric field gradient, the magnetic dipole interaction, and the spin-orbit coupling on $\langle r^{-3} \rangle$. Furthermore, the Fermi contact term depends on the density at the nucleus and the octopole coupling on the slope of the p-type orbitals, also at the nucleus.

Therefore, a comparison of theoretical and experimental (or exact) values for the various properties and interactions yields an insight into the accuracy of the description the function under consideration provides for $\rho(0)$, $|dR(r)/dr|_{r=0}$ (for p-type orbitals), $\langle r^{-3} \rangle$, $\langle r^{-1} \rangle$, $\langle r^2 \rangle$, and $\rho(r)$. A complete analysis of a function is then possible on this basis.

The preceding discussion shows how different functions and methods can be compared on an *a posteriori* basis. Is it possible, however, to predict what type of function should be used in order to minimize the error in the evaluation of different properties? Closely related are the considerations regarding the selection of an adequate method.

In this connection it is convenient to consider independently the distinct types of properties. This distinction arises when the expectation values of one-electron operators are formulated within the framework of perturbation theory. Hirschfelder, Byers Brown, and Epstein [11] and Dalgarno and Stewart [4] have suggested that given a one-electron operator $\mathscr{P}$, corresponding to a physical observable, one can write a perturbed hamiltonian operator

$$\mathscr{H}_p = \mathscr{H} + \lambda' \mathscr{P},$$

in which case

$$E_p = E + \lambda' E^{(1)} + (\lambda')^2 E^{(2)} + \ldots,$$

where E represents the eigenvalue of the unperturbed hamiltonian operator $\mathscr{H}$ and

$$E^{(1)} = \langle \mathscr{P} \rangle,$$

$$E^{(2)} = \langle \mathscr{Q} \rangle;$$

the operator $\mathscr{Q}$ is defined by

$$\mathscr{Q} = (\mathscr{P} - \langle \mathscr{P} \rangle)(\mathscr{H} - E)^{-1}(\langle \mathscr{P} \rangle - \mathscr{P}).$$

The properties defined by the expectation value $\langle \mathscr{P} \rangle$ may be considered as first-order properties (dipole and quadrupole moments, diamagnetic contribution to the susceptibility and the nuclear magnetic shielding, etc.), whereas those proportional to $\langle \mathscr{Q} \rangle$ are second-order properties (electric polarizability, paramagnetic contribution to the susceptibility and the nuclear magnetic shielding, etc.).

If the eigenfunctions Ψ of $\mathscr{H}$ are not known, the calculation must be carried out using an approximate function Φ, assumed to be an eigenfunction of the operator $\mathscr{H}^{(0)}$, such that

$$\mathscr{H} = \mathscr{H}^{(0)} + \lambda \mathscr{H}^{(1)}.$$

The first- and second-order properties are then given by

$$\langle \mathscr{P} \rangle = \langle \mathscr{P} \rangle_0 + \lambda \langle \mathscr{P} \rangle_1 + \dots,$$
$$\langle \mathscr{Q} \rangle = \langle \mathscr{Q} \rangle_0 + \lambda \langle \mathscr{Q} \rangle_1 + \dots.$$

In the case when Φ is the Hartree-Fock function for the ground state of the system under consideration, then $\langle \mathscr{P} \rangle_0$ represents the uncoupled Hartree-Fock approximation to $\langle \mathscr{P} \rangle$, and $\langle \mathscr{P} \rangle_1$ vanishes. (See Dalgarno [3].)

This fact already indicates that for first-order properties the Hartree-Fock functions are satisfactory, but it is still possible to obtain an idea of the order of magnitude of the error, as shown below.

The accuracy of a function in connection with a given property, has been discussed by Eckart [5], Buimistrov [2], Löwdin [13], and Goodisman and Klemperer [9]. Following the formulation of Goodisman and Klemperer [9], one can write for the exact function:

$$\Psi = (1 - \tfrac{1}{2}\omega^2)\Phi + \omega\Phi',$$

where Φ is an approximation to Ψ, Φ' represents an appropriate correction, and the parameter ω gives an indication of the accuracy of Φ. The functions Φ and Φ' are assumed to be orthonormal, Ψ being normalized to fourth order in ω. The approximate energy expectation value, determined from Φ, is given (to second order in ω) by

$$E_{\text{appr.}} = E_{\text{exact}} (1 - \omega^2) + \omega^2 \langle \Phi' | \mathscr{H} | \Phi' \rangle.$$

Similar expressions can be given for the expectation values of operators corresponding to physical observables. For an operator that commutes with $\mathscr{H}$ one has (to second order)

$$P_{\text{appr.}} = P_{\text{exact}} (1 - \omega^2) + \omega^2 \langle \Phi' | \mathscr{P} | \Phi' \rangle,$$

whereas for an operator that does not commute with $\mathscr{H}$ it is

$$P_{\text{appr.}} = P_{\text{exact}} - \omega[\langle \Phi' | \mathscr{P} | \Psi \rangle + \langle \Psi | \mathscr{P} | \Phi' \rangle + \omega^2[P_{\text{exact}} + \langle \Phi' | \mathscr{P} | \Phi' \rangle]. \tag{7-1}$$

In the case of Hartree or Hartree-Fock functions it follows from the Brillouin theorem [1, 14] that for one-electron operators

$$P_{\text{appr.}} = P_{\text{exact}} (1 + \omega^2) + \omega^2 \langle \Phi' | \mathscr{P} | \Phi' \rangle. \tag{7-2}$$

For other approximate functions an equation similar to Eq. (7-2) can be obtained only if Φ' is an eigenfunction of $\mathscr{P}$, which is not probable unless there is a physical connection between $\mathscr{P}$ and $\mathscr{H}$. The condition represented by Eq. (7-2) is satisfied by the so-called stable functions, defined by Hall [10]. That is, Hartree-Fock functions are stable under all one-electron properties.

Therefore, ω^2 can be taken as a measure of the accuracy of the expectation values of one-electron operators calculated from Hartree-Fock functions. For other approximate functions, however, the error is of the order of ω.

Table 7-1 Expectation Values[a] of One-electron Operators for He

OPERATOR	OPTIMIZED FIRST-ORDER ENERGY	DALGARNO	SANDERS-HIRSCHFELDER	HARTREE-FOCK	EXACT
r^5	8.07007	8.75358	9.01093	9.22	9.35833
r^4	3.57621	3.74483	3.82964	3.8877	3.94435
r^3	1.85338	1.89416	1.92413	1.9406	1.96206
r^2	1.16080	1.16959	1.18053	1.18485	1.19234
r^1	0.92181	0.92308	0.92663	0.9273	0.92929
r^{-1}	1.6875	1.6875		1.68735	1.68834
r^{-2}	5.97328	5.97667		5.9955	6.01740

a. The values in this table are given by Sanders and Hirschfelder [15], except for the Hartree-Fock results which have been taken from Fraga and Malli [6]. The exact values are those obtained by Scherr and Knight [16, 17].

The value of ω can be estimated from the coefficients of configuration interaction functions. (See the work of Goodisman and Klemperer [9] for more details.)

Techniques have been devised, however, in order to improve the results obtained with simple functions. In particular, Dalgarno and Stewart [4] have suggested the use of screening constants, determined under the condition that the first-order correction for the property under consideration will vanish. Sanders and Hirschfelder [15] have indicated that the method of Dalgarno may give a lower bound for the expectation value of any positive definite operator. Therefore, it may be possible to obtain a further improvement by maximization of the corresponding expectation value, using the function corrected to first order.

It has been also shown by Sanders and Hirschfelder [15] that the screening constants determined by the method of Dalgarno differ from those determined by optimization of the energy to first order. The implication is that improvements in the expectation values of different observables are obtained at the expense of the total energy.

These considerations are reflected in Table 7-1, which collects the expectation values of the one-electron operators* r^5 to r^{-2} for He.

The difficulties encountered in the calculation of expectation values of second-order properties have determined a proliferation of methods, which are discussed in the following chapters. It is interesting to note, however, that $\langle \mathscr{D} \rangle_1$ can be determined, as shown by Tuan, Epstein, and Hirschfelder [18], from quantities already available from the calculation of $\langle \mathscr{D} \rangle_0$. That is, second-order properties can be calculated to first order without added difficulty.

---

* The expectation values of one-electron operators r^n, with $-5 \leq n \leq 5$, have been determined by Fraga and Malli [6–8] from analytical Hartree-Fock functions for all the neutral atoms and their negative ions from He to Kr and for the isoelectronic series $1s(2)$, ^1S, to $K(2)L(8)M(18)4s(1)$, ^2S, for the same atoms.

REFERENCES

1. L. Brillouin. Act. Sci. Ind. Nos. 71, 159, 160 (1933–34).
2. V. M. Buimistrov. J. Exptl. and Theoret. Phys. (U.S.S.R.) 35, 1161 (1958).
3. A. Dalgarno. Proc. Roy. Soc. (London) A251, 282 (1959).
4. A. Dalgarno and A. L. Stewart. Proc. Roy. Soc. (London) A247, 245 (1958).
5. C. Eckart. Phys. Rev. 36, 878 (1930).
6. S. Fraga and G. Malli. Technical Report* TC-6601, Division of Theoretical Chemistry, Department of Chemistry, University of Alberta, Edmonton, Alta., 1966.
7. S. Fraga and G. Malli. Technical Report* TC-6602, Division of Theoretical Chemistry, Department of Chemistry, University of Alberta, Edmonton, Alta., 1966.
8. S. Fraga and G. Malli. Technical Report* TC-6603, Division of Theoretical Chemistry, Department of Chemistry, University of Alberta, Edmonton, Alta., 1966.
9. J. Goodisman and W. Klemperer. J. Chem. Phys. 38, 721 (1963).
10. G. G. Hall. Phil. Mag. 6, 249 (1961).
11. J. O. Hirschfelder, W. Byers Brown, and S. T. Epstein. Recent Developments in Perturbation Theory, in "Advances in Quantum Chemistry," vol. 1, edited by P. O. Löwdin. Academic Press, Inc., New York, N.Y., 1964.
12. M. Karplus, A. Kuppermann, and L. M. Isaacson. J. Chem. Phys. 29, 1240 (1958).
13. P. O. Löwdin. Ann. Rev. Phys. Chem. 11, 107 (1960).
14. C. Møller and M. S. Plesset. Phys. Rev. 46, 618 (1934).
15. W. A. Sanders and J. O. Hirschfelder. J. Chem. Phys. 42, 2904 (1965).
16. C. W. Scherr and R. E. Knight. Rev. Mod. Phys. 35, 436 (1963).
17. C. W. Scherr and R. E. Knight. J. Chem. Phys. 40, 3034 (1964).
18. D. F. T. Tuan, S. T. Epstein, and J. O. Hirschfelder. J. Chem. Phys. 44, 431 (1966).
19. T. H. Walnut. Report WIS-TCI-127, Theoretical Chemistry Institute, University of Wisconsin, Madison, Wisconsin, 15 July 1965.

---

* These Reports have been placed in The Depository of Unpublished Data, National Science Library, National Research Council, Ottawa 2, Canada.

Chapter 8   ELECTRIC MOMENTS AND POLARIZABILITIES

ELECTRIC DIPOLE MOMENT

The accuracy of an approximate function, as far as the electronic density distribution is concerned, can be tested by means of the expectation values corresponding to some simple one-electron operators.

Using the notation of Karplus [47], one can write for the n-th order moments

$$M_n(m_1, m_2, m_3) = \int x^{m_1} y^{m_2} z^{m_3} \, \rho(r) \, d\tau,$$

where $\rho(r)$ is the electronic charge distribution and m_1, m_2, and m_3 can take the values $0, 1, 2, \ldots$, subject to the condition that $m_1 + m_2 + m_3 = n$. These electronic moments are designated as dipole $(n = 1)$, quadrupole $(n = 2)$, octopole $(n = 3)$ moments, etc. The discussion here is restricted to dipole and quadrupole moments.

The electronic quadrupole moment is of interest as an accuracy criterion for nonpolar molecules. The quadrupole moment is defined as a tensor of rank two, with components $\langle x^2 - r^2/3 \rangle$, $\langle y^2 - r^2/3 \rangle$, $\langle z^2 - r^2/3 \rangle$, $\langle xy \rangle$, $\langle xz \rangle$, and $\langle yz \rangle$ (the other nondiagonal components being identical to the ones given here). Only five of the nine components are independent; the trace is identically zero and invariant under a transformation of the system of coordinates. Table 8-1 collects the expectation values (referred to a system of coordinates centered at the midpoint of the internuclear axis) for some of these components for H_2, calculated from different approximate functions. Karplus [47] and Das and Bersohn [25] have discussed the accuracy of the various functions on the basis of these values, taking into account that expectation values such as $\langle x^2 \rangle$, $\langle y^2 \rangle$, and $\langle z^2 \rangle$ give a measure of the size of the charge distribution, whereas $\langle z^2 - x^2 \rangle$, etc., define the shape of the distribution (as different from a spherical distribution, for which this and similar expectation values vanish).

Table 8-1 Second Moments[a] (in a_0^2 Units) for H_2

$\langle x^2 \rangle$	$\langle z^2 \rangle$	$\langle z^2 - x^2 \rangle$	FUNCTION
1.0371	1.385	0.348	Heitler-London [37]
1.044	1.367	0.323	Coulson [14]
0.742	0.964	0.222	Rosen [66]
0.767	1.131	0.364	Wang [82]
0.816	1.147	0.331	Wallis (CI) [81]
0.761	1.108	0.347	Wallis (limited ionic) [81]
0.738	1.082	0.344	Weinbaum [87]
0.777	1.020	0.243	Kolos-Roothaan (Hartree-Fock) [53]
0.731	1.002	0.271	Newell [57, 58]
0.745	1.009	0.264	Nordsieck [59]
0.742	1.073	0.332	Coulson (optimized) [14]
0.762	1.020	0.258	Kolos-Roothaan (accurate) [53]
0.744	1.070	0.326	Hirschfelder-Linnett [40]
0.7663	1.0604	0.2941	Experimental[b]

a. The values in this table are given by Das and Bersohn [25], with the exception of the values determined by Kolos and Roothaan [53]. See also the values given by Karplus [47]. The center of coordinates is at the midpoint of the internuclear separation; the z-axis coincides with the internuclear axis.

b. The experimental values are given by Ramsey [65].

It must be pointed out that a comparison with experimental values, in order to be meaningful, requires an averaging of each quantity over the nuclear function. In the case of H_2, however, Karplus [47] has shown that the vibrational correction is small compared with the difference between the calculated and experimental values.

In the case of polar molecules one can use the first-order moment, which contributes to the total dipole moment of the system. The other contribution arises from the nuclei in the molecule. For a diatomic molecule, the molecular dipole moment is defined by

$$\mu = -\langle z_c \rangle + \tfrac{1}{2}R(Z_b - Z_a),$$
$$= -\langle z \rangle + RZ_b, \tag{8-1}$$

where $\langle z \rangle$ denotes the total expectation value and R is the internuclear separation; Z_a and Z_b are the nuclear charges of the two nuclei. In the first expression of Eq. (8-1), the center of coordinates is at the midpoint of the internuclear axis, whereas in the second expression the center of coordinates has been taken at nucleus a, situated on the left. The value of the total dipole moment μ is invariant under a change of the system of coordinates, but the electronic and nuclear contributions do change.

The theoretical values of dipole moments are very sensitive to changes in the functions used in the calculations. (See, for example, the work of Fraga and Ransil [32], using single- and many-configuration SCF functions for diatomic molecules of the first row.) It seems, however, that Hartree-Fock functions may yield values in satisfactory agreement with experiment,

Table 8-2 Electric Dipole Moments for Some Hydrides[a]

SYSTEM	STATE	CONTRIBUTING TERMS (au)		DIPOLE MOMENT		
		$\frac{R}{2}(Z_a - Z_b)$	$-\langle z \rangle$	Calculated		Experimental[b]
				(au)	(Debye)	(Debye)
LiH	$^1\Sigma^+$	3.0150	0.6536	−2.3614	−6.002	−5.882
BeH	$^2\Sigma^+$	3.8070	3.6959	−0.1111	−0.282	
BH	$^1\Sigma^+$	4.6720	5.3539	0.6819	1.733	
CH	$^2\Pi_r$	5.3100	5.9279	0.6179	1.570	
NH	$^3\Sigma^-$	5.8842	6.5243	0.6401	1.627	
OH	$^2\Pi_i$	6.4197	7.1202	0.7005	1.780	1.72
FH	$^1\Sigma^+$	6.9312	7.6951	0.7639	1.942	1.8195
NaH	$^1\Sigma^+$	17.8300	15.0908	−2.7392	−6.962	
MgH	$^2\Sigma^+$	17.9905	17.3940	−0.5965	−1.516	
AlH	$^1\Sigma^+$	18.6840	18.7509	0.0669	0.170	
SiH	$^2\Pi_r$	18.6810	18.7999	0.1189	0.302	
PH	$^3\Sigma^-$	18.9560	19.1677	0.2117	0.538	
SH	$^2\Pi_i$	19.1325	19.4714	0.3389	0.861	
ClH	$^1\Sigma^+$	19.2696	19.7404	0.4608	1.197	1.081

a. Calculated by Cade and Huo [10] from analytical Hartree-Fock functions, at the experimental equilibrium distance. The polarity A^-H^+ is associated with a dipole moment $\mu < 0$ and the polarity A^+H^- with $\mu > 0$.

b. The experimental values are those determined by Wharton, Gold, and Klemperer [90], Phelps and Dalby [62], and Weiss [88]. See also the work of Powell and Lide [64].

as observed in Table 8-2, which collects the dipole moments for some hydrides of the first two rows. The comparison of theoretical and experimental values presents also the difficulty mentioned above for the second-order moment. The experimental value of the dipole moment represents an average value over vibrational states, whereas the theoretical value is determined for a given internuclear separation (usually the experimental distance).

In diatomic molecules it is also possible to determine the functional form of the dipole moment in terms of the internuclear distance. In particular, Goodisman [34] has investigated the behavior of this functional at the united- and separated-atom limits, where the dipole moment vanishes. For large separations, the dipole moment changes as R^{-4} (when at least one of the atoms has a quadrupole moment) or R^{-7}. On the other hand, at the united-atom limit, the dipole moment tends to zero as R^3 (for a united atom in an S or P state) or R^5 (for a united atom in a D or F state).

ELECTRIC POLARIZABILITY

The application of an external electric field, due to an electric charge, produces a distortion of the electronic charge distribution in a system, giving rise to induced moments.

The induced moments are proportional to the field or its derivatives. In the simple case of an atom, for example, one can write

$$\mu = -\alpha_D(\partial V/\partial z),$$

$$Q = \alpha_Q(\partial^2 V/\partial z^2),$$

$$O = -\alpha_O(\partial^3 V/\partial z^3),$$

$$H = \alpha_H(\partial^4 V/\partial z^4),$$

etc., for the dipole, quadrupole, octopole, and hexadecapole moments, respectively. The constants of proportionality are the corresponding dipole, quadrupole, octopole, and hexadecapole polarizabilities. V is the electrostatic potential of the external charge placed on the z-axis. Dalgarno [16] gives some alternate definitions in a very detailed review of this subject.

The total moments of the system (including the permanent moments, if different from zero) can interact with the external field. For example, the dipole moment interacts with the uniform part of the electric field, whereas the unhomogeneous part interacts with the quadrupole moment. Restricting the discussion to dipole polarizabilities and assuming that the system does not have a permanent dipole, we see that the interaction energy is given by

$$\Delta E = -\tfrac{1}{2}\, \boldsymbol{F}\boldsymbol{\alpha}\boldsymbol{F} = -\tfrac{1}{2}\sum_u\sum_v F_u\alpha_{uv}F_v, \qquad u, v = \begin{cases} x \\ y, \\ z \end{cases} \qquad (8\text{-}2)$$

where $\boldsymbol{\alpha}$ represents the polarizability tensor and F_u are the components of the electric field. The polarizability tensor can be characterized in an adequate system of coordinates by the principal polarizabilities α_{xx}, α_{yy}, and α_{zz}. It is customary to use an alternate notation in certain cases. For example, in a diatomic molecule (with cylindrical symmetry), the polarizabilities are denoted by $\alpha_{\parallel} = \alpha_{zz}$ and $\alpha_{\perp} = \alpha_{xx} = \alpha_{yy}$, assuming that the z-axis coincides with the internuclear axis.

When the system has spherical symmetry, the three principal polarizabilities are identical. For other systems without spherical symmetry, the distortion depends on the orientation of the system. It is then convenient to define an average polarizability

$$\alpha = \tfrac{1}{3}(\alpha_{xx} + \alpha_{yy} + \alpha_{zz}).$$

A number of methods have been used for the evaluation of dipole polarizabilities. Exact calculations have been carried for the one-electron atom by Epstein [28], Schrödinger [68], Wentzel [89], and Doi [26]. Very accurate results have been obtained by perturbation treatments, such as those of Schwartz [69] for H⁻ and He and those of Kelly [48] for Be. The direct application of the variational method implies the use of

Eq. (8-2). The total energy of the system, in the presence of the perturbing field, is minimized, and comparison of the interaction energy with Eq. (8-2) yields the components of the polarizability tensor. This method was first used by Slater and Kirkwood [70] and Buckingham [6], and generalized by Guy and Harrand [35]. Similar treatments are those of Wikner and Das [91], Pople and Schofield [63], Ishiguro *et al.* [43], and Das and Bersohn [25].

The Hartree-Fock formalism, however, provides the basis for a consistent evaluation of the dipole polarizability. As discussed in Chapter 7, the Hartree-Fock approximation must yield satisfactory results for one-electron properties such as the dipole polarizability. Within the general framework of this formalism, several alternate procedures are possible. The perturbation coupled Hartree-Fock (PCHF) method, with calculations carried out by second-order perturbation, has been developed by Peng [61], Allen [1], Dalgarno [15], and Kaneko [46]. A more practical formulation is exemplified by the coupled Hartree-Fock (CHF) method, developed by Cohen and Roothaan [13]. In this method, equivalent to the PCHF in the limiting case of a vanishing field, the Hartree-Fock equations are solved in the presence of a perturbing field. The procedure involves the determination of the perturbed state function, which is then used in the calculation of the induced dipole moment. The polarizability, as a function of the applied field, is then determined by the relation

$$\alpha(F) = \mu(F)/F.$$

The polarizability, independent of the field, is then defined as the limiting value of $\alpha(F)$ when the field tends to zero.

An approximate method is the uncoupled Hartree-Fock (UHF) method, proposed by Dalgarno [15]. It has the disadvantage, however, that the perturbed functions are not required to be solutions of the perturbed Hartree-Fock equations. This situation exists also in the case of the Sternheimer method, developed by Sternheimer [71] and used by Sundbom [80], Dalgarno and Parkinson [22], etc.

The various methods may lead to different values. Table 8-3 collects the values of the dipole polarizability for a number of neutral atoms (up to Kr) and their positive and negative ions. It can be observed that, as expected, the values calculated by the PCHF and the CHF scheme coincide.

For molecules most of the calculations have been carried out by a variational procedure. The values presented in Table 8-4 for H_2 provide an example of the values to be obtained by different types of functions.*

In the calculation of quadrupole polarizabilities, similar methods to those just described have been used. The theory was first developed by Sternheimer and coworkers [30, 71, 75, 76], Das and Bersohn [24], Wikner and Das [91, 92], Burns [7, 8] and Burns and Wikner [9].

---

* The reader is referred to the work of Das and Bersohn [25] for a detailed discussion on the merits of the different functions. Calculations on HF and F_2 have been carried out by Stevens and Lipscomb [77, 78].

Table 8-3 Dipole Polarizabilities (in Å³) for Some Atoms and Ions

SYSTEM	α_D	METHOD	REFERENCE
H⁻	7.3	Perturbation	Dalgarno-Stewart [23]
	11.8	PCHF	Stewart [79]
	11.8	PCHF	Dalgarno-McNamee [20]
	13.4	Sternheimer	Sternheimer [72]
	13.8	CHF	Cohen [12]
	14.88	Variation	Wikner-Das [91]
	16.7	UFH	Yoshimine-Hurst [93]
	39.28	Variation	Kolker-Michels [51]
	30.4	Exact	Schwartz [69]
	30.2	Experimental[a]	Geltman [33]
He	0.224	Sternheimer	Sternheimer [72]
	0.2205	Sternheimer	Kaneko [46]
	0.220	Sternheimer	Dalgarno-McNamee [20]
	0.220	UHF	Yoshimine-Hurst [93]
	0.218	Variation	Wikner-Das [91]
	0.1956	PCHF	Stewart [79]
	0.196	PCHF	Dalgarno-McNamee [20]
	0.196	PCHF	Kaneko [46]
	0.196	CHF	Cohen [12]
	0.2165	Variation	Kolker-Michels [51]
	0.2050	Exact	Schwartz [69]
	0.206	Perturbation	Dalgarno-Stewart [23]
	0.2068	Experimental[b]	Johnston-Oudemans-Cole [45]
	±0.0002		
Li⁺	0.0307	Sternheimer	Sternheimer [72]
	0.0305	Variation	Wikner-Das [91]
	0.0304	Sternheimer	Dalgarno-McNamee [20]
	0.0304	UHF	Yoshimine-Hurst [93]
	0.0299	Perturbation	Dalgarno-Stewart [23]
	0.0292	Variation	Kolker-Michels [51]
	0.0282	Exact	Schwartz [69]
	0.02816	PCHF	Stewart [79]
	0.0281	PCHF	Dalgarno-McNamee [20]
	0.0280	CHF	Cohen [12]
	0.0235	Experimental[c]	Sternheimer [71]
Li	25	Sternheimer	Parkinson [60]
	24.9	Sternheimer	Sternheimer [74]
	20	Sternheimer	Sundbom [80]
	21.0	UHF	Yoshimine-Hurst [93]
	22 ± 2	Experimental[d]	Chamberlain-Zorn [11]
Be⁺	2.48	UHF	Yoshimine-Hurst [93]
Be	9.6	Sternheimer	Parkinson [60]
	9.53	UHF	Yoshimine-Hurst [93]

a. Bates and Lewis [3] give a value of 34.1 Å³ for H⁻.

b. Other experimental values of 0.206, 0.204, and 0.2051 Å³ for He are given by Essen [29], Herzfeld and Wolf [38, 39], and Dalgarno and Kingston [18], respectively.

c. A value of 0.025 Å³ for Li⁺ is given by Mayer and Mayer [56].

d. Dalgarno and Kingston [17] give a value of 24.4 Å³ and Salop *et al.* [67] a value of 20 ± 3 Å³ for Li.

Table 8-3 Dipole Polarizabilities (in $\overset{\circ}{A}{}^3$) for Some Atoms and Ions (*continued*)

SYSTEM	α_D	METHOD	REFERENCE
Be	9.5	Sternheimer	Dalgarno-McNamee [21]
	4.5	UHF	Dalgarno-McNamee [21]
	4.54	UHF	Kelly-Taylor [49]
	6.75	CHF	Cohen [12]
	6.76	PCHF	Dalgarno-McIntyre [19]
	6.93	Exact	Kelly [48]
B+	1.96	UHF	Yoshimine-Hurst [93]
	1.69	PCHF	Dalgarno-McIntyre [19]
	1.682	CHF	Cohen [12]
B	5.1	Sternheimer	Dalgarno-Parkinson [22]
C	2.1	Sternheimer	Dalgarno-Parkinson [22]
N	1.3	Sternheimer	Dalgarno-Parkinson [22]
O+	0.49	Sternheimer	Parkinson [60]
O	0.89	Sternheimer	Dalgarno-Parkinson [22]
O-	3.2	Sternheimer	Parkinson [60]
F	0.6	Sternheimer	Dalgarno-Parkinson [22]
F-	1.858	Sternheimer	Sternheimer [73]
	1.81	UHF	Yoshimine-Hurst [93]
	1.8	Sternheimer	Dalgarno-Parkinson [22]
	1.206	Perturbation	Donath [27]
	0.99	Experimental	Born-Heisenberg [5]
Ne+	0.21	Sternheimer	Parkinson [60]
Ne	0.615	Sternheimer	Kaneko [46]
	0.3674	Perturbation	Donath [27]
	0.38	Sternheimer	Dalgarno-Parkinson [22]
	0.409	UHF	Yoshimine-Hurst [93]
	0.398	Experimental[e]	Landolt-Börnstein [55]
Na+	0.145	Sternheimer	Parkinson [60]
	0.152	Sternheimer	Sternheimer [73]
	0.1541	Perturbation	Donath [27]
	0.163	UHF	Yoshimine-Hurst [93]
	0.17	Experimental	Mayer-Mayer [56]
Na	27.1	UHF	Yoshimine-Hurst [93]
	22.9	Sternheimer	Sternheimer [74]
	21.5 $\pm$ 2	Experimental[f]	Chamberlain-Zorn [11]
Mg+	5.51	UHF	Yoshimine-Hurst [93]
Mg	19.4	UHF	Yoshimine-Hurst [93]
	7.0 $\pm$ 1.8	Experimental	Altick [2]
	7.4 $\pm$ 1.8		
Al+	5.89	UHF	Yoshimine-Hurst [93]
Cl-	7·19	Sternheimer	Sternheimer [73]
	6.23	UHF	Yoshimine-Hurst [93]
	3.05	Experimental	Born-Heisenberg [5]

e. Dalgarno and Kingston [18] give for Ne a value of 0.395 Å³.
f. For Na, Dalgarno and Kingston [17] give a value of 24.6 Å³ and Salop *et al.* [67] a value of 20 $\pm$ 2.5 Å³.

Table 8-3 Dipole Polarizabilities (in Å³) for Some Atoms and Ions (*continued*)

SYSTEM	α_D	METHOD	REFERENCE
A	2.40	Sternheimer	Kaneko [46]
	2.32	UHF	Yoshimine-Hurst [93]
	2.03	Variation	Pople-Schofield [63]
	1.63	Experimental[g]	Landolt-Börnstein [55]
K+	1.24	Sternheimer	Sternheimer [73]
	1.08	UHF	Yoshimine-Hurst [93]
	0.80	Experimental	Mayer-Mayer [56]
K	59.6	UHF	Yoshimine-Hurst [93]
	44.4	Sternheimer	Sternheimer [74]
	38 ± 4	Experimental[h]	Chamberlain-Zorn [11]
Ca+	14.3	UHF	Yoshimine-Hurst [93]
Ca	48.9	UHF	Yoshimine-Hurst [93]
	19.7 ± 0.6	Experimental	Altick [2]
	22.5 ± 0.6		
Cu+	0.982	Sternheimer	Sternheimer [73]
Kr	2.48	Experimental	Dalgarno-Kingston [18]

g. Dalgarno and Kingston [18] give an value of 1.64 Å³ for A.

h. Dalgarno and Kingston [17] and Salop *et al.* [67] give for K values of 41.6 and 40 ± 5 Å³, respectively. Hall and Zorn (Bull. Amer. Phys. Soc. *12*, 131 [1967]) have determined a value of 45.7 ± 6.

Table 8-4 Dipole Polarizability (in a_0^3) of H_2

$\alpha_\perp$	$\alpha_\parallel$	α	FUNCTION	REFERENCE
9.77	16.57	12.04	Coulson [14]	Das-Bersohn [25]
9.02	12.62	10.22	Heitler-London [37]	Das-Bersohn [25]
5.41	8.73	6.52	Fraga-Ransil (SCF) [31]	Kolker-Karplus [52]
3.95	5.71	4.54	Hirschfelder-Linnett [40]	Das-Bersohn [25]
4.40	5.04	4.61	Rosen [66]	Das-Bersohn [25]
5.19	7.51	5.96	Harris-Taylor [36]	Hoyland [41]
4.35	9.15	5.95	Coulson (optimized) [14]	Das-Bersohn [25]
4.89	8.00	5.93	Coulson (optimized) [14]	Hoyland [41]
4.72	5.12	4.85	Wang [82]	Das-Bersohn [25]
4.36	6.18	4.97	Weinbaum [87]	Das-Bersohn [25]
4.45	6.12	5.00	James-Coolidge [44]	Ishiguro *et al.* [43]
4.81	7.31	5.64	Correlated	Hoyland [41]
4.77	7.36	5.63	Berencz [4]	Hoyland [41]
4.70	7.15	5.52	Open-shell	Hoyland [41]
5.32	5.01	5.22	Wallis (CI) [81]	Das-Bersohn [25]
4.64	6.39	5.22	Wallis (limited ionic) [81]	Das-Bersohn [25]
4.85	6.30	5.33	Experimental	Landolt-Börnstein [55]

Table 8-5 Quadrupole Polarizabilities (in $\overset{\circ}{A}{}^5$) for Some Atoms and Their Ions

SYSTEM	α_Q	REFERENCE	SYSTEM	α_Q	REFERENCE
H^-	67.0	Das-Bersohn [24]	B^+	1.173	Lahiri-Mukherji [54]
	66.5	Sternheimer [72]		1.17	Dalgarno-McIntyre [19]
He	0.0993	Sternheimer [72]	F^-	2.38	Burns-Wikner [9]
	0.0979	Dalgarno-McNamee [20]	Ne	0.370	Burns [8]
	0.0965	Lahiri-Mukherji [54]	Na^+	0.0670	Das-Bersohn [24]
	0.0949	Das-Bersohn [24]		0.0649	Burns [7]
Li^+	0.00473	Sternheimer [72]		0.0562	Sternheimer [72]
	0.00472	Dalgarno-McNamee [20]	Cl^-	13.77	Sternheimer [72]
	0.00471	Das-Bersohn [24]		13.1	Burns-Wikner [9]
	0.00465	Lahiri-Mukherji [54]	A	2.19	Burns [8]
Be	15.1	Dalgarno-McNamee [21]	K^+	0.733	Sternheimer [72]
	14.21	Lahiri-Mukherji [54]		0.721	Burns [7]
	14.2	Dalgarno-McIntyre [19]	Cu^+	1.280	Sternheimer [72]

Sternheimer [71, 75] solves numerically the first-order perturbation equation. Das [24, 91, 92], Burns [7–9], and Ingalls [42] determine the perturbed functions by minimization of the second-order energy; and Dalgarno [15, 16], Kaneko [46], and Allen [1] have used the fully coupled approximation. The formulation of Dalgarno has been used by Khubchandani, Sharma, and Das [50], but without maintaining the coupling between the perturbed orbitals. A modified variational method for the minimization of the second-order energy within the framework of the fully-coupled Hartree-Fock approximation has been applied by Lahiri and Mukherji [54]. The unrestricted Hartree-Fock method has been used extensively by Watson and Freeman [83–86].

Table 8-5 collects the values of the quadrupole polarizabilities calculated by some of these methods.

REFERENCES

1. L. C. Allen. Phys. Rev. *118*, 167 (1960).
2. P. L. Altick. J. Chem. Phys. *40*, 238 (1964).
3. D. R. Bates and J. T. Lewis. Proc. Phys. Soc. (London) *A68*, 173 (1955).
4. F. Berencz. Acta Physica Acad. Sci. Hung. *6*, 423 (1957).
5. M. Born and W. Heisenberg. Z. Physik *23*, 388 (1924).
6. R. A. Buckingham. Proc. Roy. Soc. (London) *A160*, 94 (1937).
7. G. Burns. Phys. Rev. *115*, 357 (1959).
8. G. Burns. J. Chem. Phys. *31*, 1253 (1959).
9. G. Burns and E. G. Wikner. Phys. Rev. *121*, 155 (1961).

10. P. E. Cade and W. Huo. Technical Report, LMSS, Department of Physics, The University of Chicago, 149, 1965; J. Chem. Phys. *45*, 1063 (1966).
11. G. E. Chamberlain and J. C. Zorn. Phys. Rev. *129*, 677 (1963).
12. H. D. Cohen. J. Chem. Phys. *43*, 3558 (1965).
13. H. D. Cohen and C. C. J. Roothaan. J. Chem. Phys. *43*, S34 (1965).
14. C. A. Coulson. Trans. Faraday Soc. *33*, 1479 (1937).
15. A. Dalgarno. Proc. Roy. Soc. (London) *A251*, 282 (1959).
16. A. Dalgarno. Advanc. Phys. *11*, 281 (1962).
17. A. Dalgarno and A. E. Kingston. Proc. Phys. Soc. (London) *73*, 455 (1959).
18. A. Dalgarno and A. E. Kingston. Proc. Roy. Soc. (London) *A259*, 424 (1960).
19. A. Dalgarno and H. A. J. McIntyre. Proc. Phys. Soc. (London) *85*, 47 (1965).
20. A. Dalgarno and J. McNamee. Proc. Phys. Soc. (London) *77*, 673 (1961).
21. A. Dalgarno and J. McNamee. J. Chem. Phys. *35*, 1517 (1961).
22. A. Dalgarno and D. Parkinson. Proc. Roy. Soc. (London) *A250*, 422 (1959).
23. A. Dalgarno and A. L. Stewart. Proc. Roy. Soc. (London) *A247*, 245 (1958).
24. T. P. Das and R. Bersohn. Phys. Rev. *102*, 360 (1956).
25 T. P. Das and R. Bersohn. Phys. Rev. *115*, 897 (1959).
26. S. Doi. Proc. Phys.-Math. Soc. (Japan) *10*, 223 (1928).
27. W. E. Donath. J. Chem. Phys. *39*, 2685 (1963).
28. P. S. Epstein. Phys. Rev. *28*, 695 (1926).
29. L. Essen. Proc. Phys. Soc. (London) *66*, 189 (1953).
30. H. M. Foley, R. M. Sternheimer, and D. Tycko. Phys. Rev. *93*, 734 (1954).
31. S. Fraga and B. J. Ransil. J. Chem. Phys. *35*, 1967 (1961).
32. S. Fraga and B. J. Ransil. J. Chem. Phys. *36*, 1127 (1962).
33. S. Geltman. Astrophys. J. *136*, 935 (1962).
34. J. Goodisman. J. Chem. Phys. *38*, 2597 (1963).
35. J. Guy and M. Harrand. Compt. Rend. *234*, 616 (1952).
36. F. E. Harris and H. S. Taylor. J. Chem. Phys. *38*, 2591 (1963).
37. W. Heitler and F. London. Z. Physik *44*, 455 (1927).
38. K. F. Herzfeld and K. L. Wolf. Ann. Physik *76*, 71 (1925).
39. K. F. Herzfeld and K. L. Wolf. Ann. Physik *76*, 567 (1925).
40. J. O. Hirschfelder and W. Linnett. J. Chem. Phys. *18*, 130 (1950).
41. J. R. Hoyland. J. Chem. Phys. *41*, 3153 (1964).
42. R. Ingalls. Phys. Rev. *128*, 1155 (1962).
43. E. Ishiguro, T. Arai, M. Mizushima, and M. Kotani. Proc. Phys. Soc. (London) *65*, 178 (1952).
44. H. James and A. S. Coolidge. J. Chem. Phys. *1*, 825 (1933).
45. D. R. Johnston, G. J. Oudemans, and R. H. Cole. J. Chem. Phys. *33*, 1310 (1960).
46. S. Kaneko. J. Phys. Soc. Japan *14*, 1600 (1959).
47. M. Karplus. J. Chem. Phys. *25*, 605 (1956).
48. H. P. Kelly. Phys. Rev. *136*, B896 (1964).
49. H. P. Kelly and H. S. Taylor. J. Chem. Phys. *40*, 1478 (1964).
50. P. G. Khubchandani, R. R. Sharma, and T. P. Das. Phys. Rev. *126*, 594 (1962).
51. H. J. Kolker and H. H. Michels. J. Chem. Phys. *43*, 1027 (1965).
52. H. J. Kolker and M. Karplus. J. Chem. Phys. *39*, 2011 (1963).
53. W. Kolos and C. C. J. Roothaan. Rev. Mod. Phys. *32*, 219 (1960).
54. J. Lahiri and A. Mukherji. Phys. Rev. *141*, 428 (1966).
55. H. H. Landolt and R. Börnstein. "Zahlenwerte und Funktionen aus Physik, Chemie, Astronomie, Geophysik und Technik." Springer-Verlag, Berlin, Germany, 1950.
56. J. E. Mayer and M. G. Mayer. Phys. Rev. *43*, 605 (1933).
57. G. F. Newell. Phys. Rev. *78*, 711 (1950).
58. G. F. Newell. Phys. Rev. *80*, 476 (1950).
59. A. Nordsieck. Phys. Rev. *58*, 310 (1940).
60. D. Parkinson. Proc. Phys. Soc. (London) *75*, 169 (1960).
61. H. Peng. Proc. Roy. Soc. (London) *178*, 499 (1941).
62. D. H. Phelps and F. W. Dalby. Can. J. Phys. *43*, 144 (1965).
63. J. A. Pople and P. Schofield. Phil. Mag. *2*, 591 (1957).
64. F. X. Powell and D. R. Lide, Jr. J. Chem. Phys. *42*, 4201 (1965).
65. N. F. Ramsey. "Molecular Beams." Oxford University Press, Oxford, England, 1956.
66. N. Rosen. Phys. Rev. *38*, 2099 (1931).

67. A. Salop, E. Pollack, and B. Bederson. Phys. Rev. *124*, 1431 (1961).
68. E. Schrödinger. Ann. Physik *80*, 437 (1926).
69. C. Schwartz. Phys. Rev. *123*, 1700 (1961).
70. J. C. Slater and J. G. Kirkwood. Phys. Rev. *37*, 682 (1931).
71. R. M. Sternheimer. Phys. Rev. *96*, 951 (1954).
72. R. M. Sternheimer. Phys. Rev. *107*, 1565 (1957).
73. R. M. Sternheimer. Phys. Rev. *115*, 1198 (1959).
74. R. M. Sternheimer. Phys. Rev. *127*, 1220 (1962).
75. R. M. Sternheimer. Phys. Rev. *130*, 1423 (1963).
76. R. M. Sternheimer and H. M. Foley. Phys. Rev. *92*, 1460 (1953).
77. R. M. Stevens and W. N. Lipscomb. J. Chem. Phys. *41*, 184 (1964).
78. R. M. Stevens and W. N. Lipscomb. J. Chem. Phys. *41*, 3710 (1964).
79. A. L. Stewart. Proc. Phys. Soc. (London) *77*, 447 (1961).
80. M. Sundbom. Ark. Fys. *13*, 539 (1958).
81. R. F. Wallis. J. Chem. Phys. *23*, 1256 (1955).
82. S. Wang. Phys. Rev. *31*, 579 (1928).
83. R. E. Watson and A. J. Freeman. Phys. Rev. *131*, 250 (1963).
84. R. E. Watson and A. J. Freeman. Phys. Rev. *131*, 2566 (1963).
85. R. E. Watson and A. J. Freeman. Phys. Rev. *132*, 706 (1963).
86. R. E. Watson and A. J. Freeman. Phys. Rev. *135*, A1209 (1964).
87. S. Weinbaum. J. Chem. Phys. *1*, 593 (1933).
88. R. Weiss. Phys. Rev. *131*, 659 (1963).
89. G. Wentzel. Z. Physik *38*, 635 (1926).
90. L. Wharton, L. P. Gold, and W. Klemperer. J. Chem. Phys. *33*, 1255 (1960).
91. E. G. Wikner and T. P. Das. Phys. Rev. *107*, 497 (1957).
92. E. G. Wikner and T. P. Das. Phys. Rev. *109*, 360 (1958).
93. M. Yoshimine and R. P. Hurst. Phys. Rev. *135*, A612 (1964).

Chapter 9 MAGNETIC SUSCEPTIBILITIES

INTRODUCTION

The concept of magnetic susceptibility is associated with the interaction between a system and an external homogeneous magnetic field. The external field induces a magnetic moment in the system and the interaction takes place between the field and the resultant moment, which includes the permanent moment of the system if different from zero. The system is designated correspondingly as diamagnetic (no permanent moment) or paramagnetic (with permanent moment). (Ferromagnetism is not considered here.)

All systems exhibit a diamagnetic behavior. In paramagnetic systems it is hidden, however, because of the difference in magnitude between the induced and permanent moments. The discussion in this chapter is restricted to diamagnetism.

The interaction energy between a system with no permanent magnetic moment and a homogeneous external magnetic field H is given by

$$\Delta E = \tfrac{1}{2} H \cdot \chi \cdot H, \tag{9-1}$$

where χ represents the susceptibility tensor. Equation (9-1) can be written as

$$\Delta E = -\tfrac{1}{2} \sum_i \sum_j H_i \chi_{ij} H_j, \qquad i,j = \begin{cases} x \\ y \\ z \end{cases} \tag{9-2}$$

The susceptibility tensor can be diagonalized by means of an appropriate coordinate transformation. Equation (9-2) then becomes

$$\Delta E = -\tfrac{1}{2} \sum_i H_i \chi_{ii} H_i = -\tfrac{1}{2} \sum_i \chi_{ii} H_i^2,$$

where the components χ_{ii} are the principal susceptibilities. Except for molecules with a high symmetry, the diamagnetic susceptibility tensor will show anisotropy. The diamagnetic anisotropy can be measured either directly (in some molecular crystals) or by magnetic double refraction (Cotton-Mouton effect). See, for example, the work of Beams [4].

For a collection of systems, it is possible to define, on the basis of their random orientation, an average susceptibility

$$\chi = \tfrac{1}{3}(\chi_{xx} + \chi_{yy} + \chi_{zz}),$$

so that

$$\Delta E = -\tfrac{1}{2}\chi H^2. \tag{9-3}$$

The average susceptibility χ can then be determined if the dependence of the interaction energy on H^2 is found.

This is a problem that can be tackled by the perturbation techniques described in Chapter 5. The hamiltonian operator for a diamagnetic system in a magnetic field H is

$$\mathscr{H} = \tfrac{1}{2}\sum_j [(1/i)\nabla_j + (1/c)A_j]^2 + V$$

$$= \sum_j \{-\tfrac{1}{2}\nabla_j^2 + (1/ic)(A_j \cdot \nabla_j) + (1/2c^2)A_j^2\} + V, \tag{9-4}$$

with

$$A_j = \tfrac{1}{2}[H \times r_i]. \tag{9-5}$$

The summation extends over the electrons in the system and V represents the potential energy operator in the absence of the field. The vector r_i represents the position vector for the i-th electron, referred to an arbitrary origin (see below). Equation (9-4) can be rearranged as

$$\mathscr{H} = \mathscr{H}^{(0)} + \mathscr{H}^{(1)} + \mathscr{H}^{(2)},$$

with

$$\mathscr{H}^{(0)} = -\tfrac{1}{2}\sum_j \nabla_j^2 + V, \tag{9-6a}$$

$$\mathscr{H}^{(1)} = (1/2ic)\sum_j ([H \times r_j] \cdot \nabla_j), \tag{9-6b}$$

$$\mathscr{H}^{(2)} = (1/8c^2)\sum_j ([H \times r_j] \cdot [H \times r_j]), \tag{9-6c}$$

where $\mathscr{H}^{(1)}$ is smaller than $\mathscr{H}^{(0)}$ and $\mathscr{H}^{(2)}$ smaller than $\mathscr{H}^{(1)}$, which is the condition for a meaningful application of the perturbation method.

PERTURBATION THEORY OF SUSCEPTIBILITIES

Application of the formulas, presented in Chapter 5 for the evaluation of the energy to second order, yields

$$\Delta E^{(1)} = (1/2ic) \langle \Psi_n^{(0)}| \sum_j ([H \times r_j] \cdot \nabla_j) |\Psi_n^{(0)}\rangle, \tag{9-7a}$$

$$\Delta E^{(2)} = (1/8c^2) \langle \Psi_n^{(0)}| \sum_j ([H \times r_j][H \times r_j]) |\Psi_n^{(0)}\rangle - (1/4c^2)\sum_{k \neq n} [\langle \Psi_n^{(0)}|$$

$$\times \sum_j ([H \times r_j] \cdot \nabla_j) |\Psi_k^{(0)}\rangle \langle \Psi_k^{(0)}| \sum_j ([H \times r_j] \cdot \nabla_j) |\Psi_n^{(0)}\rangle]/(E_n^{(0)} - E_k^{(0)}),$$

$$\tag{9-7b}$$

which are the first- and second-order contributions to the interaction energy, respectively. The first-order correction, $\Delta E^{(1)}$, vanishes for diamagnetic molecules and therefore only $\Delta E^{(2)}$ need be considered. Equation (9-7b) can be rewritten as

$$\Delta E^{(2)} = (1/8c^2) \langle \Psi_n^{(0)} | \sum_j [H^2 r_j^2 - (\mathbf{H} \cdot \mathbf{r}_j)^2] | \Psi_n^{(0)} \rangle - (1/4c^2) \sum_{k \neq n} [\langle \Psi_n^{(0)} |$$
$$\times \sum_j (\mathbf{H} \cdot [\mathbf{r}_j \times \mathbf{\nabla}_j]) | \Psi_k^{(0)} \rangle \langle \Psi_k^{(0)} | \sum_j (\mathbf{H} \cdot [\mathbf{r}_j \times \mathbf{\nabla}_j]) | \Psi_n^{(0)} \rangle]/(E_n^{(0)} - E_k^{(0)}).$$
$$(9\text{-}8)$$

If we take into account that the experimental values represent averages over all the possible orientations of the system with respect to the direction of the external field, we can transform Eq. (9-8) into (see Ishiguro and Koide [38])

$$\Delta E^{(2)} = (H^2/12c^2)\{\langle \Psi_n^{(0)} | \sum_j r_j^2 | \Psi_n^{(0)} \rangle$$
$$- \sum_{k \neq n} [\langle \Psi_n^{(0)} | \sum_j [\mathbf{r}_j \times \mathbf{\nabla}_j] | \Psi_k^{(0)} \rangle \langle \Psi_k^{(0)} | \sum_j [\mathbf{r}_j \times \mathbf{\nabla}_j] | \Psi_n^{(0)} \rangle]/(E_n^{(0)} - E_k^{(0)})\}. \quad (9\text{-}9)$$

Taking into account the definition of the angular momentum vector operators and Eq. (9-3), we are able to write

$$\chi = -(N/6c^2)\{\langle \Psi_n^{(0)} | \sum_j r_j^2 | \Psi_n^{(0)} \rangle$$
$$- \sum_{k \neq n} [\langle \Psi_n^{(0)} | \sum_j \mathbf{l}_j | \Psi_k^{(0)} \rangle \langle \Psi_k^{(0)} | \sum_j \mathbf{l}_j | \Psi_n^{(0)} \rangle]/(E_n^{(0)} - E_k^{(k)})\} \quad (9\text{-}10)$$

for the molar susceptibility (as derived by Van Vleck [84]), where N is Avogadro's number.

Equation (9-10) can be rewritten* as

$$\chi = \chi^{(d)} + \chi^{(p)}, \qquad (9\text{-}11)$$

where $\chi^{(d)}$, always negative, represents the diamagnetic term of Langevin. The term $\chi^{(p)}$, which constitutes the so-called "high-frequency" contribution, is the temperature-independent paramagnetic correction of Van Vleck and is always positive for ground states. (Eshbach and Strandberg [11] have shown that $\chi^{(p)}$ can be determined from the experimental values for molecular rotational magnetic moments.)

Guy, Tillieu, and Baudet [19] have shown that the condition $\chi^{(p)} > |\chi^{(d)}|$ never occurs, and therefore the diamagnetic susceptibility, as given to second order by Eq. (9-10), is always negative. For diamagnetic systems, the susceptibility is negative and independent of the temperature, whereas for paramagnetic systems the susceptibility is positive and inversely proportional to the absolute temperature. The above result excludes the possibility of a positive susceptibility independent of the temperature.

The evaluation of the magnetic susceptibility can, in principle, be carried out by use of Eq. (9-10). These are, however, two practical difficulties, closely interrelated.

---

* See the discussion by Hurst, Karplus, and Das [36] on the physical significance.

Table 9-1 Diamagnetic Susceptibilities (in 10^{-6} cm³ mole⁻¹ Units) for Some Positive Ions, Neutral Atoms, and Negative Ions[a]

Z	SYSTEM	POSITIVE ION State	POSITIVE ION $-\chi^{(d)}$	NEUTRAL ATOM State	NEUTRAL ATOM $-\chi^{(d)}$	NEGATIVE ION State	NEGATIVE ION $-\chi^{(d)}$
2	He			^1S	1.9		
3	Li	^1S	0.7	^2S	14.8	^1S	69.7
4	Be	^2S	5.2	^1S	13.7		
5	B	^1S	6.3	^2P	12.6	^3P	31.5
6	C	^2P	6.4	^3P	10.9	^4S	20.8
7	N	^3P	6.1	^4S	9.6	^3P	17.7
8	O	^4S	5.8	^3P	8.9	^2P	14.9
9	F	^3P	5.6	^2P	8.1	^1S	12.6
10	Ne	^2P	5.4	^1S	7.4		
11	Na	^1S	5.1	^2S	21.5	^1S	78.3
12	Mg	^2S	11.2	^1S	23.5		
13	Al	^1S	13.8	^2P	26.5	^3P	58.8
14	Si	^2P	16.0	^3P	25.6	^4S	43.2
15	P	^3P	16.6	^4S	24.0	^3P	38.6
16	S	^4S	16.5	^3P	23.1	^2P	34.1
17	Cl	^3P	16.4	^2P	21.9	^1S	30.3
18	A	^2P	16.0	^1S	20.6		
19	K	^1S	15.5	^2S	40.6	^1S	126.4
20	Ca	^2S	24.8	^1S	44.8		
21	Sc	^3F	18.2	^2D	42.1	^3F	88.2
22	Ti	^4F	17.7	^3F	39.8	^4F	86.2
23	V	^5D	17.2	^4F	37.7	^5D	82.3
24	Cr	^6S	16.5	^7S	30.1	^6S	78.6
25	Mn	^5D	16.3	^6S	34.1	^5D	73.2
26	Fe	^4F	15.9	^5D	32.6	^4F	69.9
27	Co	^3F	15.5	^4F	31.2	^3F	65.8
28	Ni	^2D	15.1	^3F	30.0	^2S	38.5
29	Cu	^1S	14.7	^2S	26.3	^1S	60.1
30	Zn	^2S	17.9	^1S	27.7		
31	Ga	^1S	20.0	^2P	32.4	^3P	66.4
32	Ge	^2P	22.9	^3P	33.0	^4S	51.2
33	As	^3P	24·2	^4S	32.5	^3P	48.5
34	Se	^4S	24.7	^3P	32.6	^2P	45.3
35	Br	^3P	25.3	^2P	32.1	^1S	42.2
36	Kr	^2P	25.4	^1S	31.3		
42	Mo		29.7	^7S	44.8		
54	Xe			^1S	44.9		

a. Evaluated by Malli and Fraga [44] from the analytical Hartree-Fock functions of Clementi [6], Malli [43], Roothaan and Synek [66], Synek [79], and Synek and Stungis [80]. Calculations have also been carried out by Strand and Bonham [78], Sidwell and Hurst [70], Saxena and Narasimhan [68], and Banyard [1]. Malli and Froese [45] have evaluated $\chi^{(d)}$ for He to Rn, using the numerical Hartree-Fock functions of Froese [14].

As mentioned before, the position vectors r_j are referred to an arbitrary origin of coordinates. Van Vleck [84] has shown that the value of χ is independent of the choice of the origin but that the two contributions, $\chi^{(d)}$ and $\chi^{(p)}$, do in fact depend on the origin of reference. The problem posed by the summation in $\chi^{(p)}$, over the discrete states and the continuum, suggests the approximation of χ by $\chi^{(d)}$. (The results obtained by Snyder and Parr [71] indicate that the continuum contribution may be important. Hameka [30] has also discussed this point.) In such a situation the choice of the origin becomes important.

In the case of atoms, the nucleus seems to be the logical choice as the center of reference. Within this convention the susceptibility is approximated by $\chi^{(d)}$. Table 9-1 presents the corresponding values, calculated from analytical Hartree-Fock functions, for He to Kr.

VARIATIONAL FORMULATIONS

The variational method, either by itself or applied to the perturbation formulation, provides the solution to the problem of the vector potential origin.

The direct application of the variational method, through the use of functions with a number of parameters to be optimized, obviates such a problem. The treatments of Hoyland and Parr [35] and Hoyland [34] belong to this category.

Formulations have also been proposed in which the trial function includes the external field. Ishiguro and Koide [38] have used for H_2 a function

$$\Phi = \Phi' + \boldsymbol{H} \cdot \boldsymbol{\Phi}'',$$

where Φ' and Φ'' are James-Coolidge [39] type functions. This method, however, does not seem to be practical for application to other molecules. On the other hand, Tillieu and Guy [3, 81–83] have proposed the use of functions of the form

$$\Phi = \Phi'(1 + \boldsymbol{H} \cdot \boldsymbol{g}),$$

where g is a function of the electron coordinates and Φ' represents an approximate function. Guy and Tillieu [16–18] have applied this method to the evaluation of the susceptibilities of electron pair bonds.

The variational method can also be applied to the perturbation formulation. The direct approach is exemplified by the formalism developed by Karplus and Kolker [40], outlined in Chapter 5. On the basis of numerical results for a series of diatomic molecules, this variation-perturbation method seems to be adequate for application to other molecules. This prospect is enhanced by the possibility of using SCF or Hartree-Fock functions in the calculation, as the corresponding formulation has already been developed by Karplus and Kolker [40].

A different treatment is represented by the variational method of Rebane [65]. The difference, however, is one only of approach, as shown by McLachlan and Baker [46] and Ghosh and Sinha [15]. The basic characteristic is the use of a gauge transformation in order to reduce the contribution $\chi^{(p)}$ to zero, thus avoiding the problem of the summation within it. The term $\chi^{(d)}$ is changed at the same time but, as pointed out above, the total susceptibility remains unchanged.

Hameka [27] has reformulated the derivation of this method. Equation (9-7b) can be rewritten as

$$\Delta E^{(2)} = (1/8c^2)\{\langle \Psi_n^{(0)} | \sum_j (A_j')^2 | \Psi_n^{(0)} \rangle - 2 \sum_{k \neq n} |\langle \Psi_k^{(0)} | \sum_j [(A_j' \cdot \nabla_j)$$
$$+ (\nabla_j \cdot A_j')] | \Psi_n^{(0)} \rangle|^2 / (E_n^{(0)} - E_k^{(0)}) \}, \quad (9\text{-}12)$$

with

$$A_j' = \tfrac{1}{2}[H \times r_j] + \nabla_j \phi_j(r_j), \quad (9\text{-}13)$$

where the gauge functions, ϕ_j, are arbitary functions of the coordinates and of the magnitude of the external field. The operators in the infinite series are hermitian.

If one takes into consideration that each term of the series is positive, the condition

$$\Delta E^{(2)} \leq (1/8c^2) \langle \Psi_n^{(0)} | \sum_j (A_j')^2 | \Psi_n^{(0)} \rangle \quad (9\text{-}14)$$

must be satisfied for every set of gauge functions. Rebane [65] has shown that, at least for one-electron systems, there is a set of gauge functions, ϕ_j, that satisfy the condition

$$\sum_j ((A_j' \cdot \nabla_j) + (\nabla_j \cdot A_j')) | \Psi_n^{(0)} \rangle = 0. \quad (9\text{-}15)$$

In such a case the equality of Eq. (9-14) holds and the susceptibility may be evaluated without having to include the infinite series.

Closely connected with this method is the use of gauge invariant atomic orbitals (GIAO), first proposed by London [42] and used for the evaluation of the nuclear magnetic shielding constant (see Chapter 10) of H_2 by Pople [57] and McWeeny [48]. In this method, the same gauge functions, ϕ_j, which determine the origin of the position vectors, are used for the orbitals. A detailed formulation has been given by Hameka [21–24, 27, 28].

For comparison of the merits of these methods, the results of a number of calculations of the susceptibility of H_2 have been collected in Table 9-2. There are two sets of such calculations: the origin of the vector potential is at the center of the molecule in one set and at one of the nuclei in the other. Within each set the results are ordered according to the accuracy of the value of χ. The difference between a given calculated value and the experimental result depends, of course, on both the type of trial function used and the method of calculation. (Details of the functions can be found in the original references or in the summary given by McLean, Weiss, and

Table 9-2 Values (in 10^{-6} cgs Units) of the Susceptibliity for H_2

$-\chi^{(d)}$	$\chi^{(p)}$	$-\chi$	TYPE OF FUNCTION	METHOD	REFERENCE
			Origin of Vector Potential at Center of Molecule		
5.473	0.139	5.335	Coulson [7]	Variation	Das-Bersohn [8]
5.478	0.310	5.168	Heitler-London [32]	Variation	Das-Bersohn [8]
3.878	0.092	3.786	Rosen [67]	Variation	Das-Bersohn [8]
4.305	0.070	4.235	Open-shell [34]	Variation	Hoyland [34]
4.400	0.177	4.223	Wallis (CI) [86]	Variation	Das-Bersohn [8]
3.921	0.077	3.844	Berencz [5]	Variation	Hoyland [34]
4.052	0.185	3.867	Hirschfelder-Linnett [33]	Variation	Das-Bersohn [8]
4.030	0.117	3.913	Coulson (optimized) [7]	GIAO	Hameka [27]
4.069	0.114	3.955	Coulson (optimized) [7]	Variation	Hoyland [34]
4.014	0.056	3.958	Rosen [67]	GIAO	Hameka [27]
4.166	0.204	3.962	Wallis (limited ionic) [86]	Variation	Das-Bersohn [8]
4.150	0.075	4.075	Correlated [34]	Variation	Hoyland [34]
4.210	0.151	4.069	James-Coolidge [39]	Variation	Ishiguro-Koide [38]
4.153	0.092	4.061	Harris-Taylor [31]	Variation	Hoyland [34]
4.217	0.222	3.995	Wang [87]	Variation	Das-Bersohn [8]
4.199	0.204	3.995	Wang [87]	GIAO	Hameka [27]
4.187	0.192	3.995	Coulson (optimized) [7]	Variation	Das-Bersohn [8]
4.234	0.206	4.028	Weinbaum [88]	Variation	Das-Bersohn [8]
4.110	0.085	4.025		Experimental	Ramsey [64]
			Origin of Vector Potential at a Proton		
5.081	0.779	4.302	Open-shell [34]	Variation	Hoyland [34]
4.697	0.813	3.884	Berencz [5]	Variation	Hoyland [34]
4.929	0.812	4.117	Harris-Taylor [31]	Variation	Hoyland [34]
4.927	0.830	4.097	Correlated [34]	Variation	Hoyland [34]
4.845	0.852	3.993	Coulson (optimized) [7]	Variation	Hoyland [34]
4.800	0.750	4.050	One-center expansion [35]	Variation	Hoyland-Parr [35]
4.868	0.843	4.025	Fraga-Ransil (SCF) [13]	Variation	Karplus-Kolker [40]
4.886	0.861	4.025		Experimental	Ramsey [64]

Yoshimine [47].) Comparison can be made in particular, however, between those calculations that use the same function. The best result is the one obtained by the variation-perturbation method of Karplus and Kolker [40] using an SCF function.

In addition, a perturbed Hartree-Fock method (see Chapter 5) has been used by Lipscomb and coworkers [72–77] for the evaluation of the magnetic susceptibility of LiH, HF, F_2, and BH. Other calculations have been carried out by Hameka and coworkers [20, 25–27], Das and Ghose [9], Banyard [1, 2], and Eisenberg, Pochan, and Flygare [10].

MOLECULAR ORBITAL THEORY OF PASCAL CONSTANTS

The practical problems encountered in calculations of large molecules, coupled with the theoretical difficulties just mentioned, impose the use of approximate rules.

On the basis of an empirical scheme, Pascal [52–55] proposed the use of the following formula (see also the work of Selwood [69] and Pacault [49–51]):

$$\chi = \sum_a \chi_a + \chi', \tag{9-16}$$

where χ_a represents the contribution of atom a to the molar diamagnetic susceptibility and χ' is a correction for the different groups present in the molecule; the summation extends over all the atoms. Values for these constants are obtained by correlation with experimental results. Table 9-3 presents the values for some Pascal constants and constitutive corrections.

It is possible, however, to develop a theoretical formulation for such a rule within the framework of the molecular orbital method. Using gauge invariant atomic orbitals and introducing a systematic set of approximations,* Pople [12, 58, 59, 61, 62] has proposed the following formula for noncyclic molecules:

$$\chi = \sum_a (\chi_a^{(d)} + \chi_a^{(p)}), \tag{9-17}$$

which can be considered the molecular orbital analogue of Eq. (9-16). This point of view is reinforced by the fact that the paramangetic contributions $\chi_a^{(p)}$ depend on the chemical environment of the atom.

For saturated systems, within the LCAO approximation and neglecting overlap-type integrals, the components in the z-direction (perpendicular to the molecular plane) for the susceptibility terms from atom a are defined (when the contributions of the atomic d orbitals are not important) by

$$(\chi_a^{(d)})_{zz} = -(N\alpha^2/2) \sum_i P_{ii} \langle x^2 + y^2 \rangle_i, \tag{9-18a}$$

$$(\chi_a^{(p)})_{zz} = (N\alpha^2/2)(\Delta E)^{-1}(Q_a)_{zz}, \tag{9-18b}$$

with

$$(Q_a)_{zz} = \sum_b (Q_{ab})_{zz}, \tag{9-19a}$$

$$(Q_{ab})_{zz} = P_{x_a x_b}(2\delta_{ab} - P_{y_a y_b}) + P_{y_a y_b}(2\delta_{ab} - P_{x_a x_b}) + 2P_{x_a y_b}P_{y_a x_b}. \tag{9-19b}$$

---

* The nature of the approximations is also discussed by Hameka [29] and Pople [60].

Table 9-3 Pascal Constants and Constitutive Corrections[a] (in 10^{-6} cgs Units)

PASCAL CONSTANTS FOR THE ELEMENTS

Element		Constant	Element		Constant
H		−2.93	Cl	Aromatic	−17.2
C		−6.00	Br	Aliphatic	−30.4
N	Open chain	−5.55		Aromatic	−26.5
	Ring	−4.61	I	Aliphatic	−44.6
	Monamide	−1.54		Aromatic	−40.5
	Diamide, imide	−2.11	S		−15.2
O	Alcohol, ether	−4.60	Se		−23.5
	Aldehyde, ketone	1.66	B		−7.3
	Carboxyl[b]	−7.95	Si		−13.0
F		−6.4	P		−10.0
Cl	Aliphatic	−19.9	As		−21.0

CONSTITUTIVE CORRECTIONS FOR BONDS

Bond	Correction	Bond	Correction
C=C	5.5	N=N	1.85
C≡C	0.8	C=N	8.15
C=C—C=C	10.6	C≡N	0.8

CONSTITUTIVE CORRECTIONS FOR RINGS

Ring	Correction	Ring	Correction	Ring	Correction
Cyclopropane	3.4	Cyclohexadiene	10.7	Benzene	−1.4
Cyclobutane	1.1	Piperidine	3.6	Pyridine	0.5
Cyclopentane	0.0	Piperazine	7.5	Triazine	−1.4
Cyclohexane	3.1	Pyrazoline	8.3	Furan	−2.5
Cyclohexene	7.2	Glyoxaline	7.8	Pyrrole	−3.5

GROUP CORRECTIONS FOR HALOGENS

Group	Correction	Group	Correction
—CH_2Cl	−0.3	—CH_2Br	−1.5
—$CHCl_2$	−0.6	—$CHBr_2$	−0.5
—CCl_3	2.5	—CBr_3	10.6

a. This table, taken from Pople, Schneider, and Bernstein [63], includes the original values of Pascal [55] and those proposed by Ingold [37] for halogens in aliphatic systems.
b. For both oxygens of the carboxyl group in acids and esters.

The summation in Eq. (9-18a) extends over the atomic orbitals centered on atom a, and $\langle x^2 + y^2 \rangle$ represents the mean value for any such orbital; P_{ij} denotes the elements of the generalized charge density and bond order matrix, and ΔE is the mean excitation energy to higher states. The sub-indices $x_a, x_b, y_a,$ and y_b refer to atomic $2p$ orbitals centered on atoms a and b, respectively. Similar expressions exist for the other components.

For unsaturated noncylic systems it is necessary to introduce corrections, determined on the basis of a comparison with calculations for simple unsaturated systems.

In the case of unsaturated cyclic systems, Eq. (9-17) must be replaced by

$$\chi = \sum_a (\chi_a^{(d)} + \chi_a^{(p)}) + \chi_{\text{ring}}, \qquad (9\text{-}20)$$

where χ_{ring} represents the ring current contribution. (See, for example, Pauling [56].) Assuming localized σ-type molecular orbitals, Pople [62] has obtained the expression

$$\Delta\chi = \chi_{zz} - \tfrac{1}{2}(\chi_{xx} + \chi_{yy}) = \chi_{\text{ring}} - (N\alpha^2/3\Delta E) \sum_a \sum_b{}' P_{z_a z_b} \qquad (9\text{-}21)$$

for the overall anisotropy, relative to an axis perpendicular to the molecular plane. The summation over b extends only over those carbon atoms bonded to atom a. This equation indicates that the overall anisotropy arises not only from the ring current but also from local terms.

REFERENCES

1. K. E. Banyard. J. Chem. Phys. *33*, 832 (1960).
2. K. E. Banyard. J. Chem. Phys. *34*, 338 (1961).
3. J. Baudet, J. Tillieu, and J. Guy. Compt. Rend. *244*, 1756 (1957).
4. J. W. Beams. Rev. Mod. Phys. *4*, 133 (1932).
5. F. Berencz. Acta Physica Acad. Sci. Hung. *6*, 423 (1957).
6. E. Clementi. "Tables of Atomic Functions." IBM Corporation, San José, California, 1965.
7. C. A. Coulson. Trans. Faraday Soc. *33*, 1479 (1937).
8. T. P. Das and R. Bersohn. Phys. Rev. *115*, 897 (1959).
9. T. P. Das and T. Ghose. J. Chem. Phys. *31*, 42 (1959).
10. D. Eisenberg, J. M. Pochan, and W. H. Flygare. J. Chem. Phys. *43*, 4531 (1965).
11. J. R. Eshbach and M. W. P. Strandberg. Phys. Rev. *85*, 24 (1952).
12. A. F. Ferguson and J. A. Pople. J. Chem. Phys. *42*, 1560 (1965).
13. S. Fraga and B. J. Ransil. J. Chem. Phys. *35*, 1967 (1961).
14. C. Froese. J. Chem. Phys. *45*, 1417 (1966).
15. S. K. Ghosh and S. K. Sinha. J. Chem. Phys. *36*, 737 (1962).
16. J. Guy and J. Tillieu. Compt. Rend. *241*, 382 (1955).
17. J. Guy and J. Tillieu. Compt. Rend. *242*, 1279 (1956).
18. J. Guy and J. Tillieu. J. Chem. Phys. *24*, 1117 (1956).
19. J. Guy, J. Tillieu, and J. Baudet. Compt. Rend. *246*, 574 (1958).
20. H. Hamano, H. Kim, and H. F. Hameka. Physica *29*, 111 (1963).
21. H. F. Hameka. Mol. Phys. *1*, 203 (1958).
22. H. F. Hameka. Mol. Phys. *2*, 64 (1959).
23. H. F. Hameka. Nuovo Cimento *11*, 382 (1959).

24. H. F. Hameka. Physica 25, 626 (1959).
25. H. F. Hameka. Z. Naturforschg. 14a, 599 (1959).
26. H. F. Hameka. J. Chem. Phys. 34, 366 (1961).
27. H. F. Hameka. Rev. Mod. Phys. 34, 87 (1962).
28. H. F. Hameka. Physica 28, 908 (1962).
29. H. F. Hameka. J. Chem. Phys. 37, 3008 (1962).
30. H. F. Hameka. J. Chem. Phys. 37, 3127 (1964).
31. F. E. Harris and H. S. Taylor. J. Chem. Phys. 38, 2591 (1963).
32. W. Heitler and F. London. Z. Physik 44, 455 (1927).
33. J. O. Hirschfelder and W. Linnett. J. Chem. Phys. 18, 130 (1950).
34. J. R. Hoyland. J. Chem. Phys. 41, 3153 (1964).
35. J. R. Hoyland and R. G. Parr. J. Chem. Phys. 38, 2991 (1963).
36. R. P. Hurst, M. Karplus, and T. P. Das. J. Chem. Phys. 36, 2786 (1962).
37. C. K. Ingold. "Structure and Mechanism in Organic Chemistry." Cornell University Press, Ithaca, N.Y., 1953.
38. E. Ishiguro and S. Koide. Phys. Rev. 94, 350 (1954).
39. H. M. James and A. S. Coolidge. J. Chem. Phys. 1, 825 (1933).
40. M. Karplus and H. J. Kolker. J. Chem. Phys. 38, 1263 (1963).
41. H. Kim, H. Hamano, and H. F. Hameka. Physica 29, 117 (1963).
42. F. London. J. Phys. Radium 8, 397 (1937).
43. G. Malli. Can. J. Phys. 44, 3121 (1966).
44. G. Malli and S. Fraga. Theoret. Chim. Acta (Berlin) 5, 284 (1966).
45. G. Malli and C. Froese. Unpublished results.
46. A. D. McLachlan and M. R. Baker. Mol. Phys. 4, 254 (1961).
47. A. D. McLean, A. W. Weiss, and M. Yoshimine. Rev. Mod. Phys. 32, 211 (1960).
48. R. McWeeny. Mol. Phys. 1, 311 (1958).
49. A. Pacault. Rev. Sci. 82, 465 (1944).
50. A. Pacault. Rev. Sci. 86, 38 (1948).
51. A. Pacault. Bull. Soc. Chim. France D371 (1949).
52. P. Pascal. Ann. Chim. et Phys. 19, 5 (1910).
53. P. Pascal. Ann. Chim. et Phys. 25, 289 (1912).
54. P. Pascal. Ann. Chim. et Phys. 29, 218 (1913).
55. P. Pascal. "Chimie Generale." Masson et Cie., Editeurs, Paris, 1949.
56. L. Pauling. J. Chem. Phys. 4, 673 (1936).
57. J. A. Pople. Proc. Roy. Soc. (London) A239, 541 (1957).
58. J. A. Pople. J. Chem. Phys. 37, 53 (1962).
59. J. A. Pople. J. Chem. Phys. 37, 60 (1962).
60. J. A. Pople. J. Chem. Phys. 37, 3009 (1962).
61. J. A. Pople. J. Chem. Phys. 38, 1276 (1963).
62. J. A. Pople. J. Chem. Phys. 41, 2559 (1964).
63. J. A. Pople, W. G. Schneider, and H. J. Bernstein. "High-Resolution Nuclear Magnetic Resonance." McGraw-Hill Book Company, Inc., New York, 1959.
64. N. F. Ramsey. "Molecular Beams." Oxford University Press, Oxford, England, 1956.
65. T. K. Rebane. J. Exptl. and Theoret. Phys. (U.S.S.R.) 38, 963 (1960).
66. C. C. J. Rothaan and M. Synek. Phys. Rev. 133, A1263 (1964).
67. N. Rosen. Phys. Rev. 38, 2099 (1931).
68. K. M. S. Saxena and P. T. Narasimhan. J. Chem. Phys. 42, 4304 (1965).
69. P. W. Selwood. "Magnetochemistry." Interscience Publishers, Inc., New York, 1956.
70. T. W. Sidwell and R. P. Hurst. J. Chem. Phys. 37, 203 (1962).
71. L. C. Snyder and R. G. Parr. J. Chem. Phys. 34, 837 (1961).
72. R. M. Stevens and W. N. Lipscomb. J. Chem. Phys. 40, 2238 (1964).
73. R. M. Stevens and W. N. Lipscomb. J. Chem. Phys. 41, 184 (1964).
74. R. M. Stevens and W. N. Lipscomb. J. Chem. Phys. 41, 3710 (1964).
75. R. M. Stevens and W. N. Lipscomb. J. Chem. Phys. 42, 3666 (1965).
76. R. M. Stevens and W. N. Lipscomb. J. Chem. Phys. 42, 4302 (1965).
77. R. M. Stevens, R. M. Pitzer, and W. N. Lipscomb. J. Chem. Phys. 38, 550 (1963).
78. T. G. Strand and R. A. Bonham. J. Chem. Phys. 40, 1686 (1964).
79. M. Synek. Phys. Rev. 133, A961 (1964).
80. M. Synek and G. E. Stungis. J. Chem. Phys. 42, 3068 (1965).
81. J. Tillieu and J. Guy. Compt. Rend. 239, 1203 (1954).

82. J. Tillieu and J. Guy. Compt. Rend. *239*, 1283 (1954).
83. J. Tillieu and J. Guy. Compt. Rend. *240*, 1402 (1955).
84. J. H. Van Vleck. "The Theory of Electric and Magnetic Susceptibilities." Oxford University Press, Oxford, England, 1932.
85. J. R. de la Vega and H. F. Hameka. J. Chem. Phys. *40*, 1929 (1964).
86. R. F. Wallis. J. Chem. Phys. *23*, 1256 (1955).
87. S. Wang. Phys. Rev. *31*, 579 (1928).
88. S. Weinbaum. J. Chem. Phys. *1*, 593 (1933).

Chapter 10 NUCLEAR MAGNETIC SHIELDING

INTERNAL DIAMAGNETIC FIELDS

The molecular beam experiments of Rabi and coworkers [23, 38–40, 50, 51] showed the existence of internal diamagnetic fields when atoms are placed in a homogeneous magnetic field. The Larmor precession, which takes place, produces a shielding field at the position of the nucleus. The shielding field is small in comparison to the external field, but its existence must be taken into consideration in the measurement of nuclear magnetic moments.

It can also be observed that the value of the applied magnetic field for nuclear resonance at a fixed radio frequency for a given nucleus depends on the chemical environment. That is, it is different for the same nucleus in different systems. Such differences give rise to the chemical shifts in high resolution nuclear magnetic resonance (NMR) spectroscopy. (For references on this subject the reader is referred, for example to the works of Andrew [2] and Pople, Schneider, and Bernstein [59].)

The shielding field is proportional to the external field. Assuming that the system that contains the nucleus under consideration is held in a fixed orientation in the homogeneous external magnetic field H, the effective magnetic field acting on the nucleus is

$$H = H_0 - H_0 \cdot \sigma, \tag{10-1}$$

where σ represents the nuclear magnetic shielding tensor.

The theoretical formulation for nuclear magnetic shielding constants parallels that given in Chapter 9 for diamagnetic susceptibilities.* That is, consider a system in its ground state, which in the absence of the external field has no resultant orbital or spin angular momentum. All other nuclei

---

* Both the diamagnetic susceptibility and nuclear magnetic shielding can be related to the scattering factors (Chapter 16). In this connection the reader is referred to the work of Silverman and Obata [72].

in the system have no magnetic moment and the nucleus under consideration has a magnetic moment in the direction of the applied field and with magnitude μ. Holding the nuclear frame fixed in a given orientation, the interaction energy corresponding to the shielding effect is given by

$$\Delta E = \mu \sigma H. \tag{10-2}$$

In experimental measurements* in gases or liquids, the molecules may adopt any orientation. Therefore, Eq. (10-2) must be averaged over all possible orientations. The corresponding σ, defined as the average nuclear magnetic shielding constant,

$$\sigma = \tfrac{1}{3}(\sigma_{xx} + \sigma_{yy} + \sigma_{zz}),$$

can then be determined from the value of the interaction energy. This constant is also denoted as proton shielding constant when the nucleus considered is a proton.

Under the conditions indicated above, the hamiltonian operator† for the system may be written (see Chapter 9) as

$$\mathscr{H} = \mathscr{H}^{(0)} + \mathscr{H}^{(1)} + \mathscr{H}^{(2)},$$

where the zero-order term, $\mathscr{H}^{(0)}$, represents the hamiltonian operator in the absence of the perturbing field. The perturbation terms, $\mathscr{H}^{(1)}$ and $\mathscr{H}^{(2)}$, are defined by

$$\mathscr{H}^{(1)} = (1/ci) \sum_{j} (A_j \cdot \nabla_j), \tag{10-3a}$$

$$\mathscr{H}^{(2)} = (1/2c^2) \sum_{j} A_j^2, \tag{10-3b}$$

where A_j is the vector potential acting on the j-th electron, and the summations extend over all the electrons in the system. The vector potential is defined by

$$A_j = \tfrac{1}{2}[H \times r_j] + [\mu \times r_j]r_j^{-3}, \tag{10-4}$$

where the position vector r_j is referred to an arbitrary origin (see below). The vector μ denotes the magnetic moment vector of the nucleus considered.

The magnitudes of the perturbation terms in the hamiltonian operator suggest again the possibility of applying perturbation theory.

PERTURBATION THEORY OF THE MAGNETIC SHIELDING

The application of perturbation theory involves the use of the equations presented in Chapter 5. For a diamagnetic system, the first-order contribution to the interaction energy is zero. The interaction energy can then be

---

* It is possible, however, to determine the components in certain cases. For more details, the reader is referred to the work of Buckingham and Lovering [6], Graff [19], Lauterbur [42], and Andrew and Tunstall [3].

† The effects due to electron spins are not considered in this discussion. See, for example, the work of Wick [88].

written, to second order, as

$$\Delta E = (1/2c^2)\langle\Psi_n^{(0)}|\sum_j ([H \times r_j] \cdot [\mu \times r_j])r_j^{-3}|\Psi_n^{(0)}\rangle - (1/c^2)\sum_k \{\langle\psi_n^{(0)}|$$

$$\times \sum_j ([H \times r_j] \cdot \nabla_j)|\Psi_k^{(0)}\rangle\langle\Psi_k^{(0)}|\sum_j r_j^{-3}([\mu \times r_j] \cdot \nabla_j)|\Psi_n^{(0)}\rangle + \langle\Psi_n^{(0)}|\sum_j r_j^{-3}$$

$$\times([\mu \times r_j] \cdot \nabla_j)|\Psi_k^{(0)}\rangle\langle\Psi_k^{(0)}|\sum_j ([H \times r_j] \cdot \nabla_j)|\Psi_n^{(0)}\rangle\}/(E_n^{(0)} - E_k^{(0)}). \quad (10\text{-}5)$$

Proceeding in the manner described in Chapter 9 for the diamagnetic susceptibility, one can write for the average molar nuclear magnetic shielding

$$\sigma = (N\alpha^2/3)[\langle\Psi_n^{(0)}|\sum_j r_j^{-1}|\Psi_n^{(0)}\rangle - \sum_k \{\langle\Psi_n^{(0)}|\sum_j [r_j \times \nabla_j]|\Psi_k^{(0)}\rangle$$

$$\times \langle\Psi_k^{(0)}|\sum_j r_j^{-3}[r_j \times \nabla_j]|\Psi_n^{(0)}\rangle\langle\Psi_n^{(0)}|\sum_j r_j^{-3}[r_j \times \nabla_j]|\Psi_k^{(0)}\rangle$$

$$\times \langle\Psi_k^{(0)}|\sum_j [r_j \times \nabla_j]|\Psi_n^{(0)}\rangle\}/(E_n^{(0)} - E_k^{(0)})], \quad (10\text{-}6)$$

with the summation over k extending over all the excited states and the continuum.

Equation (10-6), first derived by Ramsey [60–63], can be written as

$$\sigma = \sigma^{(d)} - \sigma^{(p)},$$

where

$$\sigma^{(d)} = (N\alpha^2/3)\langle r^{-1}\rangle \quad (10\text{-}7)$$

is the Lamb term [41]. The term $\sigma^{(p)}$ represents the paramagnetic correction.

The problems arising in the practical application of Eq. (10-6) are analogous to those encountered in the evaluation of diamagnetic suscepti-bilities, regarding the origin of the vector potential and the summation in the paramagnetic correction.

The term $\sigma^{(d)}$, as given by Eq. (10-7), has been calculated for atoms, using various functions. Table 10-1 presents the corresponding values for He to Kr, calculated from analytical Hartree-Fock functions. Malli and Fraga [45] have given a formula for extrapolation to heavier atoms, and Malli and Froese [46] have evaluated $\sigma^{(d)}$ up to Rn, using numerical Hartree-Fock functions. Dickinson [13] has pointed out, however, that the relativistic corrections are important for heavy atoms.

For molecules, a number of methods have been proposed in order to overcome these difficulties. With the exception of the perturbation treatment of Kelly and Taylor [33], the remaining formulations are based on the variational method.

VARIATIONAL FORMULATIONS

The variational treatment of Hornig and Hirschfelder [26] offers the dis-advantage, as pointed out by McGarvey [48], of leading to divergences. On

Table 10-1 Nuclear Magnetic Shielding Constants ($10^5\sigma$) for Some Positive Ions, Neutral Atoms, and Negative Ions[a]

Z	SYSTEM	POSITIVE ION State	POSITIVE ION $\sigma^{(d)}$	NEUTRAL ATOM State	NEUTRAL ATOM $\sigma^{(d)}$	NEGATIVE ION State	NEGATIVE ION $\sigma^{(d)}$
2	He			^1S	6.0		
3	Li	^1S	9.5	^2S	10.2	^1S	10.4
4	Be	^2S	14.2	^1S	15.0		
5	B	^1S	19.4	^2P	20.2	^3P	20.7
6	C	^2P	25.1	^3P	26.1	^4S	26.7
7	N	^3P	31.4	^4S	32.6	^3P	33.2
8	O	^4S	38.4	^3P	39.5	^2P	40.3
9	F	^3P	45.8	^2P	47.1	^1S	48.0
10	Ne	^2P	53.8	^1S	55.2		
11	Na	^1S	62.4	^2S	62.9	^1S	63.2
12	Mg	^2S	70.3	^1S	70.9		
13	Al	^1S	78.4	^2P	79.0	^3P	79.3
14	Si	^2P	86.8	^3P	87.4	^4S	87.9
15	P	^3P	95.4	^4S	96.1	^3P	96.6
16	S	^4S	104.3	^3P	105.0	^2P	105.6
17	Cl	^3P	113.4	^2P	114.3	^1S	114.9
18	A	^2P	122.8	^1S	123.8		
19	K	^1S	132.5	^2S	132.9	^1S	133.2
20	Ca	^2S	141.8	^1S	142.3		
21	Sc	^3F	152.0	^2D	152.1	^3F	152.6
22	Ti	^4F	162.1	^3F	162.3	^4F	162.8
23	V	^5D	172.5	^4F	172.7	^5D	173.2
24	Cr	^6S	183.2	^7S	183.7	^6S	184.0
25	Mn	^5D	194.0	^6S	194.2	^5D	194.8
26	Fe	^4F	205.1	^5D	205.3	^4F	205.9
27	Co	^3F	216.5	^4F	216.6	^3F	217.2
28	Ni	^2D	228.1	^3F	228.2	^2S	230.8
29	Cu	^1S	239.9	^2S	240.5	^1S	240.8
30	Zn	^2S	252.0	^1S	252.2		
31	Ga	^1S	263.3	^2P	263.9	^3P	264.2
32	Ge	^2P	275.1	^3P	275.7	^4S	276.2
33	As	^3P	287.1	^4S	287.7	^3P	288.2
34	Se	^4S	299.2	^3P	299.8	^2P	300.4
35	Br	^3P	311.4	^2P	312.1	^1S	312.7
36	Kr	^2P	323.8	^1S	324.6		
42	Mo			^7S	400.3		
54	Xe			^1S	563.9		
86	Rn			^1S	1072.0		

a. Evaluated by Malli and Fraga [45] from the analytical Hartree-Fock functions of Clementi [7], Malli [44], Roothaan and Synek [66], Synek [80], and Synek and Stungis [81]. Calculations have been reported by Bonham and Strand [5], Cooper and Martin [8], Dickinson [13], Ellison [14, 15], Knight and Scherr [36], Ormand and Matsen [53], Pekeris [55], Rustgi and Tiwari [68], Saxena and Narasimhan [70], and Scherr and Knight [71]. Malli and Froese [46] have evaluated $\sigma^{(d)}$ for He to Rn using the numerical Hartree-Fock functions of Froese [17].

the other hand, the method proposed by McGarvey [49] implies the solution of an inaccurate Schrödinger equation for the first-order perturbation.

The methods of Das and Bershon [10] (also used by Das and Ghose [12]) and Stephen [73] are equivalent to the formulation developed by Tillieu and Guy [82–84] for diamagnetic susceptibilities (see Chapter 9). The main difference between the two methods lies in the number of variational parameters needed.

The variation-perturbation method of Karplus and Kolker [32], used by Kolker and Karplus [37] for diatomic molecules, seems to be adequate for application to larger molecules, using Hartree-Fock functions as unperturbed functions.

The direct approach to the problem of the origin of the vector potential is exemplified by the use of gauge invariant atomic orbitals by Hameka [21]. This method and the Rebane [65] variational procedure have been discussed in Chapter 9.

Lipscomb and coworkers [74–79] have used mainly a perturbed Hartree-Fock formulation, but Kern and Lipscomb [34] have attacked the problem by use of an appropriate choice of the gauge of the vector potential. In this formulation, the shielding constant is determined again exclusively from the ground state function by means of an approximation that involves cancellation of average excitation energies.

Table 10-2 presents the values obtained for the proton shielding constant in H_2 by various methods and by using different functions. Comparison of the values in Table 10-2, corresponding to calculations by different methods but using the same functions, provides a basis for an assessment of the formulations.

Other calculations on molecules have been carried out by Kern and Lipscomb [34].

SIMPLIFIED MOLECULAR ORBITAL FORMULATION

For large molecules, the difficulties encountered in the practical application of the preceding methods impose the use of simple approximations. The resolution of the magnetic shielding of a nucleus by the electrons in the system into local contributions, associated with the different bonds and molecular orbitals, was first proposed by Saika and Slichter [69]. The formulation, in its present state, is mainly from Pople [56–58] and McConnell [47].

The chemical shift, relative to a reference system, can be measured by the parameter

$$\delta = \sigma - \sigma_r = (H - H_r)/H_r,$$

where H and H_r are the fields for the system under consideration and the

Table 10-2 Values[a] of the Magnetic Shielding ($10^6\sigma$) for H_2

$\sigma^{(a)}$	$-\sigma^{(p)}$	σ	TYPE OF FUNCTION	METHOD	REFERENCE
2.65	0.38	2.27	Coulson [9]	Variation	Das-Bersohn [11]
2.97	0.64	2.33	Wallis (limited ionic) [85]	Variation	Das-Bersohn [11]
2.83	0.39	2.44	Heitler-London [24]	Variation	Das-Bersohn [11]
3.03	0.58	2.45	Rosen [67]	Variation	Das-Bersohn [11]
2.95	0.49	2.46	Wang [86]	Variation	Das-Bersohn [11]
3.00	0.53	2.47	Weinbaum [87]	Variation	Das-Bersohn [11]
3.21	0.45	2.76	Coulson [9]	Variation	Hoyland [27]
		2.76	James-Coolidge [31]	Variation	Ishiguro-Koide [30]
2.91	0.17	2.74	Wang [86]	Variation	McGarvey [49]
3.23	0.50	2.73	Berencz [4]	Variation	Hoyland [27]
		2.73	Coulson [9]	GIAO	Hameka [21]
3.07	0.54	2.53	Hirschfelder-Linnett [25]	Variation	Das-Bersohn [11]
3.04	0.51	2.53	Wallis (CI) [85]	Variation	Das-Bersohn [11]
2.83	0.13	2.70	Coulson [9]	Variation	McGarvey [49]
3.22	0.52	2.70	Open-shell	Variation	Hoyland [27]
3.08	0.53	2.55	Coulson (optimized) [9]	Variation	Das-Bersohn [11]
		2.68	Nordsieck [52]		Ramsey[b] [61]
3.24	0.56	2.68	Wang [86]	Variation	Ghosh-Sinha [18]
3.26	0.59	2.67	One-center expansion	Variation	Hoyland-Parr [28]
3.23	0.57	2.66	Correlated	Variation	Hoyland [27]
3.16	0.50	2.66			Hylleraas-Skavlem [29]
3.22	0.57	2.65	Fraga-Ransil (SCF) [16]	Variation	Kolker-Karplus [37]
		2.64	Wang [86]	GIAO	Hameka [21]
3.23	0.59	2.64	Harris-Taylor [22]	Variation	Hoyland [27]
2.78	0.15	2.63	Heitler-London [24]	Variation	McGarvey [49]
		2.62	Wang [86]	GIAO	Hameka [21]
3.21 ± 0.04	0.59 ± 0.03	2.62 ± 0.04		Experimental[c]	Ramsey [64]

a. No distinction has been made in this table regarding the origin of the vector potential.
b. The calculation of $\sigma^{(a)}$, using Nordsieck's function, was carried out by Anderson [1].
c. The experimental results correspond to a vector potential with origin at one of the protons.

reference system, respectively, at which resonance tàkes place (for a given frequency). Pople [58] has proposed to approximate δ by the sum of three contributions, corresponding to local diamagnetic currents, paramagnetic currents, and interatomic currents, respectively.

The diamagnetic contribution can be evaluated by the Lamb formula, using a local atomic electron density. The interatomic currents, usually diamagnetic and important in aromatic cyclic systems, have been treated by London [43], within the framework of molecular orbital theory, and by Pauling [54], using a free electron model.

In regard to the paramagnetic contributions, there are the local currents on the atom under consideration and the currents on neighboring atoms. For hydrogen atoms only the second contribution occurs. Pople [57, 58] has shown that it is possible to express this type of contribution in terms of gross populations. This formulation has been applied by Kern and Lipscomb [35].

REFERENCES

1. H. L. Anderson. Phys. Rev. *76*, 1460 (1949).
2. E. R. Andrew. "Nuclear Magnetic Resonance." Cambridge University Press, Cambridge, 1955.
3. E. R. Andrew and D. P. Tunstall. Proc. Phys. Soc. (London) *81*, 986 (1963).
4. F. Berencz. Acta Physica Acad. Sci. Hung. *6*, 423 (1957).
5. R. A. Bonham and T. G. Strand. J. Chem. Phys. *40*, 3447 (1964).
6. A. D. Buckingham and E. G. Lovering. Trans. Faraday Soc. *58*, 2077 (1962).
7. E. Clementi. "Tables of Atomic Functions." IBM Corporation, San José, California, 1965.
8. J. W. Cooper and J. B. Martin. Phys. Rev. *131*, 1183 (1963).
9. C. A. Coulson. Trans. Faraday Soc. *33*, 1479 (1937).
10. T. P. Das and R. Bersohn. Phys. Rev. *104*, 849 (1956).
11. T. P. Das and R. Bersohn. Phys. Rev. *115*, 897 (1959).
12. T. P. Das and T. Ghose. J. Chem. Phys. *31*, 42 (1959).
13. W. C. Dickinson. Phys. Rev. *80*, 563 (1950).
14. F. O. Ellison. J. Chem. Phys. *40*, 2421 (1964).
15. F. O. Ellison. J. Chem. Phys. *41*, 2018 (1964).
16. S. Fraga and B. J. Ransil. J. Chem. Phys. *35*, 1967 (1961).
17. C. Froese. J. Chem. Phys. *45*, 1417 (1966).
18. S. K. Ghosh and S. K. Sinha. J. Chem. Phys. *36*, 737 (1962).
19. G. Graff. Z. Physik *155*, 433 (1959).
20. R. B. Hake and K. E. Banyard. J. Chem. Phys. *43*, 657 (1965).
21. H. F. Hameka. Rev. Mod. Phys. *34*, 87 (1962).
22. F. E. Harris and H. S. Taylor. J. Chem. Phys. *38*, 2591 (1963).
23. R. H. Hay. Phys. Rev. *60*, 75 (1941).
24. W. Heitler and F. London. Z. Physik *44*, 455 (1927).
25. J. O. Hirschfelder and W. Linnett. J. Chem. Phys. *18*, 130 (1950).
26. J. F. Hornig and J. O. Hirschfelder. J. Chem. Phys. *23*, 474 (1955).
27. J. R. Hoyland. J. Chem. Phys. *41*, 3153 (1964).
28. J. R. Hoyland and R. G. Parr. J. Chem. Phys. *38*, 2991 (1963).
29. E. Hylleraas and S. Skavlem. Phys. Rev. *79*, 117 (1950).
30. E. Ishiguro and S. Koide. Phys. Rev. *94*, 350 (1954).
31. H. M. James and A. S. Coolidge. J. Chem. Phys. *1*, 825 (1933).
32. M. Karplus and H. J. Kolker. J. Chem. Phys. *38*, 1263 (1963).
33. H. P. Kelly and H. S. Taylor. J. Chem. Phys. *40*, 1478 (1964).

34. C. W. Kern and W. N. Lipscomb. J. Chem. Phys. *37*, 260 (1962).
35. C. W. Kern and W. N. Lipscomb. J. Chem. Phys. *37*, 275 (1962).
36. R. E. Knight and C. W. Scherr. J. Chem. Phys. *37*, 2503 (1962).
37. H. J. Kolker and M Karplus. J. Chem. Phys. *41*, 1259 (1964).
38. P. Kusch and S. Millman. Phys. Rev. *56*, 527 (1939).
39. P. Kusch, S. Millman, and I. I. Rabi. Phys. Rev. *55*, 1176 (1939).
40. P. Kusch, S. Millman, and I. I. Rabi. Phys. Rev. *57*, 765 (1940).
41. W. E. Lamb, Jr. Phys. Rev. *60*, 817 (1941).
42. P. C. Lauterbur. Phys. Letters *1*, 343 (1958).
43. F. London. J. Phys. Radium *8*, 397 (1937).
44. G. Malli. Can. J. Phys. *44*, 3121 (1966).
45. G. Malli and S. Fraga. Theoret. Chim. Acta (Berlin) *5*, 275 (1966).
46. G. Malli and C. Froese. Unpublished results.
47. H. M. McConnell. J. Chem. Phys. *27*, 226 (1957).
48. B. R. McGarvey. J. Chem. Phys. *26*, 221 (1957).
49. B. R. McGarvey. J. Chem. Phys. *27*, 68 (1957).
50. S. Millman and P. Kusch. Phys. Rev. *58*, 438 (1940).
51. S. Millman and P. Kusch. Phys. Rev. *60*, 91 (1941).
52. A. Nordsieck. Phys. Rev. *57*, 566 (1940).
53. F. T. Ormand and F. A. Matsen. J. Chem. Phys. *30*, 368 (1959).
54. L. Pauling. J. Chem. Phys. *4*, 673 (1936).
55. C. Pekeris. Phys. Rev. *115*, 1216 (1959).
56. J. A. Pople. J. Chem. Phys. *24*, 1111 (1956).
57. J. A. Pople. Proc. Roy. Soc. (London) *A239*, 541 (1957).
58. J. A. Pople. Proc. Roy. Soc. (London) *A239*, 550 (1957).
59. J. A. Pople, W. G. Schneider, and H. J. Bernstein. "High-Resolution Nuclear Magnetic Resonance." McGraw-Hill Book Company, Inc., New York, N.Y., 1959.
60. N. F. Ramsey. Phys. Rev. *77*, 567 (1950).
61. N. F. Ramsey. Phys. Rev. *78*, 699 (1950).
62. N. F. Ramsey. Phys. Rev. *83*, 540 (1951).
63. N. F. Ramsey. Phys. Rev. *86*, 243 (1952).
64. N. F. Ramsey. "Molecular Beams." Oxford University Press, Oxford, England, 1956.
65. T. K. Rebane. J. Exptl. and Theoret. Phys. (U.S.S.R.) *38*, 963 (1960).
66. C. C. J. Roothaan and M. Synek. Phys. Rev. *133*, A1263 (1964).
67. N. Rosen. Phys. Rev. *38*, 2099 (1931).
68. M. L. Rustgi and P. Tiwari. J. Chem. Phys. *39*, 2590 (1963).
69. A. Saika and C. P. Slichter. J. Chem. Phys. *22*, 26 (1954).
70. K. M. S. Saxena and P. T. Narasimhan. J. Chem. Phys. *42*, 4304 (1965).
71. C. W. Scherr and R. E. Knight. J. Chem. Phys. *40*, 3034 (1964).
72. J. N. Silverman and Y. Obata. J. Chem. Phys. *38*, 1254 (1963).
73. M. J. Stephen. Proc. Roy. Soc. (London) *A243*, 264 (1957).
74. R. M. Stevens and W. N. Lipscomb. J. Chem. Phys. *40*, 2238 (1964).
75. R. M. Stevens and W. N. Lipscomb. J. Chem. Phys. *41*, 184 (1964).
76. R. M. Stevens and W. N. Lipscomb. J. Chem. Phys. *41*, 3710 (1964).
77. R. M. Stevens and W. N. Lipscomb. J. Chem. Phys. *42*, 3666 (1965).
78. R. M. Stevens and W. N. Lipscomb. J. Chem. Phys. *42*, 4302 (1965).
79. R. M. Stevens, R. M. Pitzer, and W. N. Lipscomb. J. Chem. Phys. *38*, 550 (1963).
80. M. Synek. Phys. Rev. *133*, A961 (1964).
81. M. Synek and G. E. Stungis. J. Chem. Phys. *42*, 3068 (1965).
82. J. Tillieu and J. Guy. Compt. Rend. *239*, 1203 (1954).
83. J. Tillieu and J. Guy. Compt. Rend. *239*, 1283 (1954).
84. J. Tillieu and J. Guy. Compt. Rend. *240*, 1402 (1955).
85. R. F. Wallis. J. Chem. Phys. *23*, 1256 (1955).
86. S. Wang. Phys. Rev. *31*, 579 (1928).
87. S. Weinbaum. J. Chem. Phys. *1*, 593 (1933).
88. G. C. Wick. Phys. Rev. *73*, 51 (1948).

Chapter 11 MAGNETIC DIPOLE AND FERMI CONTACT INTERACTION

ELECTRON-NUCLEUS INTERACTIONS

There are several terms in the hamiltonian operator that represent an interaction between the electrons and nuclei of the system under consideration.

The most important term corresponds to the electrostatic interaction, which is included in the electronic hamiltonian operator. This term has the simple form $-\sum_i \sum_a (Z_a/r_{ia})$, where the summation over i extends over the electrons and the summation over a extends over the nuclei, when both the electrons and nuclei are considered as point charges; of course, if the nucleus is thought of as having a spatial extension, a more general expression must be used. The solution of the eigenequation for the electronic hamiltonian operator yields the electronic energy levels.

This simple description, based only on electrostatic interactions, neglects the existence of spins. When one takes into account, first of all, the electron spin, it is found that the so-called spin-orbit coupling determines a fine structure (fs) splitting of the electronic energy levels. The spin-orbit coupling, discussed in Chapter 14, arises from the interaction of the magnetic dipole moment associated with the electron spin and the magnetic field due to the orbital rotation of the electron. This term does not represent an electron-nucleus interaction, but it is mentioned here for an understanding of the subsequent discussion.

The further splitting of the fs levels leads to the so-called hyperfine structure (hfs). The hfs splitting, within the context of electron-nucleus interactions, is due to both electrostatic and magnetic interactions.

The nucleus can have an electric quadrupole moment, which measures the deviation from the spherical shape of the nuclear charge distribution.

This moment gives rise to an electrostatic interaction with the field gradient produced at the nucleus by the electrons of the system. This interaction is discussed in detail in Chapter 12.

Furthermore, the nucleus has, as the electron, a nuclear spin angular momentum, with an associated nuclear magnetic dipole moment. The coupling of the nuclear spin with the total electronic angular momentum of the system, via the electron spin-nuclear spin magnetic dipole-dipole interaction, contributes also to the hfs splitting. There is, in addition, an interaction between the magnetic moment of an electron and the magnetic moment of a nucleus. This interaction, which is effective only at extremely short distances, is discussed separately (see the section on Fermi contact interaction). The third type of magnetic interaction to be considered is the octopole hyperfine interaction.

HYPERFINE STRUCTURE

The hyperfine structure,* first observed by Michelson [64] and Fabry and Perot [30], was ascribed by Pauli [68] to the interaction between the electrons and the magnetic moments of the nuclei.

The first attempt to interpret the characteristic patterns of the hfs intervals is by Back and Goudsmit [4, 5], in terms of a theory similar to the vector coupling model of multiplets of Goudsmit and Bacher [37]. Later, rigorous treatments for certain configurations were developed by Fermi [31, 32], Breit [12–14], Goudsmit [36], Casimir [17], Racah [70, 71], and Breit and Wills [15], but the development of the general theory, using the tensor algebra of Racah [72–74], is by Trees [84] and Schwartz [80, 81]. In particular, Trees [84] formulated the treatment for dipole and quadrupole effects, and Schwartz [80, 81] developed the theory for any multipole interaction, though only for a single electron. (Casimir [17], Kopfermann [45], and Townes and Schawlow [83] present very complete discussions.)

If we restrict the discussion to the first two terms, that is, to the magnetic dipole and the electric quadrupole interaction, the splitting of the fs levels can be formally represented by

$$W_F = W_J + \tfrac{1}{2}A(J)K + B(J)K(K+1), \qquad (11\text{-}1a)$$

where

$$K = F(F+1) - I(I+1) - J(J+1), \qquad (11\text{-}1b)$$

$$F = I+J, I+J-1, \ldots, |I-J|; \qquad (11\text{-}1c)$$

J, I, and F are the total electronic, nuclear spin, and total angular momentum quantum numbers, respectively.

---

* Blinder [10] has reviewed in detail the theory of atomic hyperfine structure.

The fs level W_J splits into a multiplet of hfs levels because of the magnetic and electrostatic interaction between the nucleus and the electrons. The number of levels is equal to the number of possible orientations of the angular momentum vector F, $(2I + 1)$ if $J \geq I$ and $(2J + 1)$ if $I \geq J$. The splitting leaves the center of gravity of the original fs level unchanged.

The term $\frac{1}{2}A(J)K$ arises from the magnetic dipole-dipole interaction between the electrons and the nucleus, and the term $B(J)K(K + 1)$ corresponds to the interaction with the electric quadrupole moment of the nucleus.

Expressions for the dependence of $A(J)$ and $B(J)$ on the electronic quantum numbers have been given for specific electronic configurations by Casimir [17], Goudsmit [36], Breit [14], Breit and Wills [15], and Crawford [25]. The generalization to configurations involving many equivalent electrons is difficult. However, Trees [84] has succeeded in deriving the corresponding formulas* using the tensor algebra of Racah [72, 73]. It must be mentioned that these expressions are directly applicable only to light atoms (showing LS-coupling), since the relativistic effects derived by Breit [14] and Racah [70, 71] are neglected.

The relativistic treatment of Schwartz [81] has been extended to many-electron atomic systems by Sandars and Beck [79]. Evans, Sandars, and Woodgate [29] have applied the theory to the ^6S state of Mn. Bordarier, Judd, and Klapisch [11] have carried out a theoretical analysis of the 12 levels of the EuI $4f^7(^8S)6s6p$ state using the intermediate-coupling functions obtained by a least-square fit of the energies of the different levels. In this work relativistic effects for the $6p$ electron have been considered, enabling one to relate the core polarization to data of the hfs of the $6s$ electron as well as to explain the hfs anomalies.

The relativistic effects in the hfs of the first excited states of Pu have also been discussed in detail by Armstrong [3], with the conclusion that the discrepancies between the theoretical and the experimental values may be ascribed to the core polarization.

Before we present the theoretical details it is convenient to mention, though briefly, that the most common technique of measuring hfs has been the atomic beam magnetic resonance. Nierenberg [67] has summarized the experimental results obtained up to 1957. Hubbs, Marrus, Nierenberg, and Worcester [40] have reported hfs results for Pu[239], Armstrong and Marrus [2] have analyzed the hfs of Am[241] and Am[242], and Armstrong [1] has discussed the nuclear magnetic moments and hfs anomalies of Re[186], Re[188], Am[241], and Am[242]. Childs and Goodman [20, 21] have measured the spin and the magnetic hfs constants of Ge[71], as well as the hfs of Ge[73] and the nuclear magnetic dipole moment of Ge[71]. The electron nuclear double resonance [ENDOR] techniques have been used by Terhune, Lambe, Kikuchi, and Baker [82] to observe the hfs of Cr[53].

---

* Detailed expressions for $B(J)$ are given in Chapter 12.

MAGNETIC DIPOLE INTERACTION

The magnetic hyperfine structure* arises from the interaction of the nuclear magnetic moment $\boldsymbol{\mu}_I$ with the magnetic field produced at the nucleus by an electron of spin angular momentum $\boldsymbol{s}$ and orbital angular momentum $\boldsymbol{l}$.

The nucleus has a magnetic moment $\boldsymbol{\mu}_I$ and a spin angular momentum $\boldsymbol{I}$, interrelated by $\boldsymbol{\mu}_I = g_I \mu_N \boldsymbol{I} = (\mu_I/I) \mu_N \boldsymbol{I}$, where μ_N is the nuclear magneton and g_I is the nuclear g-factor; μ_I is measured in units of nuclear magnetons. A similar expression, $\boldsymbol{\mu}_e = g_e \mu_B \boldsymbol{s} = (\mu_e/s) \mu_B \boldsymbol{s}$, can be written for the magnetic moment of the electron, g_e being the electron g-factor; μ_e is measured in units of Bohr magnetons.

The magnetic field, produced by the electron at the nucleus, consists of two terms. First, there is the magnetic field due to the orbital motion of the electron,

$$B_l = -e[\boldsymbol{v}\hbar(-\boldsymbol{r})]/cr^3 = -(e\hbar/mc)(\boldsymbol{l}/r^3) = -2\mu_B(\boldsymbol{l}/r^3),$$

where $\mu_B = e\hbar/2mc$ is the Bohr magneton (m being the mass of the electron); $\boldsymbol{r}$ and $\boldsymbol{v}$ are the position and velocity vectors of the electron. In addition, the magnetic field due to the electron spin dipole is

$$B_s = -(1/r^3)[\boldsymbol{\mu}_e - 3(\boldsymbol{\mu}_e \cdot \boldsymbol{r})(\boldsymbol{r}/r^2)] = 2(\mu_B/r^3)[\boldsymbol{s} - 3(\boldsymbol{s} \cdot \boldsymbol{r})(\boldsymbol{r}/r^2)],$$

where the value (-2) has been used for the electron g-factor. The total magnetic field at the nucleus is then

$$B = -(2\mu_B/r^3)[\boldsymbol{l} - \boldsymbol{s} + 3(\boldsymbol{s} \cdot \boldsymbol{r})(\boldsymbol{r}/r^2)]. \tag{11-2}$$

Therefore the magnetic dipole-dipole hyperfine structure hamiltonian operator $\mathscr{H}_d$ is

$$\mathscr{H}_d = -(2\mu_B\mu_N\mu_I) \sum_i (\mathbf{N}_i \cdot \mathbf{I}/r_i^3), \tag{11-3}$$

where $\mathbf{N}_i$ stands for

$$\mathbf{N}_i = \mathbf{l}_i - \mathbf{s}_i + 3(\mathbf{r}_i \cdot \mathbf{s}_i)(\mathbf{r}_i/r_i^2); \tag{11-4}$$

the summation extends over all the electrons in the system.

The interaction hamiltonian consists, essentially, of the scalar product of two vectors, and therefore the matrix elements of $\mathscr{H}_d$ can be evaluated using the tensor algebra of Racah [72, 73]. These matrix elements are independent of the total angular momentum projection quantum number M_F, with values $-F \le M_F \le F$.

In order to simplify the formulation of these elements it is convenient to express the last term of Eq. (11-4) in a tensor operator form,

$$3(\mathbf{r}_i \cdot \mathbf{s}_i)(\mathbf{r}_i/r_i^2) = 3(\mathbf{s}_i \cdot \mathbf{r}_i)(\mathbf{r}_i/r_i^2) = 3(\mathbf{s}_i^{(1)} \cdot \mathbf{C}_i^{(1)}) \cdot \mathbf{C}_i^{(1)}, \tag{11-5}$$

where $\mathbf{C}_i^{(1)}$ represents a tensor operator of rank one; for completeness the vector operator $\mathbf{s}_i$ has also been assigned a superscript (1) in order to indicate

---

* The hyperfine interaction hamiltonian has been rederived by Blinder [9], Ferrell [33], Rado [76], and Frosch and Foley [34].

that it is a tensor of rank one. The coupling implicit in Eq. (11-5) can be rewritten as

$$3(\mathbf{s}_i^{(1)} \cdot \mathbf{C}_i^{(1)}) \cdot \mathbf{C}_i^{(1)} = -3(3)^{\frac{1}{2}}((\mathbf{s}^{(1)} \cdot \mathbf{C}^{(1)})_i^{(0)} \cdot \mathbf{C}_i^{(1)})$$

$$= -3(3)^{\frac{1}{2}} \sum_k (2k+1)^{\frac{1}{2}} \begin{Bmatrix} 1 & 1 & k \\ 1 & 1 & 0 \end{Bmatrix} [(\mathbf{s}_i^{(1)} \cdot (\mathbf{C}^{(1)} \cdot \mathbf{C}^{(1)})_i^{(k)})^{(1)}].$$

Taking into account that

$$(\mathbf{C}^{(1)} \cdot \mathbf{C}^{(1)})_i^{(2)} = (\tfrac{2}{3})^{\frac{1}{2}} \mathbf{C}_i^{(2)},$$

$$(\mathbf{C}^{(1)} \cdot \mathbf{C}^{(1)})_i^{(0)} = -(\tfrac{1}{3})^{\frac{1}{2}},$$

one can write

$$3(3)^{\frac{1}{2}}((\mathbf{s}^{(1)} \cdot \mathbf{C}^{(1)})_i^{(0)} \cdot \mathbf{C}_i^{(1)}) = -(3)^{\frac{1}{2}}[-(\tfrac{1}{3})^{\frac{1}{2}} \mathbf{s}_i + (\tfrac{10}{3})^{\frac{1}{2}} (\mathbf{s} \cdot \mathbf{C}^{(2)})_i^{(1)}]$$

$$= \mathbf{s}_i - (10)^{\frac{1}{2}} (\mathbf{s} \cdot \mathbf{C}^{(2)})_i^{(1)}.$$

Therefore Eq. (11-4) can be rewritten as

$$\mathbf{N}_i = \mathbf{l}_i - (10)^{\frac{1}{2}}(\mathbf{s} \cdot \mathbf{C}^{(2)})_i^{(1)}, \tag{11-6}$$

having eliminated the spin term of the original expression.

The matrix elements of $\mathscr{H}_d$ are given by

$$(\alpha J, I, F| \mathscr{H}_d |\alpha J, I, F) = 2\mu_B \mu_N (\mu_I/I)(\alpha J, I, F \,|\, \sum_i (\mathbf{N}_i \cdot \mathbf{I}/r_i^3) \,|\, \alpha J, I, F), \tag{11-7}$$

where α denotes the additional quantum numbers required to complete the description of the state under consideration. According to the Wigner-Eckart [87, 28] theorem, the matrix elements of $\sum_i (\mathbf{N}_i \cdot \mathbf{I}/r_i^3)$ for any of the $(2J+1)$ substates corresponding to a given level are proportional to those of $\mathbf{J} \cdot \mathbf{I}$,

$$(\alpha J, I, F| \sum_i (\mathbf{N}_i \cdot \mathbf{I}/r_i^3) |\alpha J, I, F) = A'(J)(\alpha J, I, F| \mathbf{J} \cdot \mathbf{I} |\alpha J, I, F)\langle r^{-3} \rangle.$$

Therefore Eq. (11-7) becomes

$$(\alpha J, I, F| \mathscr{H}_d |\alpha J, I, F) = 2\mu_B \mu_N (\mu_I/I) A'(J)(K/2)\langle r^{-3} \rangle, \tag{11-8}$$

$A'(J)$ being a constant of proportionality and K being defined as in Eq. (11-1b). Equation (11-8) can be rewritten as

$$(\alpha J, I, F| \mathscr{H}_d |\alpha J, I, F) = A(J)(K/2), \tag{11-9}$$

with

$$A(J) = 2\mu_B \mu_N (\mu_I/I) A'(J)\langle r^{-3} \rangle. \tag{11-10a}$$

Goudsmit [36] has derived for $A'(J)$, in the LS-coupling scheme, the expression (see also Trees [84])

$$A'(J) = \lambda(2-g) - \sigma[6\Gamma(2-g) - 2(g-1)L(L+1)]/(2L-1)(2L+3) \tag{11-10b}$$

(for $L \neq 0$, $J \neq 0$), with (as proved by Trees [84])

$$\lambda = [L(L+1)(2L+1)]^{-\frac{1}{2}}(\alpha SL| \ |\sum_i l_i| \ |\alpha SL), \qquad (11\text{-}10\text{c})$$

$$\sigma = -[(2L-1)(2L+3)]^{\frac{1}{2}}[S(S+1)(2S+1)L(L+1)(2L+1)]^{-\frac{1}{2}}$$
$$\times (\alpha SL| \ |\sum_i \mathbf{s}_i \cdot \mathbf{C}_i^{(2)}| \ |\alpha SL), \qquad (11\text{-}10\text{d})$$

$$\Gamma = (\tfrac{1}{2})[J(J+1) - L(L+1) - S(S+1)], \qquad (11\text{-}10\text{e})$$

$$g = 1 + [J(J+1) + S(S+1) - L(L+1)]/(2J+1), \qquad (11\text{-}10\text{f})$$

where the double barred matrices are given by Racah [72, 73].

Hubbs, Marrus, Nierenberg, and Worcester [40] have derived independently another expression for $A'(J)$ for the ground state $(J = L + S)$ of a configuration of n equivalent electrons or holes,

$$A'(J) = \{[J(J+1) + L(L+1) - S(S+1)]/2J(J+1)\}$$
$$+ 2[(2L - n^2)/n^2(2L-1)(2l-1)(2l+3)]\{L(L+1)(g-1)$$
$$- (\tfrac{3}{2})\Gamma[J(J+1) + L(L+1) - S(S+1)]/[2J(J+1)]\}, \qquad (11\text{-}11)$$

where l is the angular momentum quantum number for the shell under consideration, and Γ and g have the same meaning as before.

Equations (11-10b) and (11-11) lead to the same values of $A'(J)$. Table 11-1 presents the values of $A'(J)$ for configurations of equivalent p and d electrons.

The constant $A(J)$, defined by Eq. (11-10a), is the so-called hyperfine structure constant, also represented by a_d. Its evaluation requires, in addition to $A'(J)$, the calculation of the expectation values $\langle r^{-3} \rangle$. Tables 11-2 and 11-3 collect the values of a_d for a series of positive ions, neutral atoms, and negative ions, calculated by Malli and Fraga [52] from the analytical HF functions of Clementi [22] and Malli [50].

The satisfactory agreement between the theoretical and experimental values indicates that HF functions can be used for this type of calculations, at least for light atoms. In this connection it is interesting to note that the results obtained by Bessis, Lefebvre-Brion, and Moser [8] for B and O with PUHF functions are in better agreement with the experimental results than those evaluated from UHF functions.

Table 11-1 Values[a] of $A'(J)$ for Various Electronic Configurations for the Case $J = L + S$

CONFIGURATION	STATE	$A'(J)$	CONFIGURATION	STATE	$A'(J)$
p^1, p^5	^2P	8/15	d^2, d^8	^2F	5/7
p^2, p^4	^3P	3/5	d^3, d^7	^4F	44/63
d^1, d^9	^2D	24/35	d^4, d^6	^5D	4/7

a. Determined by Malli and Fraga [52].

Table 11-2 Magnetic Hyperfine Structure Constants a_d (in Mc/sec) for Some States[a] of Various Neutral Atoms and Negative and Positive Ions with Configurations p^n, Evaluated by Malli and Fraga [52] from HF Functions (Experimental Values Are Given in Parentheses[a])

Z	M	POSITIVE IONS		NEUTRAL ATOMS		NEGATIVE IONS	
		State	a_d	State	a_d	State	a_d
5	10			^2P	23.7	^3P	16.0
	11			^2P	70.8	^3P	47.9
					(73.3)		
6	13	^2P	158.9	^3P	136.2		
7	14	^3P	88.7			^3P	54.8
	15	^3P	−124.3			^3P	−76.8
8	17			^3P	−215.9	^2P	−156.5
9	18	^3P	406.2	^2P	307.6		
	19	^3P	2669.5	^2P	2021.1		
10	21	^2P	−212.1				
13	26			^2P	31.0	^3P	21.4
	27			^2P	80.6	^3P	55.6
					(94.3)		
14	29	^2P	−150.1	^3P	−130.6		
15	30	^3P	139.2			^3P	89.4
	31	^3P	525.0			^3P	337.1
16	33			^3P	118.9	^2P	88.0
	35			^3P	186.6	^2P	136.8
17	34	^3P	209.4	^2P	160.8		
	35	^3P	244.8	^2P	188.8		
					(205.1)		
	36	^3P	287.1	^2P	221.5		
	37	^3P	203.8	^2P	157.2		
					(170.7)		
31	67			^2P	180.7	^3P	122.1
	69			^2P	198.0	^3P	133.8
					(190.8)		
	71			^2P	251.5	^3P	170.0
					(242.4)		
32	71	^2P	339.4	^3P	300.2		
					(361.0)[b]		
	73	^2P	−60.7	^3P	−53.7		
					(−64.4)[c]		
33	75	^3P	461.4			^3P	300.4
34	77			^3P	567.7	^2P	420.9
	79			^3P	154.6	^2P	114.6
35	79	^3P	1104.6	^2P	856.6		
					(884.8)		
	81	^3P	1190.7	^2P	923.3		
					(953.8)		

a. These are the values quoted by Ramsey [77].
b. Reported by Childs and Goodman [20].
c. Reported by Childs and Goodman [21].

Table 11-3 Magnetic Hyperfine Structure Constants a_d (in Mc/sec) for Some States[a] of Various Neutral Atoms and Negative and Positive Ions with Configurations d^n, Evaluated by Malli and Fraga [52] from HF Functions

Z	M	POSITIVE IONS		NEUTRAL ATOMS		NEGATIVE IONS	
		State	a_d	State	a_d	State	a_d
21	45	^3F	110.3	^2D	127.1	^3F	98.1
22	47	^4F	361.1	^3F	43.3	^4F	34.0
	49	^4F	361.2	^3F	43.4	^4F	34.0
23	50	^5D	70.0	^4F	98.4	^5D	67.7
	51	^5D	184.4	^4F	259.9	^5D	178.6
24	53			^5D	57.8		
25	55	^5D	278.5			^5D	273.6
26	57	^4F	10.0	^5D	9.1	^4F	9.8
27	57	^3F	489.4	^4F	525.3	^3F	484.5
	58	^3F	644.6	^4F	691.9	^3F	638.1
	59	^3F	489.2	^4F	525.1	^3F	484.3
	60	^3F	257.8	^4F	276.7	^3F	255.3
28	61			^3F	31.8		

The effect of configuration interaction has been considered by Koster [46] in Ga.

FERMI CONTACT INTERACTION

The interaction between the magnetic moment of an electron and the magnetic moment of a nucleus leads to a term in the hfs splitting of the energy levels. This interaction, which is only effective at extremely short ranges, exists only for orbitals with finite nonzero spin densities at the corresponding nucleus; in atoms, for example, this term arises only from orbitals with s character.

The hamiltonian operator $\mathscr{H}_c$ for the contact term, derived by Fermi [31, 32], is expressed by

$$\mathscr{H}_c = -(8\pi/3)g_e g_n \mu_B \mu_N \sum_i (\mathbf{I} \cdot \mathbf{s}_i)\, \delta(\mathbf{r}_i)$$
$$= -(8\pi/3)(\mu_e/s)(\mu_I/I)\mu_B \mu_N \sum_i (\mathbf{I} \cdot \mathbf{s}_i)\delta(\mathbf{r}_i), \qquad (11\text{-}12)$$

where $\delta(\mathbf{r}_i)$ is a three-dimensional delta-function, and the summation extends over all the orbitals with a nonvanishing spin density at the nucleus under consideration. For an electron with α spin the corresponding term in the summation is positive, whereas it is negative for an electron with β spin. Therefore the closed shells give no contribution to the Fermi contact. Consequently only unpaired electrons need be considered, and Eq. (11-12) becomes

$$\mathscr{H}_c = -(8\pi/3)(\mu_e/s)(\mu_I/I)\mu_B \mu_N(\mathbf{I} \cdot \mathbf{s}) \sum_i \varepsilon_i \delta(\mathbf{r}_i), \qquad (11\text{-}13)$$

where ε_i takes the value ± 1 depending on the spin of the unpaired electron.

For an s orbital in an atom ($l = 0, s = \tfrac{1}{2}, j = \tfrac{1}{2}$), the scalar product

$$2(\boldsymbol{I} \cdot \boldsymbol{s}) = 2(\boldsymbol{I} \cdot \boldsymbol{j}) = f(f+1) - I(I+1) - s(s+1)$$

takes the values I (for $f = I + \tfrac{1}{2}$) or $-(I + 1)$ (for $f = I - \tfrac{1}{2}$). Therefore, the energy splitting corresponding to an unpaired electron is

$$\Delta E = (8\pi/3)\,\mu_e \mu_I \mu_B \mu_N (2 + 1/I)\rho(0) = \tfrac{1}{2}a_c(1 + 2I),$$

where $\rho(0)$ is the electronic density at the nucleus for the s orbital occupied by the unpaired electron; a_c is the hfs constant, defined by

$$a_c = (16\pi/3)\,\mu_e \mu_I \mu_N \mu_B (1/I)\rho(0).$$

Table 11-4 collects the hfs constants a_c for ^2S states of some positive ions, neutral atoms, and negative ions, evaluated from HF functions. (Similar calculations have been carried out for Li by Cohen, Goodings, and Heine [24], Goodings [35], and Sachs [78].) Inspection of the experimental values, determined by Kusch and Taub [49], shows that HF functions are not appropriate for the evaluation of a_c.

The underestimation of this effect by HF functions can be corrected by the use of pseudo-open shell functions. In such a case Nesbet [65] and Pratt [69] have shown that the magnetic field at the nucleus due to the inner s electrons does not cancel, as it does for closed shells. This polarization effect contributes to the hfs splitting, as the calculations of Sachs [78] and

Table 11-4 Hyperfine Structure Constants a_c (in Mc/sec) for the Ground States of Various Neutral Atoms, Positive Ions and Negative Ions, Evaluated[a] by Malli and Fraga [51] from HF Functions (Experimental Values Are Given in Parentheses[b])

SYSTEM	M	a_c	SYSTEM	M	a_c
Li	6	110.1	K	42	380.1
	7	290.9	Cu	63	3560.6
		(401.8)			
Na	22	246.0		64	959.5
	23	624.5		65	3813.4
		(885.8)			
	24	178.3	Be$^+$	9	511.6
K	38	259.0	Mg$^+$	25	464.5
	39	144.8	Zn$^+$	67	1689.5
		(230.9)			
	40	180.1	Ca$^+$	43	580.0
	41	79.6	Ni$^-$	61	81.5

a. Using the values of μ_I quoted by Ramsey [77].
b. The experimental values are those determined by Kusch and Taub [49].

Kerwin and Burke [44] for Li show. The use of CI functions can also lead to very satisfactory results (see, for example, the calculations on Li by Nesbet [66] and Martin and Weiss [54]); in fact, both treatments should yield essentially equivalent results when carried out to the same accuracy.

These considerations are further reinforced by the results obtained for the Fermi contact term at the proton in OH by Kayama [43], using a CI function. Mention must also be made of the work of Krauss and Wehner [47].

PROTON HYPERFINE INTERACTION

The hfs observed in the electron spin resonance (ESR) spectra of organic systems can be understood in terms of the magnetic interactions described in the preceding sections. Though it is not possible to present a detailed discussion, it is convenient to summarize here briefly the situation regarding the proton hyperfine interactions.

The large number of systems where these interactions can be detected imposes the need for such a discussion. Just as important, however, is the fact that the calculations for organic compounds are still carried out in a semiempirical way. The corresponding functions do not meet the standards of HF functions, but nevertheless interesting conclusions can be drawn from them. Therefore an inspection of the problem may prove to be stimulating.

Anisotropic proton hyperfine interaction (due to magnetic dipole-dipole coupling) has been observed for free radicals in crystals and has been discussed theoretically by McConnell and coworkers [60, 62], Derbyshire [27], and Higuchi [39]. But most of the work has been carried out on the isotropic proton hyperfine interaction, which can be observed, for example, for aromatic free radicals in solution, in the presence of a strong static magnetic field.

Weissman [85] pointed out that the splitting arises from the Fermi contact interaction, neglecting the spin-orbit interactions in order to arrive at this conclusion. However, McConnell and Chesnut [59] have indicated that the spin-orbit interactions may produce isotropic hfs splittings in solutions, though these effects are too small to account for the observed splittings. It is expected, however, that spin-orbit interactions may produce pseudocontact hfs splittings in other paramagnetic molecules in solution.

The interest in the isotropic hyperfine interaction from a theoretical point of view is due to certain peculiarities. As discussed in the previous section, the contact term arises from the interaction of an unpaired electron with a nucleus. In an aromatic radical, the unpaired electron occupies a π-type orbital, with a node at the plane of the molecule. Therefore one would expect the contact interaction to vanish, in contradiction with the observed results.

The observed splitting can be explained, however, on the basis of a σ-π exchange interaction. In fact, an unpaired electron density at the proton can be predicted within the framework of the VB (McConnell [56], Jarrett [42], and Bersohn [7]) and MO theories (Weissman [86] and McConnell and Chesnut [59]).

This hfs interaction has an indirect character. That is, it represents an interaction between the π-electron spin and the proton spin. As a matter of fact, satisfactory results can be obtained by use of a semiempirical relation between the hyperfine splitting due to the proton and the electron density at the adjacent carbon atom. The constant of proportionality is ascribed a semiempirical value based on the observed hfs splittings in aromatic radicals (see McConnell and Chesnut [59]). This relation, proposed by McConnell [55–57], does not hold, unfortunately, in all cases.

In even alternant hydrocarbons, the unpaired electron densities predicted at certain carbons by the simple theories are zero, and consequently, the protons associated with such carbons could not interact with any unpaired electron. McConnell and Chesnut [59] have overcome this difficulty through the definition of a generalized spin density which, unlike the unpaired electron density, may be positive or negative. McConnell and Chesnut [59] were able to rederive the original relation within the framework of CI; this formulation has been corrected by McConnell and Robertson [61].

Later work has introduced more refinements in the theory. In particular, McConnell [58] has presented a generalized theory, with inclusion of overlap, and Chesnut [19] has studied the isotropic hfs interaction in aliphatic radicals. On the other hand, McLachlan, Dearman, and Lefebvre [63] have given a general treatment in terms of σ-electron excitations.

Bernheim and Das [6] have indicated that the C^{13}-H^1 spin-spin coupling constant and the proton hfs constant in a free radical are interdependent; both can be estimated from a calculation of the perturbation produced by the magnetic moment of the proton on the function, as proposed by Das and Mukherjee [26]. (See the work of Brown [16] on azulene.)

It must be remembered that the ESR spectra represent a superposition of factors and that reduction of the problem to the evaluation of the unpaired electron density may be considered a simplification. The different properties (bond angle, hybridization, etc.) of the C—H bond should be included in a more rigorous treatment, as pointed out by Higuchi [38].

OCTOPOLE COUPLING CONSTANTS

In addition to the magnetic hfs interactions already discussed in this chapter, namely the dipole and the contact interaction, there can also be a so-called octopole interaction.

The effect of the magnetic octopole moment of a nucleus was first discussed by Casimir and Karreman [18] using classical arguments. This type of hfs was observed experimentally by Jaccarino, King, Satten, and Stroke [41] in I^{127} and by Kusch and Eck [48] in In^{115}.

Table 11-5 Octopole Coupling Constants* c (c/sec)

SYSTEM	STATE	THEORETICAL[a]	EXPERIMENTAL[b]
Cl^{35}	^2P	−6.299	−6.69 ± 1.2
Cl^{37}	^2P	−4.973	−5.41 ± 1.2
Cl^{35+}	^3P	−7.342	
Cl^{37+}	^3P	−5.796	
Ga^{69}	^2P	75.053	93.0
Ga^{71}	^2P	96.497	121.9
Ga^{69-}	^3P	45.218	
Ga^{71-}	^3P	58.137	

a. Evaluated by Malli and Fraga [53] from analytical HF functions.
b. Values reported by Schwartz [81].
* This table is reproduced by permission of the National Research Council of Canada.

The theory for the hfs octopole interaction has been developed by Schwartz [80, 81], using Racah tensor algebra. For a single electron in a p shell (and, equivalently, for a p^n configuration with a single hole), the octopole coupling constant is given by

$$c = (\tfrac{4}{35}) \mu_B g(0) \Omega, \qquad (11\text{-}14)$$

where Ω is the octopole moment (in nuclear magnetons barns), and $g(0)$ is defined by

$$g(0) = |(1/r)R(r)|^2_{r=0},$$

$R(r)$ denoting the radial function. Within the expansion method, using STO, only the $2p$-type basis functions contribute to $g(0)$.

The theoretical evaluation of octopole coupling constants depends on the knowledge of the nuclear octopole moments. Unfortunately, the values of octopole moments are available for only a few atoms. (A compilation of these values has been made by Cohen and Fuller [23].)

Table 11-5 contains the octopole coupling constants, calculated for Cl and Ga from analytical HF functions by Malli and Fraga [53]. It can be observed that the agreement for Cl is satisfactory, whereas for Ga the discrepancy is somewhat larger. A reason proposed to explain this discrepancy is that the HF function for Ga does not satisfy the coulomb cusp condition at the nucleus.

REFERENCES

1. L. Armstrong, Jr. Ph. D. Thesis. Report No. UCRL-16419, Lawrence Radiation Laboratory, University of California, Berkeley, Calif., September 1965.
2. L. Armstrong, Jr., and R. Marrus. Report No. UCRL-16494, Lawrence Radiation Laboratory, University of California, Berkeley, Calif., November 1965.
3. L. Armstrong, Jr. Bull. Am. Phys. Soc. *10*, 1214 (1965).
4. E. Back and S. Goudsmit. Z. Physik *33*, 321 (1927).

5. E. Back and S. Goudsmit. Z. Physik *47*, 174 (1929).
6. R. A. Bernheim and T. P. Das. J. Chem. Phys. *33*, 1813 (1960).
7. R. Bersohn. J. Chem. Phys. *24*, 1066 (1956).
8. N. Bessis, H. Lefebvre-Brion, and C. M. Moser. Phys. Rev. *128*, 213 (1962).
9. S. M. Blinder. J. Mol. Spectroscopy *5*, 17 (1960).
10. S. M. Blinder. Theory of Atomic Hyperfine Structure, *in* "Advances in Quantum Chemistry," vol. II, edited by P. O. Löwdin. Academic Press, Inc., New York, N.Y., 1965.
11. Y. Bordarier, B. R. Judd, and M. Klapisch. Proc. Roy. Soc. (London) *A239*, 81 (1965).
12. G. Breit. Phys. Rev. *35*, 1447 (1930).
13. G. Breit. Phys. Rev. *37*, 51 (1931).
14. G. Breit. Phys. Rev. *38*, 463 (1931).
15. G. Breit and L. A. Wills. Phys. Rev. *44*, 470 (1933).
16. T. H. Brown. J. Chem. Phys. *41*, 2223 (1964).
17. H. B. G. Casimir. "On the Interaction between Atomic Nuclei and Electrons." W. H. Freeman and Co., San Francisco, Calif., 1963.
18. H. B. G. Casimir and G. Karreman. Physica *9*, 494 (1942).
19. D. B. Chesnut. J. Chem. Phys. *29*, 43 (1958).
20. W. J. Childs and L. S. Goodman. Phys. Rev. *131*, 245 (1963).
21. W. J. Childs and L. S. Goodman. Phys. Rev. *141*, 15 (1966).
22. E. Clementi. "Tables of Atomic Functions." IBM Corporation, San José, California, 1965.
23. V. W. Cohen and G. H. Fuller. "Nuclear Moments. Appendix 1 to Nuclear Data Sheets." Nuclear Data Project, Oak Ridge National Laboratory, Oak Ridge, Tenn.
24. M. H. Cohen, D. A. Goodings, and V. Heine. Proc. Phys. Soc. (London) *73*, 811 (1959).
25. M. F. Crawford. Phys. Rev. *47*, 768 (1935).
26. T. P. Das and A. Mukherjee. J. Chem. Phys. *33*, 1808 (1960).
27. W. Derbyshire. Mol. Phys. *5*, 225 (1962).
28. C. Eckart. Rev. Mod. Phys. *2*, 305 (1930).
29. L. Evans, P. G. H. Sandars, and G. K. Woodgate. Proc. Roy. Soc. (London) *A289*, 108 (1965).
30. C. Fabry and A. Perot. Ann. Chim. et Phys. *12*, 459 (1897).
31. E. Fermi. Z. Physik *60*, 320 (1930).
32. E. Fermi. Mem. R. Acad. Ital. *4*, 131 (1933).
33. R. A. Ferrell. Am. J. Phys. *28*, 484 (1960).
34. R. A. Frosch and H. M. Foley. Phys. Rev. *88*, 1337 (1952).
35. D. A. Goodings. Phys. Rev. *123*, 1706 (1961).
36. S. Goudsmit. Phys. Rev. *37*, 663 (1931).
37. S. Goudsmit and R. F. Bacher. Phys. Rev. *34*, 1501 (1929).
38. J. Higuchi. J. Chem. Phys. *39*, 3455 (1963).
39. J. Higuchi. J. Chem. Phys. *41*, 2084 (1964).
40. J. C. Hubbs, R. Marrus, W. A. Nierenberg, and J. L. Worcester. Phys. Rev. *109*, 390 (1958).
41. V. Jaccarino, J. G. King, R. A. Satten, and H. H. Stroke. Phys. Rev. *94*, 1798 (1954).
42. H. S. Jarrett. J. Chem. Phys. *25*, 1289 (1956).
43. K. Kayama. J. Chem. Phys. *39*, 1507 (1963).
44. J. Kerwin and E. A. Burke. J. Chem. Phys. *36*, 2987 (1962).
45. H. Kopfermann. "Nuclear Moments." Academic Press, Inc., New York, N.Y., 1958.
46. G. F. Koster. Phys. Rev. *86*, 148 (1952).
47. M. Krauss and J. H. Wehner. J. Chem. Phys. *29*, 1287 (1958).
48. P. Kusch and T. G. Eck. Phys. Rev. *94*, 1799 (1954).
49. P. Kusch and H. Taub. Phys. Rev. *75*, 1477 (1949).
50. G. Malli. Can. J. Phys. *44*, 3121 (1966).
51. G. Malli and S. Fraga. Theoret. Chim. Acta (Berlin) *6*, 278 (1966).
52. G. Malli and S. Fraga. Theoret. Chim. Acta (Berlin) *7*, 75 (1967).
53. G. Malli and S. Fraga. Can J. Phys. *45*, 219 (1967).
54. J. B. Martin and A. W. Weiss. J. Chem. Phys. *39*, 1618 (1963).
55. H. M. McConnell. J. Chem. Phys. *24*, 632 (1956).
56. H. M. McConnell. J. Chem. Phys. *24*, 764 (1956).
57. H. M. McConnell. Ann. Rev. Phys. Chem. *8*, 105 (1957).

58. H. M. McConnell. J. Chem. Phys. *28*, 1188 (1958).
59. H. M. McConnell and D. B. Chesnut. J. Chem. Phys. *28*, 107 (1958).
60. H. M. McConnell, C. Heller, T. Cole, and R. W. Fesseden. J. Am. Chem. Soc. *82*, 766 (1960).
61. H. M. McConnell and R. Robertson. J. Chem. Phys. *29*, 1361 (1958).
62. H. M. McConnell and J. Strathdee. Mol. Phys. *2*, 129 (1959).
63. A. D. McLachlan, H. H. Dearman, and R. Lefebvre. J. Chem. Phys. *33*, 65 (1960).
64. A. Michelson. Phil. Mag. *31*, 338 (1891).
65. R. K. Nesbet. Proc. Roy. Soc. (London) *A230*, 312 (1955).
66. R. K. Nesbet. Phys. Rev. *118*, 681 (1960).
67. W. A. Nierenberg. "Recent Research in Molecular Beams," edited by I. Estermann. Academic Press, Inc., New York, N.Y., 1957.
68. W. Pauli. Naturwiss. *12*, 74 (1924).
69. G. W. Pratt. Phys. Rev. *102*, 1303 (1956).
70. G. Racah. Z. Physik *71*, 431 (1931).
71. G. Racah. Nuovo Cimento *8*, 178 (1931).
72. G. Racah. Phys. Rev. *62*, 438 (1942).
73. G. Racah. Phys. Rev. *63*, 367 (1943).
74. G. Racah. Phys. Rev. *76*, 1352 (1949).
75. G. Racah. "Group Theory and Spectroscopy." Princeton Lecture Notes, 1951.
76. G. T. Rado. Am. J. Phys. *30*, 716 (1962).
77. N. F. Ramsey. "Molecular Beams." Oxford University Press, Oxford, England, 1956.
78. L. M. Sachs. "A Theoretical Study of Simple Many-Electron Systems." Argonne National Laboratory, Report No. ANL-6310, May 1961.
79. P. G. H. Sandars and J. Beck. Proc. Roy. Soc. (London) *A289*, 97 (1965).
80. C. Schwartz. Phys. Rev. *97*, 380 (1955).
81. C. Schwartz. Phys. Rev. *105*, 173 (1957).
82. R. W. Terhune, J. Lambe, C. Kikuchi, and J. Baker. Phys. Rev. *123*, 1265 (1961).
83. C. H. Townes and A. L. Schawlow. "Microwave Spectroscopy." McGraw-Hill Book Company, Inc., New York, N.Y., 1955.
84. R. E. Trees. Phys. Rev. *92*, 308 (1953).
85. S. I. Weissman. J. Chem. Phys. *22*, 1378 (1954).
86. S. I. Weissman. J. Chem. Phys. *25*, 890 (1956).
87. E. P. Wigner. "Group Theory and Its Applications to the Quantum Mechanics of Atomic Spectra." Academic Press, Inc., New York, N.Y., 1959.

Chapter 12 ELECTRIC FIELD AND ITS GRADIENT

INTRODUCTION

Associated with the electronic density distribution in a system there are three quantities, the knowledge of which provides an insight into the problems of molecular structure and an understanding of the nature of bonding. One is referring here to the electric potential, electric field, and electric field gradient due to the electrons in the system.

Theoretically, the three quantities are of interest; experimentally, it is the electric field gradient that gives rise to weak interactions. Microwave and radio frequency spectroscopy provide data about the coupling constant eqQ, which is the product of a nuclear property, the electrostatic nuclear quadrupole moment eQ of a nucleus, and an electronic property, the electrostatic field gradient q, existing at the same nucleus, due to the electrons in the system. If the quadrupole moment of an atom is known, it is possible to determine, from the measured quadrupole coupling constants of molecules in which it appears, the field gradient itself. From this value one can derive an understanding of the nature of the bonds involving the atom under consideration and of the overall electronic density in the system. On the other hand, a knowledge of the state function of a system permits the *a priori* calculation of the field gradient at any nucleus and, therefore, affords the possibility of estimating the nuclear quadrupole moment from experimental data, thus providing a test for the accuracy of state functions.

ELECTRIC POTENTIAL AND FIELD

The electric potential V seen by a nucleus a in a system is equal to the sum of the potentials due to the other nuclei, $\sum_{b} (Z_b/R_{ab})$, plus the potentials due to all the electrons in the system, $-\sum_{i} (1/r_{ia})$.

The latter term appears in the electronic hamiltonian operator of the system under consideration and plays, therefore, an important role in the determination of state functions. The former is introduced in the evaluation of the total molecular energy E_M.

The expectation values of the operator $(1/r_i)$ are related, furthermore, to the nuclear magnetic shielding, discussed in Chapter 10.

In an electronic system at equilibrium the electric field seen by a nucleus must be equal to zero. Properly consistent functions should lead to vanishing electric fields at the nuclei for the predicted equilibrium distances R at which the energy reaches its minimum, that is, satisfying the Hellman-Feynman [27] theorem which is the equivalent of the condition $\langle (\partial \Psi / \partial R) H \Psi \rangle = 0$, more difficult to apply in practice, as indicated by Das and Bersohn [19]. Some attempts have been made to use the Hellman-Feynman theorem in connection with the determination of state functions. Efforts in this direction have been made by Bader and coworkers [1–7].

NUCLEAR QUADRUPOLE INTERACTION

As mentioned in Chapter 11, one of the terms of the hfs interaction arises from the interaction between the electrostatic quadrupole moment of a nucleus and the electrostatic field gradient at that nucleus, due to the electrons of the system.

The hamiltonian operator for the quadrupole interaction between the electronic and nuclear charge distributions, as given by Kopfermann [39], is

$$\mathcal{H}_Q = -\iint \rho_k (r_k^2 / r_e^3) \rho_e (\tfrac{3}{2} \cos^2 \Theta - \tfrac{1}{2}) \, d\tau_k \, d\tau_e, \qquad (12\text{-}1)$$

where Θ is the angle between the radius vector $\boldsymbol{r}_k$ of an element $\rho_k \, d\tau_k$ of nuclear charge and the electronic radius vector $\boldsymbol{r}_e$; ρ_k and ρ_e are the nuclear and electronic charge densities, respectively. The angular factor can be written as the scalar product of two tensor operators,* one electronic $(\mathbf{C}_e^{(2)})$ and the other nuclear $(\mathbf{C}_k^{(2)})$,

$$\tfrac{1}{2}(3 \cos^2 \Theta - 1) = \mathbf{C}_e^{(2)} \cdot \mathbf{C}_k^{(2)}.$$

The matrix element of $\mathcal{H}_Q$ for the state defined by a total angular momentum quantum number F, resulting from the coupling of the electronic state αSLJ and the nuclear state βI (α and β representing any additional quantum numbers needed for the description of the states), can then be written

$$(\alpha SLJ, \beta I, F | \mathcal{H}_Q | \alpha SLJ, \beta I, F)$$
$$= -(\alpha SLJ, \beta I, F | r_e^{-3} r_k^2 (\mathbf{C}_e^{(2)} \cdot \mathbf{C}_k^{(2)}) | \alpha SLJ, \beta I, F). \quad (12\text{-}2)$$

---

* The subscripts do not denote components of the tensors. They are used to distinguish the electronic and nuclear tensors.

The tensor operator is the product of two tensor operators acting in two different spaces, and therefore

$$(\alpha SLJ, \beta I, F| \mathcal{H}_Q |\alpha SLJ, \beta I, F) = -(-1)^{J+I-F} W(JIJI; F2)$$
$$\times (\alpha SLJ| \, |r_e^{-3}\mathbf{C}_e^{(2)}| \, |\alpha SLJ)(\beta I| \, |r_k^2\mathbf{C}_k^{(2)}| \, |\beta I)$$

where $W(JIJI; F2)$ is a Racah coefficient, related to Wigner's [68, 69] 6-j symbol, according to Edmonds [24], by

$$W(j_1 j_2 l_2 l_1; j_3 l_3) = (-1)^{j_1+j_2+l_1+l_2} \begin{Bmatrix} j_1 & j_2 & j_3 \\ l_1 & l_2 & l_3 \end{Bmatrix};$$

the double barred matrices are defined by Racah [54].

The quadrupole moment Q of a nucleus is defined by Casimir [16] as the matrix element of $[r_k^2(3\cos^2\theta_k - 1)]$ over the space of nuclear coordinates, evaluated for the largest component of I in the z-direction,

$$Q = (\beta II| \, r_k^2(3\cos^2\theta_k - 1) \, |\beta II),$$

which can be rewritten as

$$Q = 2(-1)^{2I} V(II2; -II0)(\beta I| \, |r_k^2\mathbf{C}_k^{(2)}| \, |\beta I),$$

where $V(j_1 j_2 j_3; m_1 m_2 m_3)$ is related to the 3-j symbol of Wigner [69],

$$V(j_1 j_2 j_3; m_1 m_2 m_3) = (-1)^{j_2+j_3-j_1} \begin{pmatrix} j_1 & j_2 & j_3 \\ m_1 & m_2 & m_3 \end{pmatrix}.$$

The particular values of $V(II2; -II0)$ and $W(JIJI; F2)$ are

$$V(II2; -II0) = (-1)^{2I}[I(2I-1)]^{\frac{1}{2}}[(I+1)(2I+1)(2I+3)]^{-\frac{1}{2}},$$

$$W(JIJI; F2) = 3(-1)^{I+J+F}[K(K+1) - (\tfrac{4}{3})I(I+1)J(J+1)]$$
$$\times [I(I+1)(2I-1)(2I+1)(2I+3)]^{-\frac{1}{2}}[(2J-2)!/(2J+3)!]^{\frac{1}{2}},$$

and therefore

$$Q = 2[I(2I-1)]^{\frac{1}{2}}[(I+1)(2I+1)(2I+3)]^{-\frac{1}{2}}(\beta I| \, |r_k^2\mathbf{C}_k^{(2)}| \, |\beta I),$$

$$(\alpha SLJ, \beta I, F| \mathcal{H}_Q |\alpha SLJ, \beta I, F)$$
$$= \{-3Q\langle r_e^{-3}\rangle[2I(2I-1)]^{-1}[(2J-2)!/(2J+3)!]^{\frac{1}{2}} (\alpha SLJ| \, |\mathbf{C}_e^{(2)}| \, |\alpha SLJ)\}$$
$$\times [K(K+1) - (\tfrac{4}{3})I(I+1)J(J+1)], \quad (12\text{-}3a)$$

which can be rewritten as

$$(\alpha SLJ, \beta I, F| \mathcal{H}_Q |\alpha SLJ, \beta I, F) = B(J)[K(K+1) - (\tfrac{4}{3})I(I+1)J(J+1)]$$
$$(12\text{-}3b)$$

The term $B(J)K(K+1)$ corresponds to the hfs splitting, and the remainder is included in the fs term, W_J, of Eq. (11-1a).

Taking into account that $\mathbf{C}_e^{(2)}$ commutes with $\mathbf{S}$, one obtains

$$(\alpha SLJ| \, |\mathbf{C}_e^{(2)}| \, |\alpha SLJ) = (-1)^{S-L-J}(2J+1)W(LJLJ; S2)(\alpha SL| \, |\mathbf{C}_e^{(2)}| \, |\alpha SL),$$

where

$$W(LJLJ; S2) = (-1)^{2(L+J)}[3X(X+1) - 4J(J+1)L(L+1)]$$
$$[J(J+1)(2J-1)(2J+1)(2J+3)]^{-\frac{1}{2}}[(2L-2)!/(2L+3)!]^{\frac{1}{2}},$$

with

$$X = J(J+1) + L(L+1) - S(S+1).$$

Therefore the hfs constant $B(J)$ can be expressed (taking into account the symmetry properties of the W function of Racah [54]; see the original work of Trees [66] for a detailed discussion) as

$$B(J) = -3Q\langle r_e^{-3}\rangle[2I(2I-1)]^{-1}(2J+1)[(2J-2)!/(2J+3)!] [3X(X-1)$$
$$- 4J(J+1)L(L+1)][L(L+1)(2L-1)(2L+1)(2L+3)]^{-\frac{1}{2}}$$
$$\times (\alpha SL| |\mathbf{C}_e^{(2)}| |\alpha SL). \quad (12\text{-}4)$$

One can now define two parameters, g and γ, the latter independent of J, by the relations

$$g = 1 + [J(J+1) + S(S+1) - L(L+1)][2J(J+1)]^{-1}, \quad (12\text{-}5a)$$

$$\gamma = -[(2L-1)(2L+3)]^{\frac{1}{2}}[L(L+1)(2L+1)]^{-\frac{1}{2}}(\alpha SL| |\sum_i (b_i)_i \mathbf{C}_i^{(2)}| |\alpha SL). \quad (12\text{-}5b)$$

The summation in Eq. (12-5b) extends over all the electrons of the system and the one-electron operator b_l is given by

$$b_l = (\tfrac{3}{16})Q\langle r_e^{-3}\rangle[I(2I-1)]^{-1}. \quad (12\text{-}5c)$$

After substitution one finally obtains

$$B(J) = 8\gamma\{3(2-g)[J(J+1)(2-g) - \tfrac{1}{2}] - L(L+1)\}$$
$$\times [(2J-1)(2J+3)(2L-1)(2L+3)]^{-1}, \quad J \neq 0, \tfrac{1}{2}, \quad (12\text{-}6)$$

which expresses the dependence of B on J.

Closed shells do not give any contribution to $B(J)$. Therefore, for one-electron configurations (that is, electronic configurations with only one electron outside of closed shells) and using

$$(l| |\mathbf{C}^{(2)}| |l) = -[l(l+1)(2l+1)]^{\frac{1}{2}}[(2l-1)(2l+3)]^{-\frac{1}{2}}, \quad (12\text{-}7)$$

one arrives at the result

$$B(J) = b_l[j(j+1)]^{-1}, \quad j \neq \tfrac{1}{2}, \quad (12\text{-}8)$$

l being the azimuthal quantum number of the shell under consideration.

Equations (12-6) and (12-8) have been given by Trees [66]. On the other hand, Casimir [16] has derived the expression

$$B(J) = -(\tfrac{3}{8})Q\left\langle \left\{ \sum_i [(3\cos^2\theta_i - 1)r_i^{-3}] \right\}_{M_J=J} \right\rangle [I(2I-1)J(2J-1)]^{-1}, \quad (12\text{-}9)$$

which agrees with the expression given by Racah [52, 53].

For a term consisting of equivalent electrons one can write, using the notation of Racah [54],

$$\sum_i (b_l)_i \mathbf{C}_i^{(2)} = b_l(l| \ |\mathbf{C}^{(2)}| \ |l) \mathbf{U}^{(2)}; \tag{12-10}$$

and therefore γ can be rewritten as

$$\gamma = -b_l[(2L-1)(2L+3)]^{\frac{1}{2}}[L(L+1)(2L+1)]^{-\frac{1}{2}}(l| \ |\mathbf{C}^{(2)}| \ |l)$$
$$\times (l^n \alpha SL| \ |\mathbf{U}^{(2)}| \ |l^n \alpha SL). \tag{12-11}$$

The double-barred submatrices of the double-tensor operator $\mathbf{U}^{(2)}$ are given by Racah [55] for configurations of equivalent p and d electrons and the double-barred matrix of $\mathbf{C}^{(2)}$ is defined by Eq. (12-7).

The electric field gradient q at the nucleus in an atom is defined by

$$q = \partial^2 V/\partial z^2 = \langle \Phi| \sum_i [(3\cos^2\theta_i - 1)r_i^{-3}] |\Phi\rangle, \tag{12-12}$$

which can be rewritten as

$$q = \langle \sum_i (3\cos^2\theta_i - 1)\rangle\langle r^{-3}\rangle, \tag{12-13}$$

when the total function can be factored into the product of a radial function and an angular function. The summations in Eqs. (12-12) and (12-13) extend, in principle, over all the electrons in the system. However closed shells and half-filled shells do not contribute, because of the spherical symmetry, to the field gradient at the nucleus; therefore the summations extend over only the open-shell electrons (with the exception of half-filled shells).

Inspection of Eq. (12-9) shows that, as mentioned above, the hfs term $B(J)K(K+1)$ corresponds to the nuclear quadrupole interaction. The product qQ, which appears within $B(J)$, is known as the quadrupole coupling constant. The value of this constant can be calculated, using the empirical value of Q, if the quantities $\langle r^{-3}\rangle$ and $\langle \sum_i (3\cos^2\theta_i - 1)\rangle$ are known.

The angular factor can be determined by equating Eqs. (12-6) and (12-9), after substitution of γ and b_l, given by Eqs. (12-11) and (12-5c) respectively, into Eq. (12-6). The values obtained for various terms arising from configurations with equivalent p and d electrons are given in Table 12-1.

The values of $\langle r^{-3}\rangle$ can be calculated if the corresponding electronic state functions are known. Alternatively, they may be estimated from the experimental values for the hfs and fs parameters to be discussed below and in Chapter 14.

In a molecular system, similarly, the evaluation of the interaction between the electric quadrupole moment of a given nucleus and the electronic charge distribution requires the knowledge of the electric field gradient tensor at that nucleus.

Table 12-1 Values of the Angular Factor $\left\langle \sum_i (3\cos^2\theta_i - 1) \right\rangle_{JJ}$, Determined by Malli and Fraga [45] for Atomic Configurations[a]

CONFIGURATION	STATE		CONFIGURATION	STATE	
p^1	^2P	$-2/5$	d^2	^3F	$-2/7$
p^2	^3P	$2/5$	d^3	^4F	$2/7$
	^1D	$-4/5$	d^4	^5D	$4/7$
p^4	^3P	$-2/5$	d^6	^5D	$-4/7$
	^1D	$4/5$	d^7	^4F	$-2/7$
p^5	^2P	$2/5$	d^8	^3F	$2/7$
d^1	^2D	$-4/7$	d^9	^2D	$4/7$

a. These values correspond to the largest possible value of J, that is, $J = L + S$.

For a nucleus a, this quantity may be expressed by

$$q_a = \sum_{b \neq a} Z_b (3\boldsymbol{R}_{ba}\boldsymbol{R}_{ba} - R_{ba}^2 \mathbf{1})/R_{ba}^5 - \langle \Phi | \sum_i (3\boldsymbol{r}_{ia}\boldsymbol{r}_{ia} - r_{ia} \mathbf{1})/r_{ia}^5 | \Phi \rangle$$

where Z_b represents the nuclear charge of nucleus b, $\boldsymbol{R}_{ba}$ is a vector from nucleus a to nucleus b, $\boldsymbol{r}_{ia}$ is a vector from nucleus a to electron i, and $\mathbf{1}$ denotes the unit dyadic. For specific details on an actual calculation, the reader is referred to the formulation for closed shells of Kern and Karplus [36].

In the case of linear molecules only one principal component of this tensor has to be considered. The quadrupole coupling constant, which is measured experimentally, involves that component.

NUCLEAR QUADRUPOLE MOMENTS

A discussion on nuclear quadrupole moments is outside the scope of this text. It is worth while, however, to point out certain details regarding the possibility of their calculation, either from experimental values alone or by semiempirical considerations.

The formulations of Burns [15], Wybourne [71], and Woodgate [70] exemplify some of the approaches to this problem, but only a simplified description is presented here.

One can observe that both hfs parameters, $A(J)$ and $B(J)$, corresponding to the magnetic dipole-dipole (see Chapter 11) and the nuclear quadrupole interaction, respectively, depend on the expectation value of the same operator, $\langle r^{-3} \rangle$.

Restricting the discussion to systems with a single electron outside of closed shells, the interaction parameters are defined, using the formulation of Casimir [16], by

$$A(J) = \mu_B \mu_N (\mu_I/I)[2l(l+1)/J(J+1)]\langle r^{-3} \rangle F, \qquad \text{(12-14a)}$$

$$B(J) = Q[2l/(2l+3)]\langle r^{-3} \rangle R, \qquad \text{(12-14b)}$$

where l is the azimuthal quantum number of the shell occupied by the single electron and where F and R are two small relativistic corrections. (See the original work of Casimir [16]. Tables of values for these and other relativistic corrections are given by Kopfermann [39].) The expectation value, $\langle r^{-3} \rangle$, is calculated, of course, over the function corresponding to the single electron.

Combining these two equations, one obtains for the electric nuclear quadrupole moment,

$$Q = \mu_B \mu_N (\mu_I/I)[(l+1)(2l+3)/J(J+1)][B(J)/A(J)](F/R). \quad (12\text{-}15)$$

Furthermore, Eq. (12-14a) leads, for different values of J, to the ratio

$$A(J)/A(J') = [J'(J'+1)/J(J+1)][F(J)/F(J')]. \quad (12\text{-}16)$$

For example, for a single electron in a p shell, Eqs. (12-15) and (12-16) become

$$Q = (\tfrac{8}{3})\mu_B \mu_N (\mu_I/I)[B(\tfrac{3}{2})/A(\tfrac{3}{2})](F/R),$$
$$A(\tfrac{1}{2})/A(\tfrac{3}{2}) = 5[F(\tfrac{1}{2})/F(\tfrac{3}{2})].$$

From the measured value of $[B(J)/A(J)]$ one can determine the value of the nuclear quadrupole moment Q. Davis, Feld, Zabel, and Zacharias [22] have found, however, that for Al, Ga, and In the experimental value of the ratio $A(J)/A(J')$ does not agree with the predicted value. The reason for the discrepancy may be found in the use of a single configuration function.

In order to overcome this difficulty, Fermi and Segre [25, 26] used a many-configuration function for calculations on Tl, and Koster [40] has carried out calculations on Ga and several other atoms with several electronic configurations.

One first determines the expression for $A(J)$, using a many-configuration function. By equating it to the corresponding experimental value of $A(J)$ one obtains an estimate of $\langle 1/r^3 \rangle$. Using this value in conjunction with the experimental value of $B(J)$ one can determine the nuclear quadrupole moment Q. One can omit the first part if a fairly accurate function is available, in which case it is possible to calculate *a priori* the value of $\langle 1/r^3 \rangle$. This approach has been tried by Nordsieck [49], Ishiguro [32, 33], and Newell [48], among others.

An alternate procedure is based on the determination of the field gradients from experimental data of the fine structure splittings, and this procedure is discussed in Chapter 14.

QUADRUPOLE COUPLING CONSTANTS AND FIELD GRADIENTS

Although it is not possible to review in detail all the work carried out in connection with the field gradient in both atoms and molecules, some points will be considered here.

Table 12-2 Field Gradients[a] (in au) for Ground States of Positive Ions, Neutral Atoms, and Negative Ions with Configurations p^n

CONFIGURATION	STATE	POSITIVE ION		NEUTRAL ATOM		NEGATIVE ION	
		System	q	System	q	System	q
$2p^1$	^2P	C+	0.88836	B	0.31009		
$2p^2$	^3P	N+	1.53264	C	0.67646	B−	0.18643
$2p^4$	^3P	F+	3.54416	O	1.98966	N−	0.94699
$2p^5$	^2P	Ne+	4.99729	F	3.01871	O−	1.62204
$3p^1$	^2P	Si+	1.06097	Al	0.43463		
$3p^2$	^3P	P+	1.61902	Si	0.82104	Al−	0.26632
$3p^4$	^3P	Cl+	3.11835	S	1.93455	P−	1.03969
$3p^5$	^2P	A+	4.11448	Cl	2.70626	S−	1.61086
$4p^1$	^2P	Ge+	2.44020	Ga	1.15646		
$4p^2$	^3P	As+	3.35681	Ge	1.91877	Ga−	0.69468
$4p^4$	^3P	Br+	5.49232	Se	3.70925	As−	2.18578
$4p^5$	^2P	Kr+	6.77161	Br	4.79137	Se−	3.09438

a. Absolute values determined by Malli and Fraga [45] from analytical HF functions determined by Clementi [17] and Malli [44].

The determination of field gradients has been attempted both from semiempirical data and on a theoretical basis. Townes and Dailey [65] have evaluated q for Cs, I, F, and Na in various electronic states. Barnes and Smith [8] determined q, from experimental data of the fine structure splittings, for a large number of atomic systems in different states of excitation and ionization, discussing also the polarization effects, as first proposed by Sternheimer [61–63]. Bersohn [9] has determined the field gradients of some ions in ionic crystals and has discussed the situation in these systems as compared with the molecular crystals.

Platas [50] calculated q for several ions of the five-electron isoelectronic series $1s^2 2s^2 2p$, ^2P from analytical open-shell functions, and Goodings [30]

Table 12-3 Field Gradients[a] (in au) for Some States of Positive Ions, Neutral Atoms, and Negative Ions with Configurations d^n

CONFIGURATION	STATE	POSITIVE ION		NEUTRAL ATOM		NEGATIVE ION	
		System	q	System	q	System	q
$3d^1$	^2D			Sc	0.81590		
$3d^2$	^3F	Sc+	0.33975	Ti	0.57564	Sc−	0.30245
$3d^3$	^4F	Ti+	0.49053	V	0.75578	Ti−	0.46388
$3d^4$	^5D	V+	1.31306	Cr	1.91236	V−	1.27140
$3d^6$	^5D	Mn+	2.10187	Fe	2.84453	Mn−	2.06524
$3d^7$	^4F	Fe+	1.28276	Co	1.69326	Fe−	1.26507
$3d^8$	^3F	Co+	1.54244	Ni	1.99499	Co−	1.52700
$3d^9$	^2D	Ni+	3.66946	Cu	4.65774		

a. Absolute values determined by Malli and Fraga [45] from HF functions determined by Clementi [17].

Table 12-4 Field Gradients[a] (in au) for Excited States ^1D of Positive Ions, Neutral Atoms, and Negative Ions with Configurations p^n

CONFIGURATION	POSITIVE ION		NEUTRAL ATOM		NEGATIVE ION	
	System	q	System	q	System	q
$2p^2$	N^+	2.99478	C	1.30524	B^-	0.33628
$2p^4$	F^+	7.03216	O	3.93956	N^-	1.86546
$3p^2$	P^+	3.18968	Si	1.59940	Al^-	0.48266
$3p^4$	Cl^+	6.24194	S	3.86342	P^-	2.06330
$4p^2$	As^+	6.61492	Ge	3.72602	Ga^-	1.25384
$4p^4$	Br^+	10.99658	Se	7.39978	As^-	4.33436

a. Absolute values determined by Malli and Fraga [45] from HF functions determined by Clementi [17] and Malli [44].

and Bessis, Lefebvre-Brion, and Moser [11] have also determined some field gradients. Tables 12-2 to 12-4 collect the values, determined by Malli and Fraga [45] from analytical HF functions, for a series of positive ions, neutral atoms, and negative ions, involving p^n and d^n configurations. The corresponding quadrupole coupling constants are presented in Table 12-5. The conclusion to be drawn from these results is that HF functions constitute an adequate basis for the determination of these quantities.

The situation in connection with molecules, at least for *a priori* calculations, is somewhat more complicated.

In ionic species (e.g., alkali halides) it is possible to estimate the coupling constant* by means of a simple model based on ions with polarizable charge distributions, as proposed by Burns [14] and Das and Karplus [20, 21]. In other systems the situation is not as simple, but some attempts have been made through the evaluation of the field gradients. The efforts in this direction depend, of course, on the availability of accurate functions.

Townes and Dailey [65] have given, for atoms with unfilled p shells (e.g., halogens) a semiquantitative interpretation of the experimental measurements in terms of the properties of localized bonds. Sternheimer and Foley [64] studied the polarization effects on Li_2, which was also treated in complete detail by Ishiguro, Kayama, Kotani, and Mizuno [34] who calculated the value of the field gradient for a series of functions and studied also the effect of the Sternheimer correction. This work provides a good description of the dependence of the field gradient on the state function used, a point that has been treated also by other authors. This dependence can be observed in Table 12-6, which also shows the order of magnitude of the polarization correction. Foley, Sternheimer, and Tycko [29] have confirmed the existence of an induced quadrupole moment in polar molecules.

---

* In some systems (such as those with symmetry around an axis) the scalar eqQ describes adequately the quadrupole coupling; in other systems, with more complex symmetry, a tensor representation is needed.

Table 12-5 Quadrupole Coupling Constants[a] (in Mc) for Some States of Positive Ions, Neutral Atoms, and Negative Ions

Z	SYSTEM	M	I	POSITIVE ION		NEUTRAL ATOM		NEGATIVE ION	
				State	eqQ	State	eqQ	State	eqQ
5	B	10	3			^2P	4.4	^3P	2.6
		11	3/2			^2P	2.6	^3P	1.6
7	N	14	1	^3P	7.2			^3P	4.5
8	O	17	5/2			^3P	2.3	^2P	1.9
13	Al	27	5/2			^2P	15.8	^3P	9.7
16	S	33	3/2			^3P	22.7	^2P	18.9
		35	3/2			^3P	15.9	^2P	13.3
17	Cl	35	3/2	^3P	57.3	^2P	49.7		
		36	2	^3P	12.6	^2P	10.9		
		37	3/2	^3P	45.1	^2P	39.2		
23	V	51	7/2	^5D	61.7	^4F	35.5	^5D	59.7
27	Co	59	7/2	^3F	181.2	^4F	198.9	^3F	179.4
31	Ga	69	3/2			^2P	51.4	^3P	30.9
		71	3/2			^2P	39.7	^3P	23.8
32	Ge	73	9/2	^2P	120.4	^3P	94.7		
33	As	75	3/2	^3P	236.6			^3P	154.1
34	Se	75	5/2			^3P	958.7	^2P	799.8
		79	7/2			^3P	610.1	^2P	509.0
35	Br	79	3/2	^3P	425.9	^2P	371.5		
		81	3/2	^3P	361.3	^2P	315.2		
36	Kr	83	9/2	^2P	238.7				

a. Values determined by Malli and Fraga [45], using for the nuclear quadrupole moments the values quoted by Ramsey [56]. Experimental values of eqQ, quoted also by Ramsey [56] are: B(11), 2.695; Al(27), 18.76; Cl(35), 54.873; Cl(37), 43.255; Ga(69), 62.52249; Ga(71), 39.39903; Br(79), 384.878; and Br(81), 321.516 Mc.

Table 12-6 Calculated[a] Field Gradient in Li_2 from Different Functions

FUNCTION[b]	ELECTRONIC FIELD GRADIENT	TOTAL FIELD GRADIENT	POLARIZATION CORRECTION	CORRECTED FIELD GRADIENT
Single configuration[c]	0.00444	0.00332	(−0.00088)	(0.00244)
Pure Heitler-London[c]	0.00428	0.00349	(−0.00088)	(0.00261)
Many configuration[c]	0.00636	0.00140	(−0.00015)	(0.00125)
Pure Heitler-London[d]	0.00422	0.00354	−0.00088	0.00026
Variational[d]	0.00867	−0.00091	−0.00015	−0.00106

a. Values in parentheses have been estimated.
b. For more details, see the original references, especially the work of Ishiguro, Kayama, Kotani, and Mizuno [34], from which this table has been taken.
c. Values determined by Ishiguro, Kayama, Kotani, and Mizuno [34].
d. Values determined by Sternheimer and Foley [64].

One of the cases that has received more attention is that of the quadrupole interaction of deuteron. In this case the difficulty is that the charge distribution in the neighborhood of the deuteron has practically spherical symmetry, in which respect it differs essentially from the halogens. On the other hand, the remainder of the electronic density distribution will be almost neutralized by the effect of the nuclear charges (unlike the ionic systems), and therefore the quadrupole coupling interaction is determined by a very small difference between the contributions of the electrons and of the nuclei. The experimental values of some deuteron coupling constants in various molecules, presented in Table 12-7, confirm the preceding considerations.

Das and Bersohn [19] undertook detailed calculations on HD, discussing the relation between the charge densities at the nucleus and the field and field gradient, together with the connection between the field gradient and the bonding and its relation to the anisotropy of the magnetic shielding.

Bersohn [10] has carried out calculations on the neutral molecular fragment D—C≡ and on H_2O. A study of the influence of the ionicity of the C—H bond (in terms of hybridization) on the field gradient leads to the conclusion that the electric field gradient increases in magnitude whenever charge is removed from the hydrogen atom, where it does not contribute appreciably, to the carbon atom, where it can make a rather important contribution. In general, it can be seen that simple functions lead to too large values of the field gradient and that the more contracted the functions are, the greater the field gradients are. The use of optimized orbital exponents may improve the results, as already shown by Das and Bersohn [19] for H_2 and Richardson [58].

Table 12-7 Experimental Values of Deuteron Quadrupole Coupling Constants[a] (kc)

BOND	SYSTEM	eqQ	REFERENCE
H—H	HD	227 ± 4	Ramsey [56]
	D_2	225	Ramsey [56]
H—C	DCN	$\pm 290 \pm 120$	White [67]
	DDCCCl	175 ± 20	White [67]
H—N	ND_3	200 ± 20	Herrmann [31]
H—O	HDO	305	Posener [51]
	$Li_2SO_4 \cdot D_2O$	$\pm 237 \pm 10$	Ketudat and Pound [37]
	$K \cdot D_2PO_4$	± 119	Bjorkstam and Uehling [12]
	$K_2HgCl_4 \cdot D_2O$	123 ± 2	Ketudat *et al.*[b]
	$Na_2S_2O_6 \cdot 2D_2O$	131 ± 2	Ketudat *et al.*[b]

a. Presented in part by Bersohn [10]. Other values are given by Kern and Karplus [36]. Additional values in single crystal anthracene have been determined by Ellis and Bjorkstam. (Private communication of Prof. J. L. Bjorkstam.)

b. Private communication of Prof. S. Ketudat. These values have been determined by Ketudat, Weiss, and Berthold, at room temperature (23°C). Two additional values, 244 ± 3 and 236 ± 3 kc/sec, determined for $Na_2S_2O_6 \cdot 2D_2O$ at $-30°C$, are attributed to the two different OD bonds.

Table 12-8 Deuteron Field Gradient (au) and Quadrupole Coupling Constant (kc) for LiD, Evaluated from Different Functions[a]

LCAO FUNCTION[b]	ELECTRONIC FIELD GRADIENT	TOTAL FIELD GRADIENT[c]	eqQ
Slater	−0.1506	0.0683	45.3
Best atom	−0.1495	0.0694	46.1
Best limited	−0.1615	0.0574	38.1
Experimental	−0.1737	0.0452	30 ± 3

a. Calculated by Kolker and Karplus [38] from the LCAO MO SCF functions of Ransil [57].
  b. The designations in this column indicate the type of orbital exponents in the STO.
  c. The values in this column include the nuclear field gradient (0.2189 au).

Kolker and Karplus [38] have evaluated the field gradient and quadrupole coupling constant for LiD and DF, giving a detailed discussion in terms of molecular orbitals. Table 12-8 shows the influence of the type of function on the value of the field gradient. It can also be observed that, as mentioned before, the total field gradient is given by the difference of two values that are not very different . Lowe and Flygare [43] have been able to give a similar discussion for formaldehyde.

The main point to be drawn from the field gradient problem is the possibility of obtaining information on the electronic structure. Townes and Dailey [65] used the data from nuclear quadrupole moments to determine the electronic structure of molecules.

This possibility arises from the fact that the field gradient is a quantity that depends only on the function of the ground state of the system under consideration. Therefore, the measurement (or evaluation) of field gradients provides an insight into the electronic distribution. Flygare [28] points out that it is possible to estimate the direction of the valence orbitals associated with a bond from the determination of the orientation of the field gradient tensor. (Flygare [28] presents an example for interpretation of microwave spectra and for determination of the quadrupole coupling constants [and field gradients] and the position of the tensor axes with respect to the bonds.) Comparison of the direction of the valence orbitals with the geometrical characteristics of the system provides information about the bond.

Unfortunately, the quadrupole coupling constant is very sensitive to the choice of function being used. Among other factors, the work of Kern and Karplus [36] seems to indicate that the basis functions may play a decisive role, especially those that contribute most to the valence shell. For this reason the quadrupole coupling constant could be used as an additional criterion on which to judge the accuracy of a function.

Many molecular functions have been tested in this way and there exists, therefore, a wealth of theoretical calculations, which cannot be discussed here. (Besides the treatments already mentioned, the reader is referred to the work of Das [18], Dousmanis [23], Kahalas and Nesbet [35],

Lefebvre-Brion, Moser, Nesbet, and Yamazaki [41], Lin, Hijikata, and Sakamoto [42], Mannari and Arai [46], Rosenblum and Nethercot [59], and Scrocco [60].) A final comment must be made, however: The excellent agreement with the experimental results indicates, as has already been mentioned, that HF functions are appropriate for the calculation of quadrupole coupling constants in general and of one-electron properties in particular. This is a fact, of course, pointed out by Brillouin [13] and Möller and Plesset [47] long before HF functions were available even for diatomic molecules.

REFERENCES

1. R. F. W. Bader. Can. J. Chem. *41*, 2303 (1963).
2. R. F. W. Bader. J. Am. Chem. Soc. *86*, 5070 (1964).
3. R. F. W. Bader and W. H. Henneker. J. Am. Chem. Soc. *87*, 3063 (1965).
4. R. F. W. Bader and G. A. Jones. Can. J. Chem. *39*, 1253 (1961).
5. R. F. W. Bader and G. A. Jones. Can. J. Chem. *41*, 586 (1963).
6. R. F. W. Bader and G. A. Jones. Can. J. Chem. *41*, 2251 (1963).
7. R. F. W. Bader and G. A. Jones. J. Chem. Phys. *38*, 2791 (1963).
8. R. G. Barnes and W. V. Smith. Phys. Rev. *93*, 95 (1954).
9. R. Bersohn. J. Chem. Phys. *29*, 326 (1958).
10. R. Bersohn. J. Chem. Phys. *32*, 85 (1960).
11. N. Bessis, H. Lefebvre-Brion, and C. M. Moser. Phys. Rev. *128*, 213 (1962).
12. J. L. Bjorkstam and E. A. Uehling. Phys. Rev. *114*, 961 (1959).
13. L. Brillouin. Actualités Sci. Ind. Secs. 71, 159, 160 (1933–1934).
14. G. Burns. Phys. Rev. *115*, 357 (1960).
15. G. Burns. Phys. Rev. *124*, 524 (1961).
16. H. B. G. Casimir. "On the Interaction between Atomic Nuclei and Electrons." W. H. Freeman & Co., San Francisco, Calif., 1963.
17. E. Clementi. "Tables of Atomic Functions." IBM Corporation, San José, California, 1965.
18. T. P. Das. J. Chem. Phys. *27*, 1 (1957).
19. T. P. Das and R. Bersohn. Phys. Rev. *115*, 897 (1959).
20. T. P. Das and M. Karplus. J. Chem. Phys. *30*, 848 (1959).
21. T. P. Das and M. Karplus. J. Chem. Phys. *42*, 2885 (1965).
22. L. Davis, B. T. Feld, C. W. Zabel, and J. R. Zacharias. Phys. Rev. *76*, 1076 (1949).
23. G. C. Dousmanis. Phys. Rev. *97*, 967 (1955).
24. A. R. Edmonds. "Angular Momentum in Quantum Mechanics." Princeton University Press, Princeton, N.J., 1957.
25. E. Fermi and E. Segre. Rendiconti della R. Academia d'Italia *4*, 18 (1933-XI).
26. E. Fermi and E. Segre. Z. Physik *82*, 729 (1933).
27. R. P. Feynman. Phys. Rev. *56*, 340 (1939).
28. W. H. Flygare. J. Chem. Phys. *41*, 206 (1964).
29. H. M. Foley, R. M. Sternheimer, and D. Tycko. Phys. Rev. *93*, 734 (1954).
30. D. A. Goodings. Phys. Rev. *123*, 1706 (1961).
31. G. Herrmann. J. Chem. Phys. *29*, 875 (1958).
32. E. Ishiguro. J. Phys. Soc. Japan *3*, 129 (1948).
33. E. Ishiguro. J. Phys. Soc. Japan *3*, 133 (1948).
34. E. Ishiguro, K. Kayama, M. Kotani, and Y. Mizuno. J. Phys. Soc. Japan *12*, 1355 (1957).
35. S. L. Kahalas and R. K. Nesbet. Phys. Letters *6*, 549 (1961).
36. C. W. Kern and M. Karplus. J. Chem. Phys. *42*, 1062 (1965).
37. S. Ketudat and R. V. Pound. J. Chem. Phys. *26*, 708 (1957).
38. H. J. Kolker and M. Karplus. J. Chem. Phys. *36*, 960 (1962).
39. H. Kopfermann. "Nuclear Moments." Academic Press, Inc., New York, N.Y., 1958.
40. G. F. Koster. Phys. Rev. *86*, 148 (1952).

41. H. Lefebvre-Brion, C. Moser, R. K. Nesbet, and M. Yamazaki. J. Chem. Phys. *38*, 2311 (1963).
42. C. C. Lin, K. Hijikata, and M. Sakamoto. J. Chem. Phys. *33*, 878 (1960).
43. J. T. Lowe and W. H. Flygare. J. Chem. Phys. *41*, 2153 (1964).
44. G. Malli. Can. J. Phys. *42*, 3121 (1966).
45. G. Malli and S. Fraga. Theoret. Chim. Acta (Berlin) *6*, 54 (1966).
46. J. Mannari and T. Arai. J. Chem. Phys. *28*, 28 (1958).
47. C. Möller and M. S. Plesset. Phys. Rev. *46*, 618 (1934).
48. G. F. Newell. Phys. Rev. *78*, 711 (1950).
49. A. Nordsieck. Phys. Rev. *58*, 310 (1940).
50. O. R. Platas. J. Chem. Phys. *37*, 2755 (1962).
51. D. W. Posener. Australian J. Phys. *10*, 276 (1957).
52. G. Racah. Z. Physik *71*, 431 (1931).
53. G. Racah. Nuovo Cimento *8*, 178 (1931).
54. G. Racah. Phys. Rev. *62*, 438 (1942).
55. G. Racah. Phys. Rev. *63*, 367 (1963).
56. N. F. Ramsey. "Molecular Beams," Oxford University Press, Oxford, England, 1956.
57. B. J. Ransil. Rev. Mod. Phys. *32*, 245 (1960).
58. J. W. Richardson. Rev. Mod. Phys. *32*, 461 (1960).
59. B. Rosenblum and A. H. Nethercot, Jr. J. Chem. Phys. *27*, 828 (1957).
60. E. Scrocco. Advan. Chem. Phys. *5*, 319 (1963).
61. R. M. Sternheimer. Phys. Rev. *80*, 102 (1950).
62. R. M. Sternheimer. Phys. Rev. *84*, 244 (1951).
63. R. M. Sternheimer. Phys. Rev. *95*, 736 (1954).
64. R. M. Sternheimer and H. M. Foley. Phys. Rev. *92*, 1460 (1953).
65. C. H. Townes and B. P. Dailey. J. Chem. Phys. *17*, 782 (1949).
66. R. E. Trees. Phys. Rev. *92*, 308 (1953).
67. R. L. White. J. Chem. Phys. *23*, 253 (1955).
68. E. P. Wigner. "On Matrices Which Reduce Kronecker Products of Representations of S. R. Groups." Unpublished (1951).
69. E. P. Wigner. "Group Theory and Its Applications to the Quantum Mechanics of Atomic Spectra." Academic Press, Inc., New York, N.Y., 1959.
70. G. K. Woodgate. Proc. Roy. Soc. (London) *A293*, 117 (1966).
71. B. G. Wybourne. J. Chem. Phys. *37*, 1807 (1962).

Chapter 13   ORBIT-ORBIT INTERACTIONS

INTRODUCTION

Inspection of the term values of MnII and FeIII led Trees [14, 15] to point out that the agreement between the theoretical formulas and the experimental data in the $3d^54s$ configuration improves by adding a correction term proportional to $L(L + 1)$, L being the resultant orbital angular momentum quantum number, and that the correction represents a polarization energy. Subsequently, Racah [11] found that the correction term of the form $aL(L + 1)$ is also important in many other spectra of the iron group and that the values of a obtained by the least squares analysis from different spectra are consistent. In addition Racah pointed out that the term values in complex atoms are displaced by $aL(L + 1)$ if one admits the existence of an additional interaction, $2a\boldsymbol{l}_i \cdot \boldsymbol{l}_j$, between each pair of electrons, where $\boldsymbol{l}_i$ denotes the orbital angular momentum vector of the i-th electron.

However, Yanagawa [18] has pointed out that the correction should be of opposite sign and smaller magnitude than the one mentioned above. This correction can be accounted for by the orbit-orbit interaction present in the Breit hamiltonian. For two electrons this interaction has the form (see also Darwin [4])

$$\mathcal{H}_{oo} = \frac{\alpha^2}{2} \{ r_{ij}^{-1}(\boldsymbol{\nabla}_i \cdot \boldsymbol{\nabla}_j) + \tfrac{1}{2} r_{ij}^{-3}[(\boldsymbol{r}_{ij} \cdot \boldsymbol{\nabla}_i)(\boldsymbol{r}_{ij} \cdot \boldsymbol{\nabla}_j) + (\boldsymbol{r}_{ji} \cdot \boldsymbol{\nabla}_j)(\boldsymbol{r}_{ji} \cdot \boldsymbol{\nabla}_i)]$$
$$+ \tfrac{1}{2} r_{ij}^{-3}(\boldsymbol{r}_{ij} \cdot (\boldsymbol{\nabla}_i - \boldsymbol{\nabla}_j)) \}, \quad (13\text{-}1)$$

where $\boldsymbol{r}_{ij} = \boldsymbol{r}_i - \boldsymbol{r}_j$ is the position vector (with modulus r_{ij}) from electron j to electron i; $\boldsymbol{\nabla}_i$ is the gradient operator for the i-th electron and α is the fine structure constant.

ORBIT-ORBIT INTERACTION IN ATOMS

Yanagawa [18] has expressed this interaction in terms of tensor operators. For a configuration l^n of n equivalent electrons (where l denotes the orbital angular momentum quantum number of the shell under consideration) one has

$$\mathscr{H}_{oo} = -\sum_{k \geq 1} 2(2l + 3)^{-1}(2l + 1)(2l + 1 - k)(2l + 2 + k)$$

$$\times (l \| \mathbf{C}^{(k)} \| l + 1)^2 M^{(k-1)} \sum_{i < j} \mathbf{u}^{(k)}(i) \cdot \mathbf{u}^{(k)}(j)), \qquad (13\text{-}2)$$

where $\mathbf{u}^{(k)}$ is a unit tensor operator* of rank k; $\mathbf{C}^{(k)}$ is a spherical harmonic operator of order k, both defined by Racah [10]; and $M^{(k-1)}$ are the radial integrals, defined by Marvin [9],

$$M^{(k-1)} = (\alpha^2/4) \iint_{r_j > r_i} R_{nl}^2(r_i)(r_i^{k-1}/r_j^{k+2})R_{nl}^2(r_j)\, dr_i\, dr_j,$$

where R_{nl} denotes a radial function. In Eq. (13-2) k is restricted to the first l terms of odd character, and i and j extend over the electrons in the shell.

The derivation of Eq. (13-2), starting from Eq. (13-1), is given below. One expresses first $1/r_{ij}$ in terms of the tensor operators $\mathbf{C}^{(k)}(i)$ and $\mathbf{C}^{(k)}(j)$,

$$1/r_{ij} = \sum_{k=0}^{\infty} (-1)^k a_k (2k + 1)^{\frac{1}{2}} (\mathbf{C}^{(k)}(i)\mathbf{C}^{(k)}(j))^{(0)}, \qquad (13\text{-}2a)$$

with $a_k = r_<^k / r_>^{k+1}$. Then the first term in Eq. (13-1) can be rewritten as

$$(1/r_{ij})(\mathbf{\nabla}_i \cdot \mathbf{\nabla}_j) = \sum_{k=0}^{\infty} (-1)^{k-1} a_k \sum_\lambda (2\lambda + 1)^{\frac{1}{2}} (\mathbf{U}^{(\lambda)}(i)\mathbf{U}^{(\lambda)}(j))^{(0)},$$

where the summation should be taken over $\lambda = k, k \pm 1$. $\mathbf{U}^{(\lambda)}$ is an irreducible tensor operator of rank λ obtained from two tensor operators $\mathbf{C}^{(k)}$ and $\mathbf{\nabla}$; its components are given by

$$U_\rho^{(\lambda)} = [\mathbf{C}^{(k)}\mathbf{\nabla}]_\rho^{(\lambda)} = \sum_{q,\sigma} C_q^{(k)} \nabla_\sigma (kq1\sigma \,|\, k1\lambda\rho), \qquad (13\text{-}2b)$$

where $(kq1\sigma \,|\, k1\lambda\rho)$ is a Clebsch-Gordan coefficient.

The term within square brackets in Eq. (13-1) can also be rewritten in tensor operator form. Taking into account that $\mathbf{r}_{ij} = \mathbf{r}_i - \mathbf{r}_j$, one first writes this term as

$$r_{ij}^{-3}[(\mathbf{r}_{ij} \cdot \mathbf{\nabla}_i)(\mathbf{r}_i \cdot \mathbf{\nabla}_j) - (\mathbf{r}_{ij} \cdot \mathbf{\nabla}_i)(\mathbf{r}_j \cdot \mathbf{\nabla}_j) + (\mathbf{r}_{ji} \cdot \mathbf{\nabla}_j)(\mathbf{r}_j \cdot \mathbf{\nabla}_i)$$

$$- (\mathbf{r}_{ji} \cdot \mathbf{\nabla}_j)(\mathbf{r}_i \cdot \mathbf{\nabla}_i)]. \qquad (13\text{-}2c)$$

---

* The notation $\mathbf{u}^{(k)}(i)$ indicates that this tensor operator refers to the i-th electron.

For the terms in this equation Yanagawa [18] has formulated the relations

$$r_{ij}^{-3}(\mathbf{r}_{ij} \cdot \boldsymbol{\nabla}_i) = \sum_{k,K,\sigma} (-1)^{\sigma+k+1}[(2K+1)/3]^{\frac{1}{2}}(k010 \mid k1K0)(\mathscr{D}_i^{k[K]}a_k)$$
$$\times [\mathbf{C}^{(k)}(i)\mathbf{C}^{(k)}(j)]_\sigma^{(1)}\nabla_{i,-\sigma}, \quad (13\text{-}2\text{d})$$

with $K = k \pm 1$,

$$(\mathbf{r}_i \cdot \boldsymbol{\nabla}_j) = \sum_q (-1)^q r_i C_q^{(1)}(i)\nabla_{j,-q}, \quad (13\text{-}2\text{e})$$

and

$$\nabla_{i,-\sigma}(\mathbf{r}_i \cdot \boldsymbol{\nabla}_j) = \sum_{q,L,M} (-1)^q(1q1-\sigma \mid 11LM)(1010 \mid 11L0)C_M^{(L)}(i)$$
$$\times (\mathscr{D}_i^{1[L]}r_i)\nabla_{j,-q} + \sum_q (-1)^q r_i C_q^{(1)}(i)\nabla_{i,-\sigma}\nabla_{j,-q}, \quad (13\text{-}2\text{f})$$

with $L = 0, 2$. $\mathscr{D}^{k[k+1]}$ and $\mathscr{D}^{k[k-1]}$ are defined by

$$\mathscr{D}^{k[k+1]} = \partial/\partial r - k/r,$$
$$\mathscr{D}^{k[k-1]} = \partial/\partial r + (k+1)/r.$$

They operate only on the radial function of the electron denoted by the subscript of $\mathscr{D}$. Therefore one can write

$$r_{ij}^{-3}(\mathbf{r}_{ij} \cdot \boldsymbol{\nabla}_i)(\mathbf{r}_i \cdot \boldsymbol{\nabla}_j) = \sum_{k,\lambda} (-1)^{k+\lambda+1}(2\lambda+1)^{\frac{1}{2}}[\mathbf{T}^{(\lambda)}(i)\mathbf{U}^{(\lambda)}(j)]^{(0)}$$
$$+ \sum_{k,\eta} (-1)^\eta(2\eta+1)^{\frac{1}{2}}[\mathbf{V}^{(\eta)}(i)\mathbf{U}^{(\eta)}(j)]^{(0)} \quad (13\text{-}2\text{g})$$

and

$$-r_{ij}^3(\mathbf{r}_{ij} \cdot \boldsymbol{\nabla}_i)(\mathbf{r}_j \cdot \boldsymbol{\nabla}_j) = \sum_k \sqrt{3}\,[\mathbf{X}^{(k)}(i)\mathbf{Y}^{(k)}(j)]^{(0)}, \quad (13\text{-}2\text{h})$$

where the various tensor operators are defined by

$$\mathbf{T}^{(\lambda)}(i) = \sum_{K,L} (-1)^K[(2K+1)(2L+1)]^{\frac{1}{2}}(k010 \mid k1K0)(1010 \mid 11L0)$$
$$\times W(KkL1; 1\lambda)(\mathscr{D}_i^{k[K]}a_k)(\mathscr{D}_i^{1[L]}r_i)[\mathbf{C}^{(K)}(i)\mathbf{C}^{(L)}(i)]^{(\lambda)}, \quad (13\text{-}2\text{i})$$

$$\mathbf{V}^{(\eta)}(i) = \sum_{K,\lambda} [(2K+1)(2\lambda+1)]^{\frac{1}{2}}(k010 \mid k1K0)\,W(Kk\lambda\eta; 11)$$
$$\times (\mathscr{D}_i^{k[K]}a_k)r_i[[\mathbf{C}^{(K)}(i)\mathbf{C}^{(1)}(i)]^{(\lambda)}\mathbf{V}_i]^{(\eta)}, \quad (13\text{-}2\text{j})$$

$$\mathbf{X}^{(k)}(i) = \sum_K (-1)^{1-K}(2K+1)^{\frac{1}{2}}(k010 \mid k1K0)(\mathscr{D}_i^{k[K]}a_k)[\mathbf{C}^{(K)}(i)\mathbf{V}_i]^{(k)},$$
$$(13\text{-}2\text{k})$$

and

$$\mathbf{Y}^{(k)}(i) = \sum_\lambda (-1)^{k+1-\lambda}[(2\lambda+1)/3(2k+1)]^{\frac{1}{2}}r_i$$
$$\times [[\mathbf{C}^{(k)}(i)\mathbf{C}^{(1)}(i)]^{(\lambda)}\mathbf{V}_i]^{(k)}; \quad (13\text{-}2\text{l})$$

in Eqs. (13-2i) through (13-2l), $W(abcd; ef)$ is a Racah coefficient.

The last term in Eq. (13-l) can be expressed in terms of the scalar products of $\mathbf{X}^{(k)}$ and $\mathbf{C}^{(k)}$,

$$r_{ij}^{-3}((\mathbf{r}_{ij} \cdot (\boldsymbol{\nabla}_i - \boldsymbol{\nabla}_j)) = \sum_k \{[\mathbf{X}^{(k)}(i)\mathbf{C}^{(k)}(j)]^{(0)} + [\mathbf{X}^{(k)}(j)\mathbf{C}^{(k)}(i)]^{(0)}\}.$$

For a configuration of n equivalent electrons, combining the results given above for the various terms of Eq. (13-1) and with the help of Racah tensor operator methods, one can now obtain Eq. (13-2) after some laborious algebraic manipulations.

Thus the matrix elements of the hamiltonian operator $\mathcal{H}_{oo}$ may be written in the τSL scheme (where τ is a set of additional quantum numbers necessary to specify the SL state) as

$$(l^n \tau SL| \mathcal{H}_{oo} |l^n \tau' S' L') = - \delta(\tau, \tau') \delta(S, S') \delta(L, L') \sum_{k \geq 1} [2/(2l + 3)]$$
$$\times (2l + 1)(2l - k + 1)(2l + k + 2)(l| |\mathbf{C}^{(k)}| |l + 1)^2$$
$$\times M^{(k-1)} \sum_{i<j} (\mathbf{u}^{(k)}(i) \cdot \mathbf{u}^{(k)}(j)). \quad (13-3)$$

Taking into account the orbit-orbit interactions, Yanagawa [18] has calculated the term values for the $4p^2$ and $5p^4$ configurations of GeI, AsII, and TeI, with satisfactory agreement between the theoretical and experimental values for GeI and AsII.

The summation over i and j in Eq. (13-3) can be simplified by making use of the properties of Casimir operators of the $(2l + 1)$-dimensional rotational groups which are used to classify the states for an l^n configuration. (Judd [7] presents a detailed discussion on Casimir operators.) Wybourne [17] derives in this way the relations

$$(p^n \tau SL| \mathcal{H}_{oo} |p^n \tau SL) = -2M^{(0)}[L(L + 1) - 2n], \quad (13-4)$$
$$(d^n \tau SL| \mathcal{H}_{oo} |d^n \tau SL) = \alpha L(L + 1) + \beta G(R_5) + n\delta, \quad (13-5)$$

where

$$\alpha = -2(M^{(0)} - \tfrac{6}{49}M^{(2)}), \qquad \beta = -\tfrac{360}{49}M^{(2)}, \qquad \delta = 24(M^{(0)} + \tfrac{1}{7}M^{(2)}),$$

and

$$(f^n \tau SL| \mathcal{H}_{oo} |f^n \tau SL) = \alpha' L(L + 1) + \beta' G(G_2) + \gamma' G(R_7) + n\delta', \quad (13-6)$$

with

$$\alpha' = -2(M^{(0)} - \tfrac{5}{121}M^{(4)}), \qquad \gamma' = -40M^{(2)},$$
$$\beta' = 32(M^{(2)} - \tfrac{35}{121}M^{(4)}), \qquad \delta' = 8(3M^{(0)} + M^{(2)} + \tfrac{5}{11}M^{(4)}).$$

In Eqs. (13-5) and (13-6), $G(R_5)$ and $G(R_7)$ are the eigenvalues of the Casimir operators of the rotational groups R_5 and R_7 used to classify the states of the configurations d^n and f^n, respectively; $G(G_2)$ is the eigenvalue of the Casimir operator of the group G_2, which serves to classify the state of the configuration f^n. The calculation of these eigenvalues is discussed by Rajnak and Wybourne [12].

Wybourne [17] has computed the values of the parameters α', β', and γ' for PIV $4f^2$ assuming that the radial function of the orbital $4f$ is hydrogenic; the values are $\alpha' = -10.4$ cm^{-1}, $\beta' = +147.2$ cm^{-1}, and $\gamma' = -89.9$ cm^{-1}, which gives an idea of the magnitude of these parameters.

Table 13-1 Orbit-orbit Interaction (in cm^{-1}) for Various States of Positive Ions, Neutral Atoms, and Negative Ions with p^n Configurations[a]

CONFIGURATION	STATE	POSITIVE ION System		NEUTRAL ATOM System		NEGATIVE ION System	
$2p^2$	^3P	N^+	3.95	C	1.61	B^-	0.35
$2p^3$	^4S	O^+	18.55	N	8.84	C^-	3.03
$2p^4$	^3P	F^+	26.35	O	13.82	N^-	5.78
$2p^5$	^2P	Ne^+	48.78	F	27.66	O^-	13.32
$3p^2$	^3P	P^+	0.75	Si	0.35	Al^-	0.09
$3p^3$	^4S	S^+	3.32	P	1.76	Si^-	0.70
$3p^4$	^3P	Cl^+	4.56	S	2.61	P^-	1.24
$3p^5$	^2P	A^+	8.15	Cl	4.99	S^-	2.66
$4p^2$	^3P	As^+	0.52	Ge	0.28	Ga^-	0.09
$4p^3$	^4S	Se^+	2.09	As	1.26	Ge^-	0.59
$4p^4$	^3P	Br^+	2.64	Se	1.69	As^-	0.91
$4p^5$	^2P	Kr^+	4.40	Br	2.95	Se^-	1.76

a. Evaluated by Fraga and Malli [5] from analytical HF functions.

More accurate values can be determined, however, from HF functions, in which case one can evaluate the radial integrals $M^{(k)}$. In particular, Froese [6] has calculated these integrals for neutral atoms up to radon, from numerical HF functions. Fraga and Malli [5] have also evaluated these integrals for positive ions, neutral atoms, and negative ions up to krypton, using analytical HF functions (see Chapter 15). The corresponding orbit-orbit interactions for p^n configurations, as defined by Eq. (13-4), are presented in Table 13-1. Table 13-2 collects the parameters α, β, and δ for d^n configurations. Regarding the latter it must be pointed out that Fraga and Malli [5] evaluated δ using, instead of the definition of Wybourne [17], the expression

$$\delta = 12(M^{(0)} + \tfrac{2}{7}M^{(2)}),$$

as given by Jucys and coworkers [2, 3, 13].

INTERACTIONS IN MOLECULES

The evaluation of the orbit-orbit interaction in molecules follows similar techniques to those used for atoms.

Christoffersen [1], using the Wang function for H_2, found that the orbit-orbit interaction in this molecule is 0.939 cm^{-1} for $R = 1.40$ bohr. However, Ufford and Callen [16] have shown that the orbit-orbit interaction is very sensitive to the correlation of the interacting electrons and that introduction of a reasonable correlation in the function may well affect its magnitude. Kolos and Wolniewicz [8], using their best correlated function, found that the orbit-orbit energy correction was -0.36 cm^{-1} at $R = 2.0$ bohr.

Table 13-2 Parameters α, β, and δ (in cm^{-1}) for the Orbit-orbit Interaction for Various States of Positive Ions, Neutral Atoms, and Negative Ions with d^n Configurations[a]

CONFIGURATION	STATE	POSITIVE ION				NEUTRAL ATOM				NEGATIVE ION			
		System	α	β	δ	System	α	β	δ	System	α	β	δ
$3d^1$	^2D	Sc$^+$	−0.63	−1.33	4.67	Sc	−0.82	−1.74	6.07	Sc$^-$	−0.52	−1.08	3.82
$3d^2$	^3F	Ti$^+$	−0.95	−2.01	7.04	Ti	−1.20	−2.57	8.92	Ti$^-$	−0.86	−1.82	6.38
$3d^3$	^4F	V$^+$	−1.30	−2.76	9.65	V	−1.60	−3.43	11.91	V$^-$	−1.23	−2.60	9.10
$3d^4$	^5D	Cr$^+$	−1.72	−3.66	12.76	Cr	−2.05	−4.40	15.23	Cr$^-$	−1.65	−3.50	12.24
$3d^5$	^6S	Mn$^+$	−2.12	−4.52	15.76	Mn	−2.57	−5.51	19.08	Mn$^-$	−2.06	−4.37	15.24
$3d^6$	^5D	Fe$^+$	−2.61	−5.55	19.33	Fe	−3.06	−6.57	22.74	Fe$^-$	−2.54	−5.40	18.82
$3d^7$	^4F	Co$^+$	−3.15	−6.71	23.38	Co	−3.64	−7.81	27.06	Co$^-$	−3.08	−6.55	22.83
$3d^8$	^3F	Ni$^+$	−3.76	−8.01	27.88	Ni	−4.29	−9.21	31.89				
$3d^9$	^2D					Cu	−5.01	−10.76	37.25				

a. Evaluated by Fraga and Malli [5] from analytical HF functions.

REFERENCES

1. R. E. Christoffersen. J. Chem. Phys. *42*, 2616 (1965).
2. R. Dagis, Z. Rudzikas, R. Katiljus, and A. Jucys. Liet. Fiz. Rinkinys *3*, 365 (1963).
3. R. Dagis, Z. Rudzikas, J. Vizbaraite, and A. Jucys. Liet. Fiz. Rinkinys *3*, 159 (1963).
4. C. G. Darwin. Phil. Mag. *39*, 537 (1920).
5. S. Fraga and G. Malli. J. Chem. Phys. *46*, 4754 (1967).
6. C. Froese. "Hartree-Fock Parameters for the Atoms Helium to Radon." Department of Mathematics, University of British Columbia, Vancouver, B.C., Canada, March 1966.
7. B. R. Judd. "Operator Techniques in Atomic Spectroscopy." McGraw-Hill Book Company, Inc., New York, N.Y., 1963.
8. W. Kolos and L. Wolniewicz. J. Chem. Phys. *41*, 3663 (1964).
9. H. H. Marvin. Phys. Rev. *71*, 102 (1947).
10. G. Racah. Phys. Rev. *63*, 367 (1943).
11. G. Racah. Phys. Rev. *85*, 381 (1952).
12. K. Rajnak and B. G. Wybourne. Phys. Rev. *132*, 280 (1963).
13. Z. Rudzikas, J. Vizbaraite, and A. Jucys. Liet Fiz. Rinkinys *5*, 315 (1965).
14. R. E. Trees. Phys. Rev. *83*, 756 (1951).
15. R. E. Trees. Phys. Rev. *84*, 1089 (1951).
16. C. W. Ufford and H. B. Callen. Phys. Rev. *110*, 1352 (1958).
17. B. G. Wybourne. J. Chem. Phys. *40*, 1457 (1964).
18. S. Yanagawa. J. Phys. Soc. Japan *10*, 1029 (1955).

Chapter 14   SPIN-ORBIT COUPLING

SPIN-OWN ORBIT INTERACTION IN ATOMS

The spin-orbit interaction hamiltonian operator for one-electron atomic systems (with a central field potential) is

$$\mathscr{H}_{so} = \frac{\alpha^2}{2}\,(r^{-1}\,\partial V(r)/dr)\,(\mathbf{l}\cdot\mathbf{s}) = \xi(r)(\mathbf{l}\cdot\mathbf{s});\qquad (14\text{-}1)$$

$V(r)$ is the coulombic potential due to the nucleus, α is the fine structure constant, and $\mathbf{s}$ and $\mathbf{l}$ are the electron spin and orbital angular momentum vector operators, respectively.

Taking into account that

$$2(\mathbf{s}\cdot\mathbf{l}) = (\mathbf{s}+\mathbf{l})^2 - \mathbf{l}^2 - \mathbf{s}^2 = \mathbf{j}^2 - \mathbf{l}^2 - \mathbf{s}^2,$$

one can see that the matrix element of $(\mathbf{s}\cdot\mathbf{l})$ in the slj scheme is

$$\Gamma = (slj|\,\mathbf{s}\cdot\mathbf{l}\,|slj) = \tfrac{1}{2}[j(j+1) - l(l+1) - s(s+1)];\quad (14\text{-}2a)$$

therefore the spin-orbit interaction can be expressed as $\zeta\Gamma$, ζ being the one-electron spin-orbit coupling parameter

$$\zeta = \langle\xi(r)\rangle = \frac{\alpha^2}{2}\,\langle r^{-1}(\partial V/\partial r)\rangle.\qquad (14\text{-}2b)$$

The expectation value in this equation is defined by

$$\langle r^{-1}\,\partial V(r)/\partial r\rangle = \int_0^\infty P_{nl}^2(r)\, r^{-1}\,(\partial V(r)/\partial r)\,dr;$$

the radial function $P_{nl}(r)$ of the electron in the shell characterized by the quantum numbers n and l is normalized to unity,

$$\int_0^\infty P_{nl}^2(r)\,dr = 1.$$

The characteristics of one-electron atomic spectra are reasonably well explained by this formulation. The spin-orbit interaction splits all configurations (except those involving s electrons) into two levels, corresponding to $j = l + \frac{1}{2}$ and $j = l - \frac{1}{2}$; each of these levels, of course, is $(2j + 1)$-fold degenerate. The two levels into which each configuration splits are said to constitute a doublet; the doublet separation δ is

$$\delta = E(j) - E(j-1) = \zeta j = \zeta(l + \tfrac{1}{2}), \tag{14-3}$$

where $E(j)$ and $E(j-1)$ represent the energies corresponding to $j = l + \frac{1}{2}$ and $j = l - \frac{1}{2}$, respectively.

The generalization of Eq. (14-1) to many-electron atomic systems is taken to be

$$\mathscr{H}_{so} = \sum_i \xi(r_i)(\mathbf{s}_i \cdot \mathbf{l}_i), \tag{14-4}$$

$\xi(r_i)$ being now a function of the potential due to the nucleus and all the other electrons. In this connection, when we use the Hartree-Fock description of an atomic system, the question arises as to which $V(r)$ should be used. It is not clear whether one should take the simple Hartree field for $V(r)$ or whether the exchange terms should also be included in $V(r)$, in which case one must define $\partial V(r)/\partial r$ for a nonlocal potential.

In Eq. (14-4) the two-particle magnetic interactions have been neglected. If one further assumes that the Russell-Saunders coupling holds, such that S and L are good quantum numbers, then the splitting of a multiplet (due to the spin-orbit coupling) obeys the Landé rule, and the spin-orbit coupling parameter can be obtained by calculating the matrix elements of $\mathscr{H}_{so}$ in the scheme LSJ.

The evaluation of these matrix elements has been carried out by Trees [35], using Racah tensor algebra for many-electron atomic systems. The spin-orbit interaction displaces a level by an amount $\zeta(l^n \gamma SL)\Gamma$, Γ being defined by an expression analogous to Eq. (14-2a),

$$\Gamma = \tfrac{1}{2}\{J(J + 1) - L(L + 1) - S(S + 1)\}.$$

The spin-orbit coupling constant $\zeta(l^n \gamma SL)$ is defined* by

$$\zeta(l^n \gamma SL) = \eta(l^n \gamma SL)\zeta_{nl}, \tag{14-5}$$

with

$$\eta(l^n \gamma SL) = [l(l+1)(2l+1)/S(S+1)(2S+1)L(L+1)(2L+1)]^{\frac{1}{2}}$$
$$\times (l^n \gamma SL|\,|\mathbf{V}^{(11)}|\,|l^n \gamma SL) \tag{14-6}$$

and

$$\zeta_{nl} = \frac{\alpha^2}{2}\int_0^\infty P_{nl}^2(r)\, r^{-1}\,(\partial V/\partial r)\, dr$$
$$= \frac{\alpha^2}{2}\int_0^\infty r^{-3}\, Z_{eff}\,(r)\, P_{nl}^2(r)\, dr.$$

---

* The subscript n in ζ_{nl} denotes the principal quantum number of the shell under consideration and not the number of equivalent electrons in the configuration l^n.

The symbol $Z_{eff}(r)$ denotes the charge contained within a sphere of radius r; that is, it represents the effective nuclear charge for the electron in the l shell, usually being written as

$$Z_{eff}(r) = Z - q(r),$$

where Z is the nuclear charge and $q(r)$ denotes the number of electrons within the sphere of radius r, excluding the eléctron under consideration. Therefore one can write

$$\zeta_{nl} = \frac{\alpha^2}{2}\left[Z\int_0^\infty r^{-3} P_{nl}^2 \, dr - \int_0^\infty r^{-3}q(r) \, P_{nl}^2 \, dr \right]$$

$$= \frac{\alpha^2}{2}\left[Z\langle r^{-3}\rangle - \sum_i \int_0^\infty r^{-3} P_{nl}^2(r) \int_0^r P_{n_i l_i}^2(r_i) \, dr_i \, dr \right], \qquad (14\text{-}7)$$

and the evaluation of ζ_{nl} reduces to determining $\langle r^{-3}\rangle$ and the summation term.

The determination of ζ_{nl}, through the use of Eq. (14-7), requires the knowledge of the corresponding state function (see below). On the other hand, for the determination of η, the reduced matrix elements of the double tensor operator $V^{(11)}$ are needed. These matrix elements are given by Racah [29, 30] for configurations of equivalent p and d electrons. Table 14-1 presents the values of η for atomic configurations of p and d electrons.

The determination of the spin-orbit coupling constant for configurations of equivalent f electrons requires a more elaborate formulation. The derivation for the term of highest multiplicity (from Elliott, Judd, and Runciman [13]) considered here, is completely general and applies also to equivalent p and d electrons.

Table 14-1 Values of $\eta(l^n\gamma SL)$ for Various Atomic Configurations[a]

CONFIGURATION	STATE	η	CONFIGURATION	STATE	η
p^1	^2P	1	d^3	^4F	1/3
p^2	^3P	1/2		^2G	3/10
d^1	^2D	1		^2H	1/5
d^2	^3P	1/2	d^4	^3_2P	1/6
	^3F	1/2		^3_4P	1/3
d^3	^2P	2/3		^3D	$-1/12$
	^4P	1/3		^5D	1/4
	^2_1D	1/2		^3_2F	1/6
	^2_3D	$-1/6$		^3_4F	$-1/12$
	^2F	$-1/6$		^3G	3/20
				^3H	1/10

a. Values determined by Malli and Fraga [25]. For more than half-filled shells, the sign of the values in the table must be changed. The left subscript used for some states is the seniority number, defined by Racah [30] to distinguish states with the same value of S and L.

The matrix elements of the spin-orbit interaction operator $\zeta_{nl} \sum_i (\mathbf{s}_i \cdot \mathbf{l}_i)$ between two states Ψ_{JM} and Ψ'_{JM} of a configuration l^n of equivalent electrons is

$$(\Psi_{JM} | \zeta_{nl} \sum_i (\mathbf{s}_i \cdot \mathbf{l}_i) | \Psi'_{JM}) = -n\zeta_{nl} [\tfrac{3}{2} l(l+1)(2L+1)(2L'+1)$$

$$\times (2S+1)(2S'+1)]^{\frac{1}{2}} W(JLS'1; SL') \sum_{\bar{\Psi}} (\bar{\Psi} | \}\Psi)(\bar{\Psi} | \}\Psi'') W(\bar{S}S\tfrac{1}{2}1; \tfrac{1}{2}S')$$

$$\times W(\bar{L}Ll1; lL'), \quad (14\text{-}8)$$

where W is a Racah function, and the symbol Ψ is used to denote the set of all the quantum numbers necessary to specify a state, $\bar{\Psi}$ representing the parent state. The symbols $(\bar{\Psi} | \}\Psi')$ are an abbreviation for the coefficient, of fractional parentage (CFP) introduced by Racah [31]. The summation in Eq. (14-7) takes place over the $\bar{\Psi}$; that is, it represents a summation over all the parent states $\bar{\Psi}$.

The expression for the matrix element given by Eq. (14-8) is completely general. It can be simplified, though, if one considers the case of Russell-Saunders coupling. Taking into account that the spin quantum number $\bar{S}$ of the parent state can take only two possible values, $\bar{S} = S \pm \tfrac{1}{2}$, we can write the sum over $\bar{\Psi}$ as

$$W(S - \tfrac{1}{2}S\tfrac{1}{2}1; \tfrac{1}{2}S') \sum_{\bar{\Psi}} (\bar{\Psi} | \}\Psi)(\bar{\Psi} | \}\Psi'') W(\bar{L}Ll1; lL')$$

$$+ [W(S + \tfrac{1}{2}S\tfrac{1}{2}1; \tfrac{1}{2}S') - W(S - \tfrac{1}{2}S\tfrac{1}{2}1; \tfrac{1}{2}S')] \sum_{\bar{\Psi}}' (\bar{\Psi} | \}\Psi)(\bar{\Psi} | \}\Psi'')$$

$$\times W(\bar{L}Ll1; lL'), \quad (14\text{-}9)$$

where $\sum'$ is a restricted sum over those $\bar{\Psi}$ for which $\bar{S} = S + \tfrac{1}{2}$. Furthermore, if Ψ and Ψ'' have the same multiplicity, that is, $S = S'$, the sum in the first term of Eq. (14-9) may be carried out. Therefore, using the explicit form of the Racah functions one obtains, for $L = L'$ and L-S coupling,

$$(\Psi | \zeta_{nl} \sum_i (\mathbf{s}_i \cdot \mathbf{l}_i) | \Psi'') = \zeta_{nl} \{ [J(J+1) - L(L+1) - S(S+1)]/$$

$$\times 8SL(L+1) \} \{ [(2S+2-n)L(L+1) - (n-2S)l(l+1)] \delta(\Psi, \Psi'')$$

$$+ n[(2S+1)/(S+1)] \sum_{\bar{\Psi}}' (\bar{\Psi} | \}\Psi)(\bar{\Psi} | \}\Psi'')\bar{L}(\bar{L}+1) \}. \quad (14\text{-}10)$$

For the states of the maximum multiplicity, $S = n/2$ (in the first half-shell), there are no parents with $\bar{S} = S + \tfrac{1}{2}$. Therefore the summation in Eq. (14-10) vanishes, yielding finally

$$(\Psi | \zeta_{nl} \sum_i (\mathbf{s}_i \cdot \mathbf{l}_i) | \Psi'') = (\zeta_{nl}/2S)\Gamma. \quad (14\text{-}11)$$

The parameter $(\zeta_{nl}/2S)$ represents therefore the many-electron spin-orbit coupling constant for the term of highest multiplicity of the configuration l^n. It is identical, in such a case, to $\zeta(l^n \gamma SL)$, as seen by inspection of the corresponding values of η in Table 14-1. This parameter, usually represented by λ, must be taken with the opposite sign for more-than-half-filled shells.

Elliott, Judd, and Runciman [13] have evaluated λ for all the SL states of f^n configurations capable of spin-orbit splitting. The evaluation of the spin-orbit interaction matrices for f^n configurations is simplified by the use of relationships derived by Wybourne [37]. These matrix elements have been tabulated by Spedding [34] (for f^2 configurations), Judd and Loudon [20] (for f^3 configurations), Runciman and Crozier [33] (for f^4 configurations), and Wybourne [37] (for f^5, f^6, and f^7 configurations).

As mentioned before, the values of ζ_{nl} can be determined theoretically if the corresponding state function is known. Malli and Fraga [25] have evaluated ζ_{nl} for atoms up to Krypton, using analytical HF functions. The corresponding values of λ are collected in Tables 14-2 and 14-3, together

Table 14-2 Spin-orbit Coupling Constants λ (in cm^{-1}) for Various States of Positive Ions, Neutral Atoms, and Negative Ions with p^n Configurations[a] (in Absolute Value)

CONFIGURATION	STATE	POSITIVE ION		NEUTRAL ATOM		NEGATIVE ION	
		System	λ	System	λ	System	λ
$2p^1$	^2P	C^+	57.9 (42.7)	B	15.3 (10.7)		
$2p^2$	^3P	N^+	60.4 (41.1)	C	21.5 (13.6)	B^-	4.5
$2p^4$	^3P	F^+	187.8 (170.9)	O	90.7 (79.3)	N^-	36.2
$2p^5$	^2P	Ne^+	597.3 (521.3)	F	316.7 (269.3)	O^-	146.6
$3p^1$	^2P	Si^+	183.8 (191.3)	Al	68.4 (74.7)		
$3p^2$	^3P	P^+	152.1 (151.9)	Si	70.7 (73.1)	Al^-	20.8
$3p^4$	^3P	Cl^+	338.2 (348.5)	S	195.3 (198.4)	P^-	97.1
$3p^5$	^2P	A^+	952.4 (954.7)	Cl	585.9 (587.3)	S^-	324.6
$4p^1$	^2P	Ge^+	1050.0 (1178.1)	Ga	479.1 (550.8)		
$4p^2$	^3P	As^+	747.1 (739.5)	Ge	412.2 (426.4)	Ga^-	143.5
$4p^4$	^3P	Br^+	1303.7) (1569.5)	Se	852.4 (994.7)	As^-	485.4
$4p^5$	^2P	Kr^+	3314.5 (3580.7)	Br	2273.0 (2456.7)	Se^-	1421.1

a. The theoretical values have been calculated by Malli and Fraga [25] from analytical HF functions. The experimental values, given in parentheses, have been calculated from the data of Moore [28].

Table 14-3 Spin-orbit Coupling Constants λ (in cm^{-1}) for Various States of Positive Ions, Neutral Atoms, and Negative Ions with d^n Configurations[a] (in Absolute Value)

CONFIGURATION	STATE	POSITIVE ION		NEUTRAL ATOM		NEGATIVE ION	
		System	λ	System	λ	System	λ
$3d^1$	^2D			Sc	96.0 (67.3)		
$3d^2$	^3F	Sc$^+$	39.3 (26.1)	Ti	74.1 (54.2)	Sc$^-$	34.8
$3d^3$	^4F	Ti$^+$	41.5 (28.5)	V	70.1 (51.0)	Ti$^-$	39.2
$3d^4$	^5D	V$^+$	45.1 (32.6)	Cr	71.3 (53.1)	V$^-$	43.7
$3d^6$	^5D	Mn$^+$	83.0 (67.0)	Fe	120.2 (104.0)	Mn$^-$	81.5
$3d^7$	^4F	Fe$^+$	143.5 (123.9)	Co	201.7 (181.3)	Fe$^-$	141.5
$3d^8$	^3F	Co$^+$	273.9 (237.6)	Ni	375.7 (333.0)	Co$^-$	271.4
$3d^9$	^2D	Ni$^+$	687.6 (602.8)				

a. The theoretical values have been calculated by Malli and Fraga [25] from analytical HF functions. The experimental values, given in parentheses, have been calculated from the data of Moore [28].

with the experimental values.* Comparison of the theoretical and experimental values shows that HF functions give reasonably good estimates of ζ_{nl}.

A more refined treatment of the theory of spin-orbit coupling in atoms has been presented by Blume and Watson [2, 3] who have derived an expression for the spin-orbit coupling constant within the Hartree-Fock description of the atom by considering the two-body mutual spin-orbit interactions between electrons. The reader is referred for further details to their work, but a brief outline of the two-body interactions will be presented below.

The experimental data of the fs splitting δ, corresponding to the spin-orbit interaction, have been used (as pointed out in Chapter 12) for the evaluation of field gradients, if the effective nuclear charge involved in the definition of the expectation value $\langle r^{-1}(\partial V/\partial r)\rangle$ can be evaluated. According to Casimir [7], its value may be obtained from the relation

$$\delta = (dn^*/dn)[Z_0^2 Z_{eff}^2/(n^*)^3 l(l+1)]\alpha^2 RH,$$

* The experimentally observed splittings of a multiplet can be obtained from the data given by Moore [28]. The experimental values of λ are determined by the relation $\lambda J = E(J) - E(J-1)$.

where n^* is the corresponding effective principal quantum number for the shell with orbital angular momentum quantum number l. The values of n^* and (dn^*/dn) can be determined from the term energies. The parameter Z_0 takes the values $1, 2, \ldots$, etc. for neutral atoms, singly-charged positive ions, etc., respectively. H represents a small relativistic correction, introduced by Casimir [7]. (Tables of various relativistic corrections are given by Kopfermann [21].)

Taking into account the definition of field gradient q, one can write

$$\delta/Z_{eff} = [(2l + 1)(2l + 3)/4l]R\alpha^2 Hq,$$

which relates δ and q. This equation has been used by Barnes and Smith [1] for the semiempirical evaluation of field gradients and by Malli and Fraga [26] for the determination of the ratio δ/Z_i from the values of q evaluated from analytical HF functions.

SPIN-OTHER ORBIT COUPLING IN ATOMS

First of all, one has to consider the spin-other orbit coupling arising from the interaction of the spin angular momentum of one electron with the orbital motion of another electron.

For a system of N electrons the hamiltonian operator $\mathscr{H}_{soo}$ for the spin-other orbit coupling has been expressed by Marvin [27] as

$$\mathscr{H}_{soo} = \frac{\alpha^2}{2} \sum_{i \neq j} [\nabla_i(1/r_{ij}) \times \boldsymbol{p}_i] \cdot (\mathbf{s}_i + 2\mathbf{s}_j). \qquad (14\text{-}12)$$

This expression can be rewritten, as shown by Horie [19] and Blume and Watson [2], in terms of tensor operators. For a term of the summation in Eq. (14-12) one has

$$\frac{\alpha^2}{2} [\nabla_1(1/r_{12}) \times \boldsymbol{p}_1] \cdot (\mathbf{s}_1 + 2\mathbf{s}_2) = V_1 + V_2 + V_3, \qquad (14\text{-}13)$$

where*

$$V_1 = \frac{\alpha^2}{2} \sum_{kqq'\mu} (-1)^k \, 4\pi[k(k+1)/(2k+1)]^{\frac{1}{2}} \begin{pmatrix} k & k & 1 \\ q & q' & -\mu \end{pmatrix}$$
$$\times Y_{q'}^{(k)}(\boldsymbol{r}_1)Y_q^{(k)}(\boldsymbol{r}_2)(\mathbf{s}_1 + 2\mathbf{s}_2)_{-\mu} \, (r_<^{k-1}/r_>^{k+2})r_2 \, \partial/\partial r_1, \qquad (14\text{-}13a)$$

$$V_2 = \frac{\alpha^2}{2} \sum_{kqq'\mu} (-1)^k 4\pi(2k+1)^{\frac{1}{2}} \Big\{ -\begin{pmatrix} k-1 & k & 1 \\ q' & q & -\mu \end{pmatrix} T_q^{(k-11)k}(1)$$
$$\times Y_{q'}^{(k-1)}(\boldsymbol{r}_2)(r_2^{k-1}/r_1^{k+2})\varepsilon(r_1 - r_2) + \begin{pmatrix} k+1 & k & 1 \\ q' & q & -\mu \end{pmatrix} T_q^{(k+11)k}(1) \, Y_{q'}^{(k+1)}(\boldsymbol{r}_2)$$
$$\times (r_1^{k-1}/r_2^{k+2})\varepsilon(r_2 - r_1)\}(\mathbf{s}_1 + 2\mathbf{s}_2)_{-\mu}, \qquad (14\text{-}13b)$$

---

* The tensor operator $\mathbf{T}^{(k-11)K}$ is defined by its components,
$$T_Q^{(k-11)K} = \sum_{\sigma\nu} Y_\sigma^{(\lambda)} 1_\nu (\lambda 1\sigma\nu \mid \lambda 1KQ).$$

$$V_3 = \frac{\alpha^2}{2} \sum_{kqq'\mu} (-1)^k 4\pi (2k+1)^{-\frac{1}{2}} \begin{pmatrix} k & k & 1 \\ q' & q & -\mu \end{pmatrix} T_q^{(k1)k}(1) \; Y_{q'}^{(k)}(r_2)$$

$$(s_1 + 2s_2)_{-\mu} [k(r_2^k/r_1^{k+3})\varepsilon(r_1 - r_2) - (k+1)(r_1^{k-2}/r_2^{k+1})\varepsilon(r_2 - r_1)]. \quad (14\text{-}13c)$$

In these expressions $\varepsilon(x) = 1$ if $x > 0$, and $\varepsilon(x) = 0$ if $x < 0$; μ takes the values $\pm 1, 0$. The spherical components A_μ of a vector A are defined in terms of the ordinary cartesian components by $A_{\pm 1} = \mp (1\sqrt{2})(A_x \pm iA_y)$, $A_0 = A_z$.

The tensor operators $T^{(\lambda 1)\lambda'}$, with components $T_{\sigma'}^{(\lambda 1)\lambda'}$, are essentially the tensor products of the angular momentum vector operator 1 with a spherical harmonic $Y_\sigma^{(\lambda)}$. Their matrix elements are given by

$$(l'm'| \, T_{\sigma'}^{(\lambda 1)\lambda'} \, |lm) = (-1)^{\lambda + \lambda' + m'} (2l+1)[(2\lambda + 1)(2\lambda' + 1)l(l+1)$$

$$\times (2l'+1)/4\pi]^{\frac{1}{2}} \begin{pmatrix} l' & \lambda & l \\ 0 & 0 & 0 \end{pmatrix} \begin{pmatrix} l' & \lambda' & l \\ -m' & \sigma' & m \end{pmatrix} \begin{Bmatrix} l' & l & \lambda \\ 1 & \lambda & l \end{Bmatrix},$$

where the 3j- and 6j-symbols are those defined in Chapter 2.

The matrix elements of $\mathcal{H}_{soo}$ can then be calculated in a straightforward manner with the help of Racah algebra. In particular, for a configuration of equivalent electrons l^n it can be shown that only V_2 leads to nonvanishing matrix elements. In this connection it must be mentioned that the closed-shell core is neglected as it can be proved that the matrix elements of the core electrons among themselves vanish. There remain, however, the matrix elements between the outer electrons and the core electrons, but Elliott [12] and Horie [19] have shown that part of the latter interaction behaves like an effective one-particle spin-orbit potential.

For simplicity it is assumed that the open shell is less than half filled, although the results are also applicable to more than half-filled shells with a slight modification. For the ground state, given by Hund's rule, all the electrons in the open shell have the same spin (α or β), occupying one-electron functions with azimuthal quantum numbers $m_l = l, \, l - 1, \ldots,$ $l - n + 1$, where l is the orbital quantum number of the shell and n is the number of electrons. Such a state, for which

$$S = \frac{n}{2}, \quad L = l + (l-1) + \cdots + (l-n+1),$$

can be represented by a single Slater determinant.

Using the familiar rules of evaluating the diagonal matrix elements of two-particle operators between determinantal functions (see Condon and Shortley [10]), one can write

$$\langle \Phi | \, \mathcal{H}_{soo} \, | \Phi \rangle = \frac{\alpha^2}{2} \sum_{i,j} [(\psi_i \psi_j| \, V_2 \, |\psi_i \psi_j) - (\psi_i \psi_j| \, V_2 \, |\psi_j \psi_i)], \quad (14\text{-}14)$$

where the summations run over all the occupied spin-orbitals ψ in the state

$|SL, J = L + S, M = S + L\rangle$. The expressions for these matrix elements, given by Blume and Watson [2] and Horie [19], are extremely lengthy and complicated. Blume and Watson [3] have calculated the spin-orbit and spin—other orbit coupling constants for a large number of atomic systems using Hartree-Fock functions; and Blume, Freeman, and Watson [4] have extended the calculations to atoms with unfilled $4d$ or $4f$ shells. The results are encouraging for lighter atoms but rather poor for heavier atoms.

SPIN-ORBIT COUPLING IN MOLECULES

The treatment of the spin-orbit coupling in a molecule is of much greater complexity than in the case of an atomic system. The discussion* in this text is restricted, therefore, to diatomic molecules belonging to Hund's case b (see Herzberg [18]) following the formulation by Chiu [8].

In a molecule one has to consider, first of all, the motion of the electrons. In addition, the nuclei can vibrate around their equilibrium positions and the molecule as a whole is free to rotate in space. Associated with each of these motions there is a state function. One is forced to treat these motions approximately and, of course, independently; the justification for the latter can be found in the arguments of Born and Oppenheimer [5]. According to the Born-Oppenheimer approximation, the total state function $\Psi_{Nv\Lambda}$ of a rotational state of a diatomic molecule can be written as a product of a vibrational state function $\Psi_v(R)$ (v being the vibrational quantum number and R the internuclear distance), an electronic state function $\Psi_\Lambda(x_i, y_i, z_i; R)$, and a rotational state function $\Psi_{Nm\Lambda}(\alpha\beta\gamma)$. The quantum number N corresponds to the angular momentum N (a resultant of the angular momentum of nuclear rotation, O, and the electronic orbital angular momentum along the internuclear axis, Λ), which is a constant of the motion in pure Hund's case b; m and Λ are the quantum numbers for the components of the angular momentum N along the fixed z-axis and the moving figure axis, respectively. The Euler angles, α, β, and γ, describe the orientation of the figure axis with respect to a fixed coordinate system, and $x_i, y_i,$ and z_i are the coordinates of the i-th electron with respect to the moving system.

The rotational state function $\Psi_{Nm\Lambda}(\alpha\beta\gamma)$ can be written as

$$\Psi_{Nm\Lambda}(\alpha\beta\gamma) = [(2N + 1)/8\pi^2]^{\frac{1}{2}} D_{m\Lambda}^{(N)*}(\alpha\beta\gamma),$$

where $D_{m\Lambda}^{(N)}(\alpha\beta\gamma)$ is the rotational matrix within the approximation of the symmetric top. (See Edmonds [11] and Rose [32] for more details.) It is, also common to combine the rotational and the electronic state functions, writing

$$\Psi_{Nm\Lambda} = \Psi_\Lambda(x_i, y_i, z_i; \rho)\Psi_{Nm\Lambda}(\alpha\beta\gamma),$$

---

* It is assumed here that the reader is familiar with the coupling of various angular momenta in molecules. Van Vleck [36] has discussed it thoroughly.

which is useful in considering the behavior of $\Psi_{Nm\Lambda}$ under the various symmetry operations of the molecule.

The symmetry properties of the total state function $\Psi_{Nv\Lambda}$ are still preserved; for example, the symmetry of inversion of all the electronic coordinates (g or u), of inversion of the coordinates of all the particles in the molecule ($+$ or $-$), of reflection on a plane containing the internuclear axis

for Σ states (Σ^{+} or Σ^{-}), and of interchanging the two nuclei (symmetric and asymmetric). For example, the effect of the inversion operator i on $D_{m\Lambda}^{(N)}(\alpha\beta\gamma)$ can be written as

$$iD_{m\Lambda}^{(N)}(\alpha\beta\gamma) = -(1)^{N} D_{m-\Lambda}^{(N)}(\alpha\beta\gamma).$$

Thus when Λ is equal to or greater than 1 (Π, Δ, Φ, ... states), the states with $+\Lambda$ and $-\Lambda$ are degenerate and one must take a linear combination of both states to obtain a state of definite symmetry, namely

$$\Psi_{Nm\Lambda} = (1/\sqrt{2})[\Psi_{\Lambda}(x_i, y_i, z_i; R)\Psi_{Nm\Lambda}(\alpha\beta\gamma) \pm (-1)^{N}\Psi_{-\Lambda}(x_i, y_i, z_i; R)$$
$$\times \Psi_{Nm-\Lambda}(\alpha\beta\gamma)].$$

Denoting by $\Xi_{S,M-m}$ the spin function of the electrons with total spin quantum number S, one can couple the spin function and the rotational-electronic state function $\Psi_{Nm\Lambda}$ to obtain the resultant state function $\Psi_{JMN\Lambda S}$, corresponding to the total electronic quantum number J (resultant of Λ and S) with projection M along an arbitrary axis. This is achieved by the usual method of coupling of two angular momenta via a Clebsch-Gordan coefficient,* i.e.,

$$\Psi_{JMN\Lambda S} = \sum_{m} \Psi_{Nm\Lambda}\, \Xi_{S,M-m} C(NSJ; m, M - m).$$

The necessity of this coupling is evident, because for the matrix elements of spin-orbit and spin-spin interactions (see Chapter 15) one must combine the electronic orbital angular momentum Λ with the electronic spin angular momentum S as in the case of atoms.

The hamiltonian operator for the spin-orbit interaction is invariant under inversion. Its matrix elements can then be expressed as

$$(\Psi_{JMN'\Lambda'S'}|\, \mathscr{H}_{so}\,|\Psi_{JMN\Lambda S}) = (JMN'\Lambda'S'|\, \mathscr{H}_{so}\,|JMN\Lambda S)$$
$$\pm (-1)^{N'}\,(JMN' - \Lambda'S'|\, \mathscr{H}_{so}\,|JMN\Lambda S)$$

for two doubly degenerate states. The two sign possibilities correspond to

---

* See Chapter 2 for more details on vector-coupling coefficients. It must be pointed out that the notation used here, more appropriate for the present case, is equivalent to that given in Chapter 2; that is,

$$C(NSJ; m, M - m) = (NmSM - m \mid NSJM),$$

being also equivalent to $(NSmM - m \mid JM)$, used by other authors. Chiu [8] uses the notation $C(NSJ; m, M - m, M)$.

the $+$ and $-$ rotational states. When one of the states is a Σ state ($\Lambda' = 0$), one has

$$(\Psi_{JMN'0S'}| \mathscr{H}_{so} |\Psi_{JMN\Lambda S}) = \sqrt{2}(JMN'0S'| \mathscr{H}_{so} |JMN\Lambda S),$$

and if both states are nondegenerate,

$$(\Psi_{JMN'0S'}| \mathscr{H}_{so} |\Psi_{JMN0S}) = (JMN'0S'| \mathscr{H}_{so} |JMN0S).$$

It must be mentioned that if the resultant nuclear spin is zero or can be neglected, then the total angular momentum J is conserved under the perturbation due to the spin-orbit interaction. In such a case the matrix elements of the interaction hamiltonian are diagonal with respect to the total electronic angular momentum quantum number J.

The hamiltonian operator $\mathscr{H}_{so}$ for the spin-orbit and spin—other orbit interactions* for two electrons in a diatomic molecule can be written as

$$\mathscr{H}_{so} = \alpha^2\{a(\mathbf{l}_1 \cdot \mathbf{s}_1) + b(\mathbf{l}_2 \cdot \mathbf{s}_2) + c(\mathbf{l}_1 \cdot \mathbf{s}_2) + d(\mathbf{l}_2 \cdot \mathbf{s}_1)\}, \quad (14\text{-}15\text{a})$$

where a, b, c, and d are functions of the radial coordinates of electrons 1 and 2, of the internuclear distance R, and of the interelectronic distance r_{12} and where α is the fine structure constant.

Two separate cases must be considered:

(1) If the matrix of $\mathscr{H}_{so}$ is diagonal with respect to the total electron spin quantum number S, then one can write

$$\mathscr{H}_{so} = \alpha^2\{a'(\mathbf{l}_1 \cdot \mathbf{S}) + b'(\mathbf{l}_2 \cdot \mathbf{S})\}, \quad (14\text{-}15\text{b})$$

with $\mathbf{S} = \mathbf{s}_1 + \mathbf{s}_2$.

(2) If, however, the states of different multiplicities interact, the matrix of $\mathscr{H}_{so}$ will have off-diagonal elements with respect to S, and in this case $\mathscr{H}_{so}$ can be written as

$$\mathscr{H}_{so} = \alpha^2\{a''(\mathbf{l}_1 \cdot \mathbf{s}_1) + b''(\mathbf{l}_2 \cdot \mathbf{s}_2). \quad (14\text{-}15\text{c})$$

The coupling coefficients have been given by Fontana [15],

$$a' = \tfrac{1}{4}(Z_a/r_{1a}^3 + Z_b/r_{1b}^3 - 3/r_{12}^3], \quad (14\text{-}16\text{a})$$

$$b' = \tfrac{1}{4}(Z_b/r_{2b}^3 + Z_a/r_{2a}^3 - 3/r_{12}^3], \quad (14\text{-}16\text{b})$$

$$a'' = \tfrac{1}{2}(Z_a/r_{1a}^3 + Z_b/r_{1b}^3 + 1/r_{12}^3], \quad (14\text{-}16\text{c})$$

$$b'' = \tfrac{1}{2}(Z_b/r_{2b}^3 + Z_a/r_{2a}^3 + 1/r_{12}^3], \quad (14\text{-}16\text{d})$$

where r_{ia} and r_{ib} are the distances of the i-th electron from the nuclei a and b, respectively, and r_{12} is the interelectronic distance.

Just as in the atomic case, the spin-orbit interaction can be expressed as the scalar product of two irreducible spherical tensors of rank one, $\mathbf{l}^{(1)}$ and

---

* For more details the reader is referred to the work of Chiu [8], Fontana [15], and Kovacs [22, 23].

$\mathbf{S}^{(1)}$, in order to evaluate its matrix elements using Racah tensor algebra. Matrix elements can exist between states for which $\Delta S = 0, \pm 1$, $\Delta N = 0, \pm 1$, and $\Delta \Lambda = 0, \pm 1$, or any combination of these.

For case (1) one has $\Delta S = 0$, and the matrix element of $\mathcal{H}_{so}$ is given by

$$(JMN'\Lambda'S|\,\mathcal{H}_{so}\,|JMN\Lambda S) = \alpha^2(-1)^{N'+S-J}W(NSN'S; J1)[(2N'+1)$$
$$\times\ (2S+1)]^{\frac{1}{2}}\,(N'\Lambda'|\,|a'\mathbf{1}^{(1)}(x_1',y_1',z_1') + b'\mathbf{1}^{(1)}(x_2',y_2',z_2')|\,|N\Lambda)$$
$$\times\ (S|\,|\mathbf{S}^{(1)}|\,|S), \quad (14\text{-}17)$$

where $W(NSN'S; J1)$ is a Racah coefficient and the reduced matrix element $(S|\,|\mathbf{S}^{(1)}|\,|S)$ is equal to $[S(S+1)]^{\frac{1}{2}}$; x_i', y_i', and z_i' are the coordinates of the i-th electron with respect to the fixed system.

After a transformation of the coordinate system, the tensor $\mathbf{1}^{(1)}(x',y',z')$ in the fixed system can be expressed as a tensor $\mathbf{1}^{(1)}(x,y,z)$ in the moving system (relative to the figure axis) using the relations given by Fontana [15]. One can then write the reduced matrix element, involving $\mathbf{1}^{(1)}$ (1) and $\mathbf{1}^{(1)}$ (2), as

$$(N'\Lambda'|\,|a'\mathbf{1}^{(1)}(x_1',y_1',z_1') + b'\mathbf{1}^{(1)}(x_2',y_2',z_2')|\,|N\Lambda) = (-1)^{N'-N+\eta}C(N'1N; \Lambda'\eta)$$
$$\times\ (\Lambda'|\,a'1_{-\eta}^{(1)}(x_1,y_1,z_1) + b'1_{-\eta}^{(1)}(x_2,y_2,z_2)\,|\Lambda), \quad (14\text{-}18)$$

with $\eta = \Lambda - \Lambda'$.

Using these expressions for the reduced matrix elements, one can obtain all the diagonal and off-diagonal elements of $\mathcal{H}_{so}$ for the case $\Delta S = 0$. The simplest matrix elements (see Chiu [8] and Fontana [15]) are

$$(JMN-1\Lambda S=1|\,\mathcal{H}_{so}\,|JMN\Lambda S=1) = -\alpha^2[(J+N+2)$$
$$\times\ (J+N-1)(N-J+1)(J-N+2)(N-\Lambda)(N+\Lambda)/4N^2(2N-1)$$
$$\times\ (2N+1)]^{\frac{1}{2}}(\Lambda|\,a'1_z^{(1)}(x_1,y_1,z_1) + b'1_z^{(1)}(x_2,y_2,z_2)\,|\Lambda). \quad (14\text{-}19)$$

For case (2), where $\Delta S = \pm 1$, one can write

$$(JMN'\Lambda'S-1|\,\mathcal{H}_{so}\,|JMN\Lambda S) = \alpha^2(-1)^{N'+S-J}W(NSN'S'; J1)$$
$$\times\ [(2N'+1)(2S-1)]^{\frac{1}{2}}(N'\Lambda'|\,|a''\mathbf{1}^{(1)}(x_1',y_1',z_1') - b''\mathbf{1}^{(1)}(x_2',y_2',z_2')|\,|N\Lambda)$$
$$\times\ (S-1|\,|\mathbf{s}^{(1)}(1)|\,|S), \quad (14\text{-}20)$$

where use has been made of the relation

$$(S-1|\,|\mathbf{s}^{(1)}(1)|\,|S) = (S-1|\,|\mathbf{s}^{(1)}(2)|\,|S).$$

Taking into account that $s_1 = s_2 = \frac{1}{2}$ and $S = 1$, one arrives at

$$(S-1|\,\mathbf{s}^{(1)}(1)|\,|S) = -[S(2-S)(2+S)/4(2S-1)]^{\frac{1}{2}} = \sqrt{3}/2.$$

Using these expressions, we can evaluate the matrix elements between singlet and triplet states. Some of the results are

$$(JMN\Lambda S = 0| \mathscr{H}_{so} |JMN\Lambda S = 1) = \alpha^2[(J + N + 2)(N - J + 1)$$
$$\times (J - N + 1)(J + N)]^{\frac{1}{2}}[\Lambda/4N(N + 1)](\Lambda| a''\mathbf{1}_z^{(1)}(x_1, y_1, z_1)$$
$$- b''\mathbf{1}_z^{(1)}(x_2, y_2, z_2) |\Lambda),$$

$$(JMN - 1\Lambda S = 0| \mathscr{H}_{so} |JMN\Lambda S = 1) = -\alpha^2[(J + N + 2)(J + N + 1)$$
$$\times (N - J + 1)(N - J)(N - \Lambda)(N + \Lambda)/16N^2(2N + 1)(2N - 1)]^{\frac{1}{2}}$$
$$\times (\Lambda| a''\mathbf{1}_z^{(1)}(x_1, y_1, z_1) - b''\mathbf{1}_z^{(1)}(x_2, y_2, z_2) |\Lambda).$$

The matrix elements $(\Lambda| a\mathbf{1}_z^{(1)}(x_1, y_1, z_1) - b\mathbf{1}_z^{(1)}(x_2, y_2, z_2) |\Lambda)$ are to be evaluated over the appropriate electronic state functions.

These matrix elements have been evaluated by Chiu [9], in order to study the "forbidden predissociation" of the metastable $C^3\Pi_u$ state of H_2 via the repulsive $b^3\Sigma_u^+$ state. This mechanism was assumed by Lichten [24], after finding that the fine structure levels of different J values of the $C^3\Pi_u$ state have different lifetimes. The lifetimes calculated (including the spin-spin interactions) by Chiu [9] are in reasonably good agreement with the experimental results. Theoretical studies have also been carried out by Frey and Mizushima [16] and Browne [6].

The spin-orbit interactions and their effect on the zero-field splitting (that is, in the absence of external magnetic fields) for polyatomic molecules have been discussed by Hameka [17] (for benzene) and Fogel and Hameka [14] (for the linear CH_2 radical).

REFERENCES

1. R. G. Barnes and W. V. Smith. Phys. Rev. *93*, 95 (1954).
2. M. Blume and R. E. Watson. Proc. Roy. Soc. (London) *A270*, 127 (1962).
3. M. Blume and R. E. Watson. Proc. Roy. Soc. (London) *A271*, 565 (1963).
4. M. Blume, A. J. Freeman, and R. E. Watson. Phys. Rev. *134*, A320 (1964).
5. M. Born and J. R. Oppenheimer. Ann. Physik *84*, 457 (1927).
6. J. C. Browne. J. Chem. Phys. *40*, 43 (1964).
7. H. B. G. Casimir. "On the Interaction between Atomic Nuclei and Electrons." W. H. Freeman & Co., San Francisco, Calif., 1963.
8. L. Y. C. Chiu. J. Chem. Phys. *40*, 2276 (1964).
9. L. Y. C. Chiu. J. Chem. Phys. *41*, 2197 (1964).
10. E. U. Condon and G. H. Shortley. "The Theory of Atomic Spectra." The University Press, Cambridge, 1935.
11. A. R. Edmonds. "Angular Momentum in Quantum Mechanics." Princeton University Press, Princeton, New Jersey, 1960.
12. J. P. Elliott. Proc. Roy. Soc. (London) *A218*, 345 (1953).
13. J. P. Elliott, B. R. Judd, and W. A. Runciman. Proc. Roy. Soc. (London) *A240*, 509 (1957).
14. S. J. Fogel and H. F. Hameka. J. Chem. Phys. *42*, 132 (1965).
15. P. R. Fontana. Phys. Rev. *125*, 220 (1962).
16. D. A. Frey and M. Mizushima. Phys. Rev. *128*, 2683 (1962).
17. H. F. Hameka. J. Chem. Phys. *31*, 315 (1958).
18. G. Herzberg. "Molecular Spectra and Molecular Structure, I. Spectra of Diatomic Molecules." D. Van Nostrand Company, Inc., Princeton, New Jersey, 1957.

19. H. Horie. Prog. Theor. Phys. (Japan) *10*, 296 (1953).
20. B. R. Judd and R. Loudon. Proc. Roy. Soc. (London) *A251*, 127 (1951).
21. H. Kopfermann. "Nuclear Moments." Academic Press, Inc., New York, N.Y., 1958.
22. I. Kovacs. Can. J. Phys. *36*, 309 (1958).
23. I. Kovacs. Can. J. Phys. *36*, 329 (1958).
24. W. Lichten. Bull. Am. Phys. Soc. *7*, 43 (1963).
25. G. Malli and S. Fraga. Theoret. Chim. Acta (Berlin) *7*, 80 (1967).
26. G. Malli and S. Fraga. Anales R. Soc. Espan. Fis. Quim. (in press).
27. H. H. Marvin. Phys. Rev. *71*, 102 (1947).
28. C. E. Moore. Natl. Bur. Standards (U.S.), Circ. No. 467 (1949).
29. G. Racah. Phys. Rev. *62*, 438 (1942).
30. G. Racah. Phys. Rev. *63*, 367 (1943).
31. G. Racah. Phys. Rev. *76*, 1352 (1949).
32. M. E. Rose. "Elementary Theory of Angular Momentum." John Wiley & Sons, Inc., New York, N.Y., 1957.
33. W. A. Runciman and M. H. Crozier. Unpublished results.
34. F. H. Spedding. Phys. Rev. *58*, 255 (1940).
35. R. E. Trees. Phys. Rev. *92*, 308 (1953).
36. J. H. Van Vleck. Rev. Mod. Phys. *23*, 213 (1951).
37. B. G. Wybourne. J. Chem. Phys. *35*, 334 (1961).

Chapter 15   SPIN-SPIN
INTERACTION

INTRODUCTION

In an atomic or molecular system, the electron and nuclear spins are responsible for a series of mutual interactions, which are included in the total hamiltonian operator for the system.

In Chapter 1 the interaction operators for the electron spin-electron spin, electron spin-nuclear spin, and nuclear spin-nuclear spin couplings have been presented. Of these, the magnetic dipole-dipole electron spin-nuclear spin interaction has already been discussed in Chapter 11, together with the Fermi contact interaction.

There remains, therefore, the dipole-dipole electron spin-electron spin and the nuclear spin-nuclear spin interactions to consider.

DIPOLE-DIPOLE ELECTRON SPIN COUPLING

Interactions in Atoms

Heisenberg [16] derived, from purely classic considerations by associating with each electron a magnetic moment $-(e/mc)\boldsymbol{s}$, the hamiltonian operator for the spin-spin interaction between two electrons. The interpretation of this interaction has proved useful in explaining energy level structures that show deviations from Landé's interval rule. It has been recognized that spin-spin contributions are appreciable in the spectra of light atoms. The later work of Araki [3, 4] and Trees [37] indicates that these contributions may be significant also in the spectra of heavy atoms.

Marvin [25] formulated the treatment for configurations with two equivalent electrons, using the method of one-electron eigenfunctions, and calculated the matrix elements involving s, p, and d electrons. Aller, Ufford, and Van Vleck [2] developed similar techniques for the $2p^3$ configuration. However, it was Trees [37] who applied Racah tensor algebra to obtain the matrix elements for d^n configurations. Trees [37] also observed that the matrix elements are diagonal with respect to the seniority number v, a quantum number first introduced by Racah [28] on the basis of group theoretical considerations to distinguish those states which, arising from a given atomic configuration, have the same SL quantum numbers. Innes [18] and Horie [17], independently and simultaneously, expressed the spin-spin interaction operator in terms of products of tensor operators and derived the matrix elements using the methods of Racah for any configuration l^n of n equivalent electrons.

The spin-spin interaction operator $\mathcal{H}_{ss}$ between two electrons i and j, having spin angular momenta $\mathbf{s}_i$ and $\mathbf{s}_j$, is written as (see Horie [17])

$$\mathcal{H}_{ss}(i,j) = \alpha^2 r_{ij}^{-5}[(\mathbf{s}_i \cdot \mathbf{s}_j)r_{ij}^2 - 3(\mathbf{s}_i \cdot \mathbf{r}_{ij})(\mathbf{s}_j \cdot \mathbf{r}_{ij})], \qquad (15\text{-}1)$$

where $\mathbf{r}_{ij}$ is the position vector (modulus r_{ij}) for one electron relative to the other. In Eq. (15-1) a term representing the contact interaction of the two spins should be added. However, it is constant for the configuration and does not lead to any splitting of the multiplet and for this reason it is not included in $\mathcal{H}_{ss}$ at this moment (see below).

The operator $\mathcal{H}_{ss}$ is a tensor of rank two in the spin and orbital parts separately, but a scalar in the product space. Such an operator is also called a double tensor operator,* which in this special case is denoted by $\mathbf{T}^{(22)}$. In general, the tensor operator $\mathbf{T}^{(\kappa k)}$, with $(2\kappa + 1)$ $(2k + 1)$ components $\mathbf{T}_{\pi q}^{(\kappa k)}$, is said to be a double tensor if it behaves as a tensor of rank k with respect to the total orbital angular momentum and as a tensor of rank κ with respect to the total spin angular momentum.

The commutation relations for $\mathbf{T}^{(\kappa k)}$ with the orbital and spin angular momentum operators are

$$[\mathcal{L}_z, T_{\pi q}^{(\kappa k)}] = q T_{\pi q}^{(\kappa k)}, \qquad (15\text{-}2a)$$

$$[\mathcal{L}_{\pm}, T_{\pi q}^{(\kappa k)}] = [k(k + 1) - q(q \pm 1)]^{\frac{1}{2}} T_{\pi q \pm 1}^{(\kappa k)}, \qquad (15\text{-}2b)$$

$$[\mathcal{S}_z, T_{\pi q}^{(\kappa k)}] = \pi T_{\pi q}^{(\kappa k)}, \qquad (15\text{-}2c)$$

$$[\mathcal{S}_{\pm}, T_{\pi q}^{(\kappa k)}] = [\kappa(\kappa + 1) - \pi(\pi \pm 1)]^{\frac{1}{2}} T_{\pi \pm 1 q}^{(\kappa k)}. \qquad (15\text{-}2d)$$

From these relations one can see that the double tensors have commutation properties similar to the ordinary tensor operators discussed in Chapter 3. Therefore one can generalize the theory of ordinary tensor operators to obtain the following expression for the Wigner-Eckart theorem for double

---

* The theory of double tensors is presented in detail by Judd [21].

tensors $T_{\pi q}^{(\kappa k)}$:

$$(\gamma S M_S L M_L| \, T_{\pi q}^{(\kappa k)} \, |\gamma' S' M'_{S'} \, L' M'_{L'}) = (-1)^{S+L-M_S-M_L} \begin{pmatrix} S & \kappa & S' \\ -M_S & \pi & M'_{S'} \end{pmatrix}$$

$$\times \begin{pmatrix} L & k & L' \\ -M_L & q & M'_{L'} \end{pmatrix}(\gamma SL| \, |\mathbf{T}^{(\kappa k)}| \, |\gamma' S' L'). \quad (15\text{-}3)$$

The double tensor formalism also allows one to evaluate the matrix elements of two-particle operators involving both spin and orbital variables. By a process of recoupling, the matrix elements of such an operator can be expressed as a sum over weighted products of the matrix elements of double tensors. Innes and Ufford [19], in particular, have extended the double tensor formalism to obtain the matrix elements of two-particle operators between coupled groups of equivalent electrons. Innes [18] expressed the spin-spin interaction operator $\mathcal{H}_{ss}$ in terms of a double tensor and evaluated the matrix elements of $\mathcal{H}_{ss}$ using the generalization of Racah tensor algebra for the matrix elements of the double tensors. However, the discussion here is restricted to the treatment of Horie [17] because of its greater simplicity.

It can be shown that

$$\mathcal{H}_{ss} = \alpha^2 (\mathbf{s}_i \cdot \mathbf{\nabla}_i)(\mathbf{s}_j \cdot \mathbf{\nabla}_j)(1/r_{ij}), \quad (15\text{-}4)$$

where $\mathbf{\nabla}_i$ and $\mathbf{\nabla}_j$ operate only on the corresponding coordinate in $1/r_{ij}$. Furthermore the term $1/r_{ij}$ can be expanded in terms of a series of scalar products of spherical harmonics, namely

$$1/r_{ij} = \sum_{k=0}^{\infty} (r_<^k/r_>^{k+1})P_k(w) = \sum_k (r_<^k/r_>^{k+1})(\mathbf{C}^{(k)}(i) \cdot \mathbf{C}^{(k)}(j)), \quad (15\text{-}5)$$

where $r_<$ and $r_>$ are the lesser and the greater, respectively, of r_i and r_j. $\mathbf{C}^{(k)}$ is a tensor operator with components (see Chapter 3)

$$C_q^{(k)} = [4\pi/(2k+1)]^{\frac{1}{2}}Y_q^{(k)}, \quad q = -k, \ldots, +k.$$

Further it can be proved that

$$\nabla_\sigma C_q^{(k)} = \sum_{KQ} (k100 \,|\, k1K0)(k1q\sigma \,|\, k1KQ)C_Q^{(K)}\mathcal{D}_\sigma^{(K)}, \quad (15\text{-}6)$$

where $(j_1 j_2 m_1 m_2 \,|\, j_1 j_2 jm)$ is a Clebsch-Gordan coefficient and $\mathcal{D}^{(K)}$ are the operators defined by

$$\mathcal{D}_i^{(k-1)} = \partial/\partial r_i + (k+1)/r_i, \quad (15\text{-}7a)$$

$$\mathcal{D}_i^{(k+1)} = \partial/\partial r_i - k/r_i. \quad (15\text{-}7b)$$

Therefore the interaction operator $\mathcal{H}_{ss}$ can be written as

$$\mathcal{H}_{ss} = \alpha^2 \sum (-1)^{\sigma+\sigma'+q} S_{1\sigma} S_{2\sigma'}(k100 \,|\, k1K0)(k100 \,|\, k1K'0)$$

$$\times (k1q - \sigma \,|\, k1KQ)(k1 - q - \sigma' \,|\, k1K'Q')C_Q^{(K)}(i)C_{Q'}^{(K')}(j)(\mathcal{D}_i^{(K)}\mathcal{D}_j^{(K')}a_k), \quad (15\text{-}8)$$

where $a_k = r_<^k/r_>^{k+1}$. The summation in this equation extends over k, q, σ, σ' K, Q, K', and Q'.

Using the symmetry property of the Clebsch-Gordan coefficients,

$$(l_1 l_2 m_1 m_2 \mid l_1 l_2 l_3 m_3) = (-1)^{l_2 + m_2}[(2l_3 + 1)/(2l_1 + 1)]^{\frac{1}{2}}$$
$$\times (l_3 l_2 - m_3 m_2 \mid l_3 l_2 \, l_1 - m_1),$$

and defining a new irreducible tensor operator of rank k, $\mathbf{t}^{(1K;k)}$, with components

$$t_q^{(1K;k)} = (2K + 1)(1K00 \mid 1Kk0) \sum_{\sigma Q} (1K\sigma Q \mid 1Kkq)S_\sigma C_Q^{(K)}, \quad (15\text{-}9)$$

one can finally write

$$\mathscr{H}_{ss} = \alpha^2 \sum_{kKK'} [1/(2k + 1)^2](\mathbf{t}^{(1K;k)}(i) \cdot \mathbf{t}^{(1K;k)}(j))(\mathscr{D}_i^{(K)}\mathscr{D}_j^{(K')}a_k). \quad (15\text{-}10)$$

That is, $\mathscr{H}_{ss}$ consists of the scalar products of tensor operators which operate upon only the spin and the orbital parts of the individual electron functions, and the remaining factor depends upon only the radial parts.

It can now be seen, from Eq. (15-7), that the radial factor vanishes if $K = K' = k \pm 1$ and that

$$[1/(2k + 1)^2](\mathscr{D}_1^{(k-1)}\mathscr{D}_2^{(k+1)}a_k) = -r_1^{k-1}/r_2^{k+2}, \quad (r_1 \leq r_2) \quad (15\text{-}11\text{a})$$

$$[1/(2k + 1)^2](\mathscr{D}_1^{(k+1)}\mathscr{D}_2^{(k-1)}a_k) = -r_2^{k-1}/r_1^{k+1}, \quad (r_2 \leq r_1). \quad (15\text{-}11\text{b})$$

One can then finally write for a l^n configuration

$$\mathscr{H}_{ss} = -\sum_k \sum_{i<j} [(\mathbf{t}^{(1k-1;k)}(i) \cdot \mathbf{t}^{(1k+1;k)}(j)) + (\mathbf{t}^{(1k+1;k)}(i) \cdot \mathbf{t}^{(1k-1;k)}(j))]M^{(k-1)}$$

$$= -2 \sum_k \sum_{i<j} (\mathbf{t}^{(1k-1;k)}(i) \cdot \mathbf{t}^{(1k+1;k)}(j))M^{(k-1)}, \quad (15\text{-}12)$$

where $M^{(k)}$ denotes the radial integrals which have been defined by Marvin [25] and which have already been introduced in Chapter 13.

In order to facilitate the calculation of matrix elements, Eq. (15-12) can be expressed in terms of the symmetric tensor operators $\mathbf{T}^{(1K;k)}$ with respect to n electrons, defined by

$$\mathbf{T}^{(1K;k)} = \sum_{i=1}^n \mathbf{t}^{(1K;k)}(i).$$

Equation (15-12) transforms then into

$$\mathscr{H}_{ss} = -\sum_k [(\mathbf{T}^{(1k-1;k)} \cdot \mathbf{T}^{(1k+1;k)}) - \sum_i (\mathbf{t}^{(1k-1;k)})(i) \cdot \mathbf{t}^{(1k+1;k)}(i))]M^{(k-1)}. \quad (15\text{-}13)$$

Furthermore, from the theory of tensor operators, it can be shown that the second term in Eq. (15-13) vanishes identically, as the tensor operator of rank two composed of single spin operators cannot exist. Therefore Eq. (15-13) can be simplified to

$$\mathscr{H}_{ss} = -\sum_k (\mathbf{T}^{(1k-1;k)} \cdot \mathbf{T}^{(1k+1;k)})M^{(k-1)}. \quad (15\text{-}14)$$

The matrix elements of $\mathscr{H}_{ss}$ can be evaluated merely by a direct application of Racah methods for tensor operators. For the l^n configuration one has (in the $SLJM$ scheme)

$$(l^n \alpha SLJM| \mathscr{H}_{ss} |l^n \alpha' S'L'JM) = (-1)^{S+L'-J} W(SLS'L'; J2)$$
$$\times (l^n \alpha SL| |\mathscr{H}_{ss}| |l^n \alpha' S'L'), \quad (15\text{-}15)$$

where

$$(l^n \alpha SL| |\mathscr{H}_{ss}| |l^n \alpha' S'L') = \sum_k f_k M^{(k-1)} \sum_{\alpha'' S'' L''} W(SlS'l; S''2)$$
$$W(Lk - 1 L'k + 1; L''2)(l^n \alpha SL| |\mathbf{V}^{(1k-1)}| |l^n \alpha'' S'' L'')$$
$$(l^n \alpha S'' L''| |\mathbf{V}^{(1k+1)}| |l^n \alpha' S'L'), \quad (15\text{-}16)$$

and

$$f_k = (-1)^k 4[5k(k + 1)(2k - 1)(2k + 1)(2k + 3)]^{\frac{1}{2}} (l| |\mathbf{C}^{(k-1)}| |l)$$
$$\times (l| |\mathbf{C}^{(k+1)}| |l). \quad (15\text{-}17)$$

From Eq. (15-17), it follows that f_k does not vanish only when k is an odd integer and $k \leq 2l - 1$. Therefore the radial integrals necessary for the matrix of the spin-spin interaction for the l^n configuration are $M^{(0)}$, $M^{(2)}, \ldots, M^{(2l-2)}$, their coefficients in the matrix elements being given by Eqs. (15-15) to (15-17). If one uses the senority number, v, of Racah [29] to characterize each term of the configuration, one can deduce some properties of the double barred matrix elements of Eq. (15-15). Since k, as mentioned above, can be only an odd integer, the matrix elements, represented by Eq. (15-16), are diagonal with respect to v. Consequently these matrix elements are completely determined by assigning a set of values v, S, and L, irrespective of n. Talmi [35] gave independently this rule for a general tensor force interaction, and Innes [18] has also given this rule for the spin-spin interaction. Moreover, it follows that the elements are unaltered by the process of conjugation (that is, if one substitutes $l^{2(2l+1)-n}$ for l^n) and that for the self conjugate configurations l^{2l+1} (half-filled shells) the matrix elements vanish between terms belonging to different classes.

For $k = 1$, the calculations are extremely simple. The coefficient of $M^{(0)}$ in the double-barred matrix elements is given by

$$4[30\, l(l + 1)(2l + 1)/(2l - 1)(2l + 3)]^{\frac{1}{2}}[S(S + 1)(2S + 1)]^{\frac{1}{2}}$$
$$\times W(S1S'1; S1)(l^n \alpha SL| |\mathbf{V}^{(12)}| |l^n \alpha' S'L').$$

Racah [27, 28] has given tables of the matrix elements of $\mathbf{V}^{(12)}$ for p^n and d^n configurations; Trees [37] has also given tables of these matrix elements. The matrix elements of $\mathbf{V}^{(12)}$ for f^n configurations are given by Racah [27, 28] and Judd [21].

The spin-spin interactions between an electron in an incomplete shell and any other closed shell are expected to vanish because of the transformation property of the interaction operators with respect to rotations in the spin space. Formal proof of this fact has been given recently by Elliott [7].

The effects of spin-spin interactions have been examined by Horie [17] and Trees [37]. Their results indicate that these interactions must be taken into account for elements heavier than those having $2p^n$ configurations.

The parameters $M^{(0)}, \ldots, M^{(2l-2)}$, can be calculated from HF functions, providing a comparison between theoretically calculated and experimentally observed splittings due to spin-spin interactions. Tables 15-1 and 15-2

Table 15-1 Radial Integrals $M^{(0)}$ (in cm^{-1}) for Various States of Positive Ions, Neutral Atoms, and Negative Ions with p^n Configurations[a]

CONFIGURATION	STATE	POSITIVE ION		NEUTRAL ATOM		NEGATIVE ION	
		System	$M^{(0)}$	System	$M^{(0)}$	System	$M^{(0)}$
$2p^1$	^2P	C$^+$	0.58	B	0.19		
$2p^2$	^3P	N$^+$	0.99	C	0.40	B$^-$	0.09
$2p^3$	^4S	O$^+$	1.55	N	0.74	C$^-$	0.25
$2p^4$	^3P	F$^+$	2.20	O	1.15	N$^-$	0.48
$2p^5$	^2P	Ne$^+$	3.05	F	1.73	O$^-$	0.83
$3p^1$	^2P	Si$^+$	0.12	Al	0.04		
$3p^2$	^3P	P$^+$	0.19	Si	0.09	Al$^-$	0.02
$3p^3$	^4S	S$^+$	0.28	P	0.15	Si$^-$	0.06
$3p^4$	^3P	Cl$^+$	0.38	S	0.22	P$^-$	0.10
$3p^5$	^2P	A$^+$	0.51	Cl	0.31	S$^-$	0.17
$4p^1$	^2P	Ge$^+$	0.09	Ga	0.04		
$4p^2$	^3P	As$^+$	0.13	Ge	0.07	Ga$^-$	0.02
$4p^3$	^4S	Se$^+$	0.17	As	0.10	Ge$^-$	0.05
$4p^4$	^3P	Br$^+$	0.22	Se	0.14	As$^-$	0.08
$4p^5$	^2P	Kr$^+$	0.28	Br	0.18	Se$^-$	0.11

a. Evaluated by Fraga and Malli [8] from the analytical HF functions of Clementi [5] and Malli [24].

present the values of these integrals for p^n and d^n configurations, as evaluated by Fraga and Malli [8]. Froese [9] has also evaluated these parameters for f^n configurations.

Interactions in Molecules

A large amount of work has also been done on the electron spin-spin interactions in molecules. The theoretical formalism is very similar to the one presented for atoms and for that reason it will not be discussed here. One must mention, though, some calculations where further details on the subject can be found.

Tinkham and Strandberg [36] have discussed in detail the spin-spin interactions in O_2 in its ground state $^3\Sigma_g^-$ and Dousmanis [6] discusses the spin-spin interaction in NO. These papers describe the theory in great detail and are representative of the work on the homonuclear and heteronuclear diatomic molecules. They constitute, at the same time, the basis

Table 15-2 Radial Integrals $M^{(0)}$ and $M^{(2)}$ (in cm^{-1}) for Various States of Positive Ions, Neutral Atoms, and Negative Ions with d^n Configurations[a]

CONFIGURATION	STATE	POSITIVE ION			NEUTRAL ATOM			NEGATIVE ION		
		System	$M^{(0)}$	$M^{(2)}$	System	$M^{(0)}$	$M^{(2)}$	System	$M^{(0)}$	$M^{(2)}$
$3d^1$	^2D	Sc$^+$	0.34	0.18	Sc	0.44	0.24	Sc$^-$	0.28	0.15
$3d^2$	^3F	Ti$^+$	0.51	0.27	Ti	0.64	0.35	Ti$^-$	0.46	0.25
$3d^3$	^4F	V$^+$	0.70	0.38	V	0.86	0.47	V$^-$	0.66	0.35
$3d^4$	^5D	Cr$^+$	0.92	0.50	Cr	1.10	0.60	Cr$^-$	0.88	0.48
$3d^5$	^6S	Mn$^+$	1.14	0.62	Mn	1.38	0.75	Mn$^-$	1.10	0.59
$3d^6$	^5D	Fe$^+$	1.40	0.76	Fe	1.64	0.89	Fe$^-$	1.36	0.73
$3d^7$	^4F	Co$^+$	1.69	0.91	Co	1.95	1.06	Co$^-$	1.65	0.89
$3d^8$	^3F	Ni$^+$	2.01	1.09	Ni	2.30	1.25			
$3d^9$	^2D				Cu	2.69	1.46			

a. Evaluated by Fraga and Malli [8] from the analytical HF functions of Clementi [5].

for the work on polyatomic molecules and should be consulted to gain an understanding of spin-spin interactions in molecules in general.

Kayama [22] has recently studied in great detail the electron spin-spin interaction in the $^3\Sigma_g^-$ state of O_2, using several approximate functions of the LCAO MO and the Heitler-London types. The discrepancy between the experimental value, determined by Tinkham and Strandberg [36], and the theoretical values has been reduced by the later work of Kayama and Baird [23].

Sharma [33] has calculated the spin-spin interaction for the methylene radical in its ground state, $^3\Sigma_g^-$, predicting that the splitting of the rotational lines in the electronic spectrum of CH_2 should be observable in the UV region of the spectrum with an instrument with a resolving power of 0.5 cm^{-1}. Sharma [33] also predicts a resonance line* near 2.2 cm^{-1} in the ESR spectrum of the solid system. Raynes [32] has developed expressions for the matrix elements of the spin-spin interaction for a nonlinear, nonrigid polyatomic molecule in a multiplet electronic state.

NUCLEAR SPIN COUPLING

The nuclear spins give rise to dipole-dipole interactions, similar to those discussed for electrons. There are, however, certain peculiarities in nuclear resonance experiments that cannot be explained as having been produced by this type of interaction. The interpretation of the phenomena imposes the need for an indirect interaction, through the interactions of the nuclei with the electrons in the molecule.

The discussion is restricted here to the so-called electron-coupled interactions between nuclear spins, but a brief mention of the direct interactions is made below.

Direct Interactions

The hamiltonian operator for the direct magnetic interaction between pairs of nuclear spins in a molecule is

$$\mathscr{H}_{nss} = -\sum_a \sum_{b>a} \gamma_a \gamma_b \{3(\mathbf{I}_a \cdot \mathbf{r}_{ab})(\mathbf{I}_b \cdot \mathbf{r}_{ab})r_{ab}^{-5} - (\mathbf{I}_a \cdot \mathbf{I}_b)r_{ab}^{-3}\}, \quad (15\text{-}18)$$

where $\mathbf{I}_a$ is the spin angular momentum of nucleus a, with a gyromagnetic ratio γ_a. (The reader is referred, for example, to the work of Ramsey [30]. Compare also Eq. (15-18) with Eq. (15-1), for the dipole-dipole interaction between electron spins.)

This interaction vanishes identically when averaged over all directions. This is the reason that to first order the direct interaction averages to zero

---

* Sharma [33] gives a value of 1.1 cm^{-1}, but Dr. Y. N. Chiu has pointed out that this value should be multiplied by 2.

as in paramagnetic resonance experiments, when the molecules adopt all possible orientations because of collisions. It is important, however, in molecular beam experiments.

ELECTRON-COUPLED INTERACTIONS

There are splittings of nuclear resonance lines that are dependent on the strength of the external magnetic field, in contrast to the magnetic shielding effects. (See the work of Proctor and Yu [26], Hahn et al. [13–15], and Gutowsky et al. [10–12].) Gutowsky et al. [10] and Hahn and Maxwell [14, 15] pointed out that the experimental results can be interpreted under the assumption of an interaction of the form $h \, \delta_{ab} \, \mathbf{I}_a \cdot \mathbf{I}_b$.

This form of interaction can be attained by inclusion of the magnetic shielding of the nuclear spin-spin interaction due to the orbital motion of the electrons. The predicted values for the parameter δ_{ab} are, however, too small. Satisfactory values, as well as a correct form for the interaction, can be obtained in terms of the electron-coupled nuclear interaction model, first proposed by Ramsey and Purcell [31].

The mathematical formulation for this interaction has been developed by Ramsey [30], on the basis of perturbation theory, and by Stephen [34] and Ishiguro [20], using a variational approach. Only the perturbation formulation is presented here.

A number of terms are included under the designation of electron-coupled nuclear spin-spin interactions. These terms arise when second-order perturbation theory is applied to the magnetic interactions. However, the largest contribution arises from the Fermi contact interaction, and this is the term discussed below.

The corresponding hamiltonian, as presented in Chapter 11 (see Abragam and Pryce [1]), is

$$\mathcal{H}_c = (16\pi\mu_B/3) \sum_i \sum_a \gamma_a \, \mathbf{s}_i \cdot \mathbf{I}_a \, \delta(\mathbf{r}_{ia}),$$

where the summation over i extends over the electrons in the system. Second-order perturbation theory leads to

$$\sum_a \sum_{b \geq a} E_{ab} = -\sum_{k \neq n} \langle \Phi_n | \, \mathcal{H}_c \, | \Phi_k \rangle \langle \Phi_k | \, \mathcal{H}_c \, | \Phi_n \rangle / (E_k - E_n), \quad (15\text{-}19)$$

where E_{ab} denotes the energy of interaction between two nuclei, a and b, by the electron-coupled model. One can then obtain for this energy E_{ab} the expression

$$E_{ab} = -2(16\pi\mu_B/3)^2 \gamma_a \gamma_b \sum_k \sum_i \sum_j \langle \Phi_n | \, (\mathbf{s}_i \cdot \mathbf{I}_a) \, \delta(\mathbf{r}_{ia}) \, | \Phi_k \rangle$$
$$\times \langle \Phi_k | \, (\mathbf{s}_j \cdot \mathbf{I}_b) \, \delta(\mathbf{r}_{jb}) \, | \Phi_b \rangle / (E_k - E_n). \quad (15\text{-}20)$$

This equation can be rewritten as

$$E_{ab} = h \mathbf{I}_a \cdot \boldsymbol{\delta}_{ab} \cdot \mathbf{I}_b + h \, \delta_{ab} \mathbf{I}_a \cdot \mathbf{I}_b \quad (15\text{-}21)$$

with

$$\delta_{ab} = -(2/3h)(16\pi\mu_B/3)^2 \, \gamma_a\gamma_b \sum_k \sum_i \sum_j \langle \Phi_n | \, \mathbf{s}_i \, \delta(\mathbf{r}_{ia}) \, | \Phi_k \rangle$$
$$\cdot \langle \Phi_k | \, \mathbf{s}_j \, \delta(\mathbf{r}_{jb}) \, | \Phi_n \rangle/(E_k - E_n), \quad (15\text{-}22a)$$

$$\boldsymbol{\delta}_{ab} = -(2/h)(16\pi\mu_B/3)^2 \gamma_a\gamma_b \sum_k \sum_i \sum_j \langle \Phi_n | \, \mathbf{s}_i \, \delta(\mathbf{r}_{ia}) \, | \Phi_k \rangle$$
$$\times \langle \Phi_k | \, \mathbf{s}_j \, \delta(\mathbf{r}_{jb}) \, | \Phi_n \rangle/(E_k - E_n) - \delta_{ab}\mathfrak{J}; \quad (15\text{-}22b)$$

$\mathfrak{J}$ is the unit dyadic and $\boldsymbol{\delta}_{ab}$ is a tensor of rank two, whose trace is zero.

For a consistent comparison with experimental results, it is necessary to average over all possible orientations, in consideration of the molecular collisions. In that case $\boldsymbol{\delta}_{ab}$ averages to zero (because of its vanishing trace), and therefore Eq. (15-21) reduces to

$$E_{ab} = h\delta_{ab}\, \mathbf{I}_a \cdot \mathbf{I}_b, \quad (15\text{-}23)$$

which has the correct form required in order to explain the experimental results.

The evaluation of δ_{ab} can be simplified by assuming a suitable mean value, Δ, for the energy differences $(E_k - E_n)$. One can then write

$$\delta_{ab} = -(2/3h\Delta)(16\pi\mu_B/3)^2 \, \gamma_a\gamma_b \, \langle \Phi_n | \sum_i \sum_j (\mathbf{s}_i \cdot \mathbf{s}_j) \, \delta(\mathbf{r}_{ia}) \, \delta(\mathbf{r}_{jb}) \, | \Phi_n \rangle.$$
$$(15\text{-}24)$$

The numerical results obtained by Ramsey [30] and Stephen [34] for the system HD indicate that, at least for this molecule, the experimental results are satisfactorily interpreted in terms of this interaction. For other molecules, however, the electron orbital contributions may be larger. (The reader is referred to the work of Ramsey [30], Stephen [34], and Ishiguro [20] for more details.)

REFERENCES

1. A. Abragam and M. H. L. Pryce. Proc. Roy. Soc. (London) *A205*, 135 (1951).
2. L. H. Aller, C. W. Ufford, and J. H. Van Vleck. Astrophys. J. *109*, 42 (1949).
3. G. Araki. Prog. Theor. Phys. (Japan) *3*, 152 (1948).
4. G. Araki. Prog. Theor. Phys. (Japan) *3*, 262 (1948).
5. E. Clementi. "Tables of Atomic Functions." IBM Corporation, San José, California, 1965.
6. C. Dousmanis. Phys. Rev. *97*, 967 (1955).
7. J. P. Elliott. Proc. Roy. Soc. (London) *A218*, 345 (1953).
8. S. Fraga and G. Malli. Unpublished results.
9. C. Froese. "Hartree-Fock Parameters for the Atoms Helium to Radon." Department of Mathematics, University of British Columbia, Vancouver, B.C., Canada, March 1966.
10. H. S. Gutowsky and D. W. McCall. Phys. Rev. *82*, 748 (1951).
11. H. S. Gutowsky, D. W. McCall, and C. P. Slichter. Phys. Rev. *84*, 589 (1951).
12. H. S. Gutowsky, D. W. McCall, C. P. Slichter, and E. B. McNeil. Phys. Rev. *84*, 1245 (1951).
13. E. L. Hahn. Phys. Rev. *80*, 580 (1950).
14. E. L. Hahn and D. E. Maxwell. Phys. Rev. *84*, 1246 (1951).

15. E. L. Hahn and D. E. Maxwell. Phys. Rev. *88*, 243 (1952).
16. W. Heisenberg. Z. Physik *39*, 499 (1926).
17. W. Horie. Prog. Theor. Phys. (Japan) *10*, 296 (1953).
18. F. R. Innes, Phys. Rev. *91*, 31 (1953).
19. F. R. Innes and C. W. Ufford. Phys. Rev. *111*, 194 (1958).
20. E. Ishiguro. Phys. Rev. *111*, 203 (1958).
21. B. R. Judd. "Operator Techniques in Atomic Spectroscopy." McGraw-Hill Book Company, Inc., New York, N.Y., 1963.
22. K. Kayama. J. Chem. Phys. *42*, 622 (1965).
23. K. Kayama and J. C. Baird. J. Chem. Phys. *43*, 1082 (1965).
24. G. Malli. Can. J. Phys. *44*, 3121 (1966).
25. H. H. Marvin. Phys. Rev. *71*, 102 (1947).
26. W. G. Proctor and F. C. Yu. Phys. Rev. *81*, 20 (1951).
27. G. Racah. Phys. Rev. *62*, 438 (1942).
28. G. Racah. Phys. Rev. *63*, 367 (1943).
29. G. Racah. Phys. Rev. *76*, 1352 (1949).
30. N. F. Ramsey. Phys. Rev. *91*, 303 (1953).
31. N. F. Ramsey and E. M. Purcell. Phys. Rev. *85*, 143 (1952).
32. W. T. Raynes. J. Chem. Phys. *41*, 3020 (1964).
33. R. D. Sharma. J. Chem. Phys. *38*, 2350 (1963).
34. M. J. Stephen. Proc. Roy. Soc. (London) *A243*, 274 (1957).
35. I. Talmi. Phys. Rev. *89*, 1065 (1953).
36. M. Tinkham and M. W. P. Strandberg. Phys. Rev. *97*, 937 (1955).
37. R. E. Trees. Phys. Rev. *71*, 102 (1947).

Chapter 16 SCATTERING FACTORS

ELECTRON AND X-RAY DIFFRACTION

The theory of electron and x-ray diffraction is discussed here, though briefly, because of the importance of the corresponding experimental values. Independently of more widely known applications (such as x-ray crystallography), diffraction experiments are valuable as they provide information on electronic density distributions.

The total scattered intensity is composed of two parts, coherent and incoherent. The coherent scattering is associated with processes in which the scattering system remains in the same energy state. The incoherent scattering involves transitions from one state to another as a result of the perturbation. The electron-nucleus radial distribution is related to the coherent scattering, whereas the electron-electron distribution can be determined from the incoherent scattering (see Bartell and Gavin, Jr. [1, 2]).

The total intensity of electrons or x-rays scattered from an atom in an initial state described by Ψ_m is given, using the notation of Bonham [6], by

$$I(\omega) = \sum_n p_n \langle \Psi_m | \mathscr{P}_n | \Psi_n \rangle \langle \Psi_n | \mathscr{P}_n^* | \Psi_m \rangle, \qquad (16\text{-}1)$$

where the summation extends over all those states Ψ_n for which the energy difference $(E_n - E_m)$ is smaller than the energy of the incident beam; ω is the scattering angle.

For electron scattering (in the first Born approximation), the parameters p_n are defined by the ratio, (k_n/k), of the amplitudes of the wave vectors of the outgoing and incident particles, with k_n defined by

$$k_n = [k^2 - (E_n - E_m)]^{\frac{1}{2}} \qquad (16\text{-}2a)$$

(with the energies given per unit of surface).

The operator $\mathscr{P}_n$, for electron scattering, is

$$\mathscr{P}_n = \sqrt{I_{c1}} \, [-N + \sum_j exp \, \{is_n \cdot r_j\}], \qquad (16\text{-}2b)$$

where the summation extends over the electrons in the system. The vector r_j is the position vector for the j-th electron and s_n represents the difference between the incident and scattered vectors, with amplitude

$$s_n = \{2k^2 - (E_n - E_m) - 2k[k^2 - (E_n - E_m)]^{\frac{1}{2}} \cos \omega\}^{\frac{1}{2}}. \quad \text{(16-2c)}$$

The classical intensity I_{cl} is defined by the Rutherford [31] scattering law.

For x-ray scattering (in a nonrelativistic formulation), the parameters p_n are defined* by $(\nu_n/\nu)^3$, with

$$\nu_n = \nu - (E_n - E_m)/h, \quad \text{(16-3a)}$$

ν being the frequency of the incident beam.

The operator $\mathcal{P}_n$, for x-ray scattering, is defined by

$$\mathcal{P}_n = \sqrt{I_{cl}} \sum_j \exp \{i(\kappa s - [(E_n - E_m)/h\nu]k_s) \cdot r_j, \quad \text{(16-3b)}$$

where the summation extends again over all the electrons in the system. The parameter $\kappa = 2\pi/\lambda$ represents the wave number of the incident electromagnetic wave (with wave length λ). The vector s represents the difference between the unit vectors in the incident and scattered directions, with modulus s equal to $2 \sin \omega/2$. The vector k_s, in the scattered direction, has a magnitude determined by the conservation of energy. The angle of scattering ω is twice the Bragg angle α. The classical intensity I_{cl} is defined by the Thomson [34] scattering law.

For coherent scattering, Eq. (16-1) reduces to

$$I_c(\omega) = \langle \Psi'_m | \mathcal{P} | \Psi'_m \rangle \langle \Psi'_m | \mathcal{P}^* | \Psi'_m \rangle = |\langle \Psi'_m | \mathcal{P} | \Psi'_m \rangle|^2, \quad \text{(16-4a)}$$

with the operator $\mathcal{P}$ defined by Eqs. (16-2b) and (16-3b), respectively, with $E_n - E_m = 0$. The intensity for incoherent scattering is then given by

$$I_i(\omega) = I(\omega) - I_c(\omega). \quad \text{(16-4b)}$$

The determination of the incoherent scattering for electrons and x-rays may involve certain approximations, introduced in order to use the closure relation when summing the contributions of the excited states. Bonham [6], however, has developed a rigorous treatment for the use of the closure relation, using a time-dependent formalism, as suggested originally by Lamb [25] and Zemach and Glauber [39, 40].

Bonham [6] has determined, to third order, the corrections to be added to the zero-order contribution for the total scattered intensity. The zero-order contribution can be written as

$$I(\omega) = \langle \Psi'_m | \mathcal{P} \mathcal{P}^* | \Psi'_m \rangle = \langle \Psi'_m | |\mathcal{P}|^2 | \Psi'_m \rangle,$$

with the operator $\mathcal{P}$ defined as for Eq. (16-4a). This equation represents

---

* They are the Breit-Dirac recoil factors. For more details see Breit [8].

the Morse expression for the total electron scattering or the Waller-Hartree [35] equation for x-ray scattering. The incoherent intensity is then given by

$$I_i(\omega) = \langle \Psi'_m | \, |\mathscr{P}|^2 \, |\Psi'_m \rangle - |\langle \Psi'_m | \, \mathscr{P} \, |\Psi'_m \rangle|^2. \qquad (16\text{-}5)$$

Bonham [6] points out that the corrections are important in the limit of low energy for the incident beam and for heavy atoms.

In addition, other corrections must be considered. These are, for example, the relativistic and polarization effects, but their importance has not been completely assessed. Exchange corrections have also been discussed within the framework of the Hartree-Fock approximation. (Details are given by Mott and Massey [28], Gjonnes [16], and Bonham [6].)

In the remainder of this chapter the discussion is centered on Eqs. (16-4a) and (16-5).

ATOMIC SCATTERING FACTORS FOR X-RAYS

Studies of the diffuse scattering of x-rays are important in investigations of such phenomena as order-disorder and lattice vibrations in crystals, and they are useful in studies of the properties of amorphous solids. Since these investigations involve intensity measurements, a knowledge of the x-ray scattering factors is needed. (The reader is referred to the work of James [21] for more details.)

The conventional notation for the preceding equations is

$$I(\omega)/I_{el} = F^2(\omega) + S(\omega),$$

$$I_c(\omega)/I_{el} = F^2(\omega),$$

$$I_i(\omega)/I_{el} = S(\omega),$$

where $F(\omega)$ and $S(\omega)$, defined from the general equations as

$$F(\omega) = \langle \Psi'_m | \sum_p exp \{i\kappa s \cdot r_p\} |\Psi'_m \rangle,$$

$$S(\omega) = \langle \Psi'_m | \, | \sum_p exp \{i\kappa s \cdot r_p\}|^2 \, |\Psi'_m \rangle - F^2(\omega),$$

are known as the coherent and incoherent scattering factors, respectively.

The scattering of x-rays has been treated by Waller and Hartree [35], Wentzel [36, 37], and Klein [24]. In particular, Waller and Hartree [35], approximating the total functions Ψ'_m by a single Slater determinant, have obtained

$$I/I_{el} = \langle \Psi'_m | \, | \sum_p exp \{i\kappa s \cdot r_p\}|^2 \, |\Psi'_m \rangle = N + \sum_j \sum_{k \neq j} (f_{jj}f_{kk}^* - |f_{jk}|^2),$$

$$(16\text{-}6)$$

with

$$f_{jk} = \left\{ \int \phi_j^*(p) \, exp \{i\kappa s \cdot r_p\} \phi_k(p) \, d\tau_p \right\} \delta(\eta_j, \eta_k), \qquad (16\text{-}7)$$

with N denoting the number of electrons in the atom. The summation over p extends over the electrons, whereas the summations over j and k extend over the spin-orbitals; η_j and η_k represent the corresponding spin functions.

Equation (16-6) can be rewritten as

$$I/I_{cl} = N + \left[\sum_j f_{jj}\right]^2 - \sum_j |f_{jj}|^2 - \sum_j \sum_{k \neq j} |f_{jk}|^2, \qquad (16\text{-}8)$$

with

$$\left[\sum_j f_{jj}\right]^2 = \sum_j |f_{jj}|^2 + \sum_j \sum_{k \neq j} f_{jj} f_{kk}^*.$$

The coherent scattered intensity is given by

$$I_c/I_{cl} = |\langle\Psi_m| \sum_p exp\ \{i\kappa s \cdot r_p\} |\Psi_m\rangle|^2 = |\sum_j f_{jj}|^2. \qquad (16\text{-}9)$$

Subtraction of this quantity in Eq. (16-8) yields the Waller-Hartree expression

$$I_i/I_{cl} = N - \sum_j |f_{jj}|^2 - \sum_j \sum_{k \neq j} |f_{jk}|^2 \qquad (16\text{-}10)$$

for the incoherent scattered intensity.

The incoherent scattered intensity increases from zero with increasing scattering angle, approaching the number of electrons in the atom. The coherent scattered intensity decreases from its maximum value of N^2 and approaches zero with increasing angle. However, the sum of the two values in any one direction is a constant, as shown by Wentzel [36, 37], for all values of the scattering variable.

The scattering vector for a spherically symmetric atom may be taken parallel to the polar axis since the scattering for such a system is independent of the atomic orientation. With this assumption, the operator involved in the calculation of the expectation values may be expanded by using the plane wave expansion

$$exp\ \{i\mu r\ cos\ \theta\} = \sum_p i^p [4\pi(2p + 1)]^{\frac{1}{2}} Y_0^{(p)}(\theta) j_p(\mu r)$$

for a wave traveling along the positive z-axis of the atom, where θ is the polar angle and μ stands for $4\pi(\sin \alpha)/\lambda$. The functions $j_p(\mu r)$ are the spherical Bessel functions, expressible in terms of the ordinary Bessel functions of the first kind and of order half an odd integer.

A detailed expression for the individual f_{jk} terms can be obtained when the orbitals are expanded,

$$\phi_i = \sum_q \chi_q c_{qi}$$

in terms of appropriate basis functions of the required symmetry. The following discussion is restricted to the case when the basis functions are Slater-type orbitals,

$$\chi_q = N_q R_q(r) Y_{m_q}^{(l_q)}(\theta, \phi),$$

with

$$R_q(\mathbf{r}) = r^{n_q-1} e^{-\zeta_q r},$$

where N_q is the normalization constant, n_q is the principal quantum number, and ζ_q is the orbital exponent. The functions $Y_{m_q}^{(l_q)}(\theta, \phi)$ are the normalized spherical harmonics, l_q and m_q being the quantum numbers that define the symmetry.

The individual f_{jk} terms are then given by

$$f_{jk} = \sum_p \sum_q \sum_t i^p [4\pi(2p+1)]^{\frac{1}{2}} N_q N_t c_{qj} c_{tk} \int R_q(r) R_t(r) j_p(\mu r) Y_0^{(p)}(\theta) Y_{m_q}^{(l_q)*}(\theta, \phi)$$
$$\times Y_{m_t}^{(l_t)}(\theta, \phi) \, r^2 \sin\theta \, dr \, d\theta \, d\phi; \quad (16\text{-}11)$$

the summation over q corresponds to ϕ_j and the summation over t to ϕ_k.

If we write the explicit expression for the spherical harmonics in terms of Legendre functions $P_m^{(l)}$,

$$Y_m^{(l)}(\theta, \phi) = (1/\sqrt{2\pi}) P_m^{(l)}(\theta) e^{im\phi},$$

and integrate over the azimuthal angle, Eq. (16-11) becomes

$$f_{jk} = (1/2\pi) \sum_p \sum_q \sum_t i^p (2p+1)[2/(2p+1)]^{\frac{1}{2}} N_q N_t c_{qj} c_{tk} \langle j_{pqt} \rangle \, \delta(m_q, m_t)$$
$$\times \int P_0^{(p)}(\theta) P_{m_q}^{(l_q)}(\theta) P_{m_t}^{(l_t)}(\theta) \sin\theta \, d\theta, \quad (16\text{-}12)$$

with

$$\langle j_{pqt} \rangle = \int R_q(r) R_t(r) j_p(\mu r) \, r^2 \, dr.$$

The notation of Condon and Shortley [10] for integrals over three associated Legendre functions, $P_m^{(l)}$, simplifies the writing of Eq. (16-12) to

$$f_{jk} = \sum_p \sum_q \sum_t i^p (2p+1) \, N_q N_t c_{qj} c_{tk} c^p(l_q m; l_t m) \langle j_{pqt} \rangle, \quad (16\text{-}13)$$

where m represents the common value of m_q and m_t. Values of the parameters $c^p(lm; l'm')$ are given by Condon and Shortley [10]. These parameters are proportional to the Clebsch-Gordan coefficients.

Because of the coupling of angular momenta, the summation over p in Eq. (16-13) is restricted to only those values (in steps of two) for which the triangular condition

$$|l_q - l_t| \leq p \leq |l_q + l_t|$$

is satisfied. The coefficients of the radial integrals $\langle j \rangle$ in the expansion of Eq. (16-13) are presented in Table 16-1 for s-, p-, d-, and f-type Slater functions; the normalization constants and the orbital expansion coefficients are not included.

If the electron distribution is no longer spherically symmetric (such as in the open shells of p or d electrons), the scattering depends on the orientation of the scattering vector. The evaluation of the individual f_{jk} terms is then carried out for an arbitrary orientation of s.

McWeeny [27] has shown that the scattering from a p orbital oriented in an arbitrary direction can be described by two factors, $f_\parallel$ and $f_\perp$, and the

Table 16-1 Coefficients of $\langle j_{pqt} \rangle$ in the Matrix Elements f_{jk} for s, p, d, and f Orbitals

q	t	COMMON COEFFICIENT	COEFFICIENT OF						
			$\langle j_0 \rangle$	$\langle j_1 \rangle$	$\langle j_2 \rangle$	$\langle j_3 \rangle$	$\langle j_4 \rangle$	$\langle j_5 \rangle$	$\langle j_6 \rangle$
s	s	1	1						
s	p_0	$i\sqrt{3}$		1					
s	d_0	$\sqrt{5}$			-1				
s	f_0	$i\sqrt{7}$				-1			
p_0	p_0	1	1		-2				
p_0	d_0	$3i/\sqrt{15}$		2		-3			
p_0	f_0	$\sqrt{3/7}$			-3		4		
d_0	d_0	1	1		$-10/7$		$18/7$		
d_0	f_0	$i/3\sqrt{35}$		27		-28		50	
f_0	f_0	$1/33$	33		-44		54		-100
p_{+1}	p_{+1}	1	1		1				
p_{+1}	d_{+1}	$3i/\sqrt{5}$		1		1			
p_{+1}	f_{+1}	$3\sqrt{2/7}$			-1		-1		
d_{+1}	d_{+1}	1	1		$-5/7$		$-12/7$		
d_{+1}	f_{+1}	$i\sqrt{2}/3\sqrt{35}$		18		-7		-25	
f_{+1}	f_{+1}	1	1		-1		$3/11$		$25/11$
d_{+2}	d_{+2}	1	1		$10/7$		$3/7$		
d_{+2}	f_{+2}	$i/3\sqrt{7}$		9		14		5	
f_{+2}	f_{+2}	1	1		0		$-21/11$		$-10/11$
f_{+3}	f_{+3}	1	1		$5/3$		$9/11$		$5/33$

angle between the orbital axis and the vector s. In this notation, $f_\perp$ is the scattering factor for a p orbital oriented perpendicular to s, with $f_\parallel$ being the scattering factor when s is parallel to the orbital axis. This method is not easily generalized to orbitals of higher angular momentum.

Freeman [13] has considered the problem of scattering from open shells from a group theoretical point of view. By a coordinate transformation of the one-electron functions, the vector s can be brought parallel to the z-axis in the rotated frame of reference. The transformation involves the rotation of the spherical harmonics from one frame of reference to another. The transformation of the spherical harmonics is complicated by the fact that the addition theorem for spherical harmonics is no longer satisfied. The results obtained by Freeman [13] for p orbitals are equivalent to the results of McWeeny [27]. In addition, Freeman [13] has derived formulas for the matrix elements involving d orbitals. The main disadvantage of this method is that the orbitals in the rotated system are no longer eigenfunctions of the orbital angular momentum operators.

Benesch and Malli [4] have developed a treatment of the scattering from nonspherical charge distributions, following the method outlined by Pohler and Hanson [29]. Instead of the plane wave expansion for a wave traveling in the positive z-direction, the expansion (see Edmonds [12])

$$exp\{i\mu r\, cos\,\theta\} = 4\pi \sum_{p=0}^{\infty} \sum_{m=-p}^{+p} i^p j_p(\mu r) Y_m^{(p)}(\theta, \phi) Y_m^{(p)*}(\theta', \phi') \quad (16\text{-}14)$$

for the wave in an arbitrary direction specified by the coordinates θ' and ϕ' is used. The average incoherent scattering factor for a nonspherical electronic charge distribution can be found by integrating (averaging) Eq. (16-10a) over all orientations of s,

$$\langle I_i/I_{cl} \rangle = N - \sum_j \langle |f_{jj}|^2 \rangle - \sum_j \sum_{k \neq j} \langle |f_{jk}|^2 \rangle. \quad (16\text{-}15)$$

For orbitals expanded again in terms of Slater-type functions, the individual scattering factors are defined by

$$f_{jk} = \sum_p \sum_q \sum_t i^p [4\pi(2p + 1)]^{\frac{1}{2}} N_q N_t c_{qj} c_{tk} Y_{m_q-m_t}^{(p)}(\theta', \phi') c^p(l_q m_q; l_t m_t) \langle j_{pqt} \rangle. \quad (16\text{-}16)$$

Multiplying Eq. (16-16) by its complex conjugate and integrating over θ', ϕ', we get

$$\langle |f_{jk}|^2 \rangle = (1/4\pi) \int |f_{jk}|^2 \, sin\,\theta'\, d\theta'\, d\phi' = \sum_p \sum_q \sum_t (2p + 1) N_q^2 N_t^2 c_{qj}^2 c_{tk}^2$$

$$\times [c^p(l_q m_q; l_t m_t)]^2 \langle j_{pqt} \rangle^2. \quad (16\text{-}17)$$

Comparison of Eqs. (16-13) and (16-17) shows an important difference concerning the parameters $c^p(lm; l'm')$. In Eq. (16-13) only those terms remain in the expansion for which $m_q = m_t$. This selection rule no longer holds in Eq. (16-17). This is a result of using the general plane wave expansion.

The scattering from an open shell is proportional to that from an equivalent closed shell, the constant of proportionality being the ratio of the occupation number of the open shell to that of the closed shell. This result is verified by determining the coefficients for any of the radial matrix elements using the selection rule and the values in Table 16-1 and comparing them to those found by summing the values given by Condon and Shortley [10], weighted by the appropriate occupation number and the value of $(2p + 1)$.

The only contributions to the coherent scattering factor, as a consequence of the assumption of spherical symmetry, arise from integrals involving the zero-order Bessel function, $j_0(\mu r) = (sin\,\mu r)/\mu r$.

The radial matrix elements remain to be evaluated in order to find the individual f_{jk} terms. The n-th order spherical Bessel function may be

Table 16-2 Atomic Factor $f_e^{(1)}$ (0) (in Å) for Electron Scattering for Positive Ions, Neutral Atoms, and Negative Ions[a]

SYSTEM	POSITIVE ION		NEUTRAL ATOM		NEGATIVE ION	
	State	$f_e^{(1)}(0)$	State	$f_e^{(1)}(0)$	State	$f_e^{(1)}(0)$
He			^1S	0.42		
Li	^1S	0.16	^2S	3.29	^1S	15.50
Be	^2S	1.16	^1S	3.05		
B	^1S	1.40	^2P	2.79	^3P	7.02
C	^2P	1.42	^3P	2.43	^4S	4.63
N	^3P	1.37	^4S	2.13	^3P	3.93
O	^4S	1.29	^3P	1.97	^2P	3.30
F	^3P	1.25	^2P	1.80	^1S	2.81
Ne	^2P	1.19	^1S	1.65		
Na	^1S	1.13	^2S	4.78	^1S	17.42
Mg	^2S	2.49	^1S	5.22		
Al	^1S	3.07	^2P	5.90	^3P	13.08
Si	^2P	3.57	^3P	5.69	^4S	9.60
P	^3P	3.69	^4S	5.34	^3P	8.58
S	^4S	3.67	^3P	5.14	^2P	7.58
Cl	^3P	3.65	^2P	4.87	^1S	6.75
A	^2P	3.57	^1S	4.59		
K	^1S	3.44	^2S	9.03	^1S	28.13
Ca	^2S	5.51	^1S	9.98		
Sc	^3F	4.04	^2D	9.37	^3F	19.62
Ti	^4F	3.93	^3F	8.85	^4F	19.18
V	^5D	3.81	^4F	8.38	^5D	18.31
Cr	^6S	3.67	^7S	6.70	^6S	17.49
Mn	^5D	3.63	^6S	7.60	^5D	16.28
Fe	^4F	3.55	^5D	7.25	^4F	15.55
Co	^3F	3.44	^4F	6.95	^3F	14.63
Ni	^2D	3.37	^3F	6.67	^2S	8.57
Cu	^1S	3.26	^2S	5.85	^1S	13.37
Zn	^2S	3.98	^1S	6.16		
Ga	^1S	4.45	^2P	7.21	^3P	14.78
Ge	^2P	5.09	^3P	7.33	^4S	11.41
As	^3P	5.38	^4S	7.24	^3P	10.80
Se	^4S	5.50	^3P	7.25	^2P	10.09
Br	^3P	5.62	^2P	7.14	^1S	9.39
Kr	^2P	5.65	^1S	6.97		

a. Values calculated from the analytical Hartree-Fock functions of Clementi [9] and Malli [26]. Strand and Bonham [33] have also calculated these values for neutral atoms.

reduced to a polynomial in r, involving sines and cosines. Using the recurrence formula

$$j_n(\mu r) = [(2n - 1)/\mu r]j_{n-1}(\mu r) - j_{n-2}(\mu r)$$

and the two basic relations

$$j_0(\mu r) = (sin\ \mu r)/\mu r, \qquad j_{-1}(\mu r) = (cos\ \mu r)/\mu r,$$

we can write the integral $\langle j_{pqt} \rangle$ as a combination of integrals

$$\int R_q(r)R_t(r) \begin{Bmatrix} sin\ \mu r \\ cos\ \mu r \end{Bmatrix}(1/\mu r)r^2\ dr = \int r^{n_q + n_t} e^{-(\zeta_q + \zeta_t)r} \begin{Bmatrix} sin\ \mu r \\ cos\ \mu r \end{Bmatrix}(1/\mu r)\ dr.$$

These integrals, written in general as

$$S_n(\mu r) = (1/\mu)\int r^n e^{-\zeta r}\ sin\ \mu r\ dr,$$

$$C_n(\mu r) = (1/\mu)\int r^n e^{-\zeta r}\ cos\ \mu r\ dr,$$

are defined (see Rustgi and Tiwari [30]) by

$$S_n(\mu r) = n!(\zeta^2 + \mu^2)^{-n-1} \sum_{p=1}^{n'} (-1)^{p+1}\binom{n+1}{2p-1}\zeta^{n-2(p-1)}\mu^{2(p-1)},$$

$$C_{n+1}(\mu r) = n!(\zeta^2 + \mu^2)^{-n-2} \sum_{p=1}^{n'} (-1)^{p+1}\binom{n+1}{2p-1}\zeta^{n-2(p-1)}\mu^{2(p-1)}$$

$$\times (A\mu^2 + B\zeta^2),$$

with

$$A = 2(p - n) - 3, \qquad B = 2p - 1,$$

$$n' = \begin{cases} \frac{1}{2}(n + 1), & \text{for } n \text{ odd,} \\ \frac{1}{2}n + 1, & \text{for } n \text{ even.} \end{cases}$$

The coherent and incoherent scattering factors for all atoms from He to Kr have been evaluated by Benesch and Malli [4] using analytical Hartree-Fock functions. (Mention must be made of the calculations of James and Brindley [22] by an interpolation procedure. Calculations have also been carried out by Berghuis et al. [5], Keating and Vineyard [23], Hurst, Miller, and Matsen [18], Freeman [13–15], Silverman, Platas, and Matsen [32], Hurst [17], Womack, Silverman, and Matsen [38], Bonham and Strand [7], Rustgi and Tiwari [30], Cornille and Roux [11], Pohler and Hanson [29], and others.) As an example the corresponding formulas for Kr are presented below in detail.

The summation terms in Eq. (16-15) are given* by

$$2(f_{1s}^2 + f_{2s}^2 + f_{3s}^2 + f_{4s}^2) + 6(f_{2p}^2 + f_{3p}^2 + f_{4p}^2) + 10f_{3d}^2$$
$$+4(f_{1s,2s}^2 + f_{1s,3s}^2 + f_{1s,4s}^2 + f_{2s,3s}^2 + f_{2s,4s}^2 + f_{3s,4s}^2)$$
$$+12(f_{1s,2p}^2 + f_{1s,3p}^2 + f_{1s,4p}^2 + f_{2s,2p}^2 + f_{2s,3p}^2 + f_{2s,4p}^2 + f_{3s,2p}^2$$
$$+f_{3s,3p}^2 + f_{3s,4p}^2 + f_{4s,2p}^2 + f_{4s,3p}^2 + f_{4s,4p}^2)$$
$$+20(f_{1s,3d}^2 + f_{2s,3d}^2 + f_{3s,3d}^2 + f_{4s,3d}^2)$$
$$+12(f_{2p,2p}^2 + f_{3p,3p}^2 + f_{4p,4p}^2 + f_{2p(0)3p}^2 + f_{2p(0)4p}^2 + f_{3p(0)4p}^2)$$
$$+24(f_{2p(2)3p}^2 + f_{2p(2)4p}^2 + f_{3p(2)4p}^2)$$
$$+24(f_{2p(1)3d}^2 + f_{3p(1)3d}^2 + f_{4p(1)3d}^2)$$
$$+36(f_{2p(3)3d}^2 + f_{3p(3)3d}^2 + f_{4p(3)3d}^2)$$
$$+\tfrac{100}{7} f_{3d(2)3d}^2 + \tfrac{180}{7} f_{3d(4)3d}^2. \tag{16-18}$$

The number of terms contributing, for an atom with s, p, and d electrons, is

$$\tfrac{1}{2}n(n+1) + \tfrac{1}{2}n_p(n_p + 1) + n_p n_d + 2n_d,$$

where n is the total number of occupied orbitals, and n_p and n_d are the number of occupied orbitals of p and d symmetry, respectively.

The coherent scattered intensity is given by

$$I_c = [2(f_{1s} + f_{2s} + f_{3s} + f_{4s}) + 6(f_{2p} + f_{3p} + f_{4p}) + 10f_{3d}]^2. \tag{16-19}$$

The notation used in Eqs. (16-18) and (16-19) is that of Keating and Vineyard [23], extended by Freeman [14], with

$$f_{ns} = \sum_q \sum_t N_q N_t c_{qns} c_{tns} \int R_q(r) R_t(r) j_0(\mu r) r^2 \, dr,$$

$$f_{ns,n's} = \sum_q \sum_t N_q N_t c_{qns} c_{tn's} \int R_q(r) R_t'(r) j_0(\mu r) r^2 \, dr,$$

$$f_{np} = \sum_q \sum_t N_q N_t c_{qnp} c_{tnp} \int R_q(r) R_t(r) j_0(\mu r) r^2 \, dr,$$

$$f_{np,np} = \sum_q \sum_t N_q N_t c_{qnp} c_{tnp} \int R_p(r) R_t(r) j_2(\mu r) r^2 \, dr,$$

$$f_{np(m)n'p} = \sum_q \sum_t N_q N_t c_{qn'p} c_{tn'p} \int R_q(r) R_t'(r) j_m(\mu r) r^2 \, dr, \, m = 0, 2$$

$$f_{ns,n'p} = \sum_q \sum_t N_q N_t c_{qns} c_{tn'p} \int R_q(r) R_t'(r) j_1(\mu r) r^2 \, dr,$$

$$f_{np(m)n'd} = \sum_q \sum_t N_q N_t c_{qnp} c_{tn'd} \int R_q(r) R_t'(r) j_m(\mu r) r^2 \, dr, \qquad m = 1, 3$$

$$f_{nd} = \sum_q \sum_t N_q N_t c_{qnd} c_{tnd} \int R_q(r) R_t(r) j_0(\mu r) r^2 \, dr,$$

$$f_{nd(m)n'd} = \sum_q \sum_t N_q N_t c_{qnd} c_{tn'd} \int R_q(r) R_t'(r) j_m(\mu r) r^2 \, dr, \qquad m = 0, 2, 4.$$

The summations extend over the corresponding basis functions.

---

* The writing of this and other expressions is simplified by grouping the terms that are similar with the common factor explicitly written. The new notation for the scattering factors is defined below. The subindices denote orbitals.

Benesch [3] has tabulated the values (from He to Kr) for the coherent atomic scattering factor, $F(\mu)$, the incoherent atomic scattering factor, $S(\mu)$, and the coherent scattered intensity, $F^2(\mu)$, for a wide range of values of the scattering variable, $\mu = (4\pi/\lambda) \sin \alpha$. These tables also include the sums of the squares of the diagonal and off-diagonal elements.

ELECTRON SCATTERING FACTORS

The electron scattering is amenable to a treatment* similar to the one described for x-rays. The corresponding operator is

$$\mathscr{P} = \sqrt{I_{cl}}\,(-N + \sum_p \exp\{i\kappa s \cdot r_p\}),$$

the classical intensity being different from the one for scattering of the x-rays.

Using the notation introduced above, we can write the total scattered intensity as

$$I/I_{cl} = N^2 - 2NF + F^2 + S = (N - F)^2 + S, \qquad (16\text{-}20)$$

and the coherent intensity is

$$I_c/I_{cl} = (N - F)^2. \qquad (16\text{-}21)$$

The coherent scattering factor, designated as $f_e^{(1)}(\mu)$, represents the square root of the quantity defined by Eq. (16-21). Benesch [3] also presents the values of this factor for the neutral atoms from He to Kr, including $f_e^{(1)}(0)$. By taking limits, we can obtain the expression

$$f_e^{(1)}(0) = \tfrac{1}{3}\langle r^2 \rangle. \qquad (16\text{-}22)$$

This expression, known as Ibers formula [19], has been rederived by Bonham and Strand [7].

Table 16-2 presents the values of $f_e^{(1)}(0)$ for a series of positive ions, neutral atoms, and negative ions. These values have been determined by Eq. (16-22), with the total expectation value $\langle r^2 \rangle$ determined from the analytical Hartree-Fock functions of Clementi [9] and Malli [26]. Values for the neutral atoms have also been given by Strand and Bonham [33] and Bonham and Strand [7].

REFERENCES

1. L. S. Bartell and R. M. Gavin, Jr. J. Am. Chem. Soc. *86*, 3493 (1964).
2. L. S. Bartell and R. M. Gavin, Jr. J. Chem. Phys. *43*, 856 (1965).

---

* See, for example, the work of Iijima, Bonham, and Ando [20] and Bartell and Gavin, Jr. [1].

3. R. Benesch. M.Sc. thesis, University of Alberta (1967).

4. R. Benesch and G. Malli. Unpublished results.

5. J. Berghuis, I. M. Haanappel, M. Potters, B. O. Loopstra, C. H. MacGillavry, and A. L. Veenendaal. Acta Cryst. *8*, 478 (1955).

6. R. A. Bonham. J. Chem. Phys. *43*, 1460 (1965).

7. R. A. Bonham and T. G. Strand. J. Chem. Phys. *39*, 2200 (1963).

8. G. Breit. Phys. Rev. *27*, 262 (1924).

9. E. Clementi. "Tables of Atomic Functions." IBM Corporation, San José, California, 1965.

10. E. U. Condon and G. H. Shortley. "The Theory of Atomic Spectra." The University Press, Cambridge, 1935.

11. M. Cornille and M. Roux. Compt. Rend. *259*, 1815 (1964).

12. A. R. Edmonds. "Angular Momentum in Quantum Mechanics." Princeton University Press, Princeton, N.J., 1957.

13. A. J. Freeman. Phys. Rev. *113*, 169 (1959).

14. A. J. Freeman. Acta Cryst. *12*, 261 (1959).

15. A. J. Freeman and J. H. Wood. Acta Cryst. *12*, 271 (1959).

16. J. Gjonnes. J. Phys. Soc. Japan (suppl. 2) *17*, 137 (1962).

17. R. P. Hurst. Acta Cryst. *13*, 634 (1960).

18. R. P. Hurst, J. Miller, and F. A. Matsen. Acta Cryst. *11*, 320 (1958).

19. J. A. Ibers. Acta Cryst. *11*, 178 (1958).

20. T. Iijima, R. A. Bonham, and T. Ando. J. Phys. Chem. *67*, 1472 (1963).

21. R. W. James. "The Optical Principles of the Diffraction of X rays." G. Bell & Sons, London, 1948.

22. R. W. James and G. W. Brindley. Phil. Mag. *12*, 81 (1931).

23. D. T. Keating and G. H. Vineyard. Acta Cryst. *9*, 895 (1956).

24. O. Klein. Z. Physik *41*, 407 (1927).

25. W. Lamb. Phys. Rev. *55*, 190 (1939).

26. G. Malli. Can. J. Phys. *44*, 3121 (1966).

27. R. McWeeny. Acta Cryst. *4*, 513 (1951).

28. N. F. Mott and H. S. W. Massey. "The Theory of Atomic Collisions." Oxford University Press, London, 1949.

29. R. F. Pohler and H. P. Hanson. J. Chem. Phys. *42*, 2347 (1965).

30. M. L. Rustgi and P. Tiwari. J. Chem. Phys. *39*, 2590 (1963).

31. E. Rutherford. Phil. Mag. *21*, 669 (1911).

32. J. N. Silverman, O. Platas, and F. A. Matsen. Acta Cryst. *13,* 539 (1960).

33. T. G. Strand and R. A. Bonham. J. Chem. Phys. *40*, 1686 (1964).

34. J. J. Thomson. "Conduction of Electricity through Gases." The University Press, Cambridge, 1906.

35. I. Waller and D. R. Hartree. Proc. Roy. Soc. (London) *A124*, 119 (1929).

36. G. Wentzel. Z. Physik *43*, 1 (1927).

37. G. Wentzel. Z. Physik *43*, 779 (1927).

38. C. M. Womack, Jr., J. N. Silverman, and F. A. Matsen. Acta Cryst. *14*, 744 (1961).

39. A. C. Zemach and R. J. Glauber. Phys. Rev. *101*, 118 (1956).

40. A. C. Zemach and R. J. Glauber. Phys. Rev. *101*, 129 (1956).

APPENDIX

Units and Constants

The fundamental constants presented below have been taken from J. W. M. DuMond and E. R. Cohen, "Physical Constants," in the *Fundamental Formulas of Physics*, edited by D. H. Menzel, Dover Publications, Inc., New York, 1960. (Through the permission of the publisher.)

Speed of Light

$$c = 2.99793 \cdot 10^{10} \text{ cm sec}^{-1} = 137.0373 \text{ au}$$

Charge of the Electron

$$e = 4.80286 \cdot 10^{-10} \text{ esu} = 1 \text{ au}$$

Mass of the Electron

$$m = 9.1083 \cdot 10^{-28} \text{ g} = 1 \text{ au}$$

Mass of the Proton

$$M = 1.67239 \cdot 10^{-24} \text{ g} = 1836.117 \text{ au}$$

Bohr Radius $a_0 = \hbar^2/me^2$

$$a_0 = 0.5291 \cdot 10^{-8} \text{ cm} = 0.5291 \text{ Å} = 1 \text{ au}$$

Bohr Magneton $\mu_B = e\hbar/2mc$

$$\mu_B = 0.92731 \cdot 10^{-20} \text{ erg gauss}^{-1} = 3.642 \cdot 10^{-3} \text{ au}$$

Nuclear Magneton $\mu_N = e\hbar/2Mc$

$$\mu_N = 0.505038 \cdot 10^{-23} \text{ erg gauss}^{-1} = 1.984 \cdot 10^{-6} \text{ au}$$

Fine Structure Constant $\alpha = e^2/\hbar c$

$$\alpha = 7.29729 \cdot 10^{-3}$$

$$1/\alpha = 137.0373$$

$$\alpha^2 = 5.32504 \cdot 10^{-5}$$

Avogadro Number

$$N = 6.02486 \cdot 10^{23} \, mole^{-1}$$

Planck Constant $\hbar = h/2\pi$

$$h = 6.62517 \cdot 10^{-27} \, erg \, sec = 2\pi \, au$$

$$\hbar = 1.05443 \cdot 10^{-27} \, sec = 1 \, au$$

Boltzmann Constant

$$k = 1.38044 \cdot 10^{-16} \, erg \, deg^{-1}$$

The Conversion Factors for Energy Values are

	cm^{-1}	ev	au
1 cm^{-1}	1	$1.2394 \cdot 10^{-4}$	$4.5550 \cdot 10^{-6}$
1 ev	$8.0683 \cdot 10^3$	1	$3.6751 \cdot 10^{-2}$
1 au	$2.1954 \cdot 10^5$	27.210	1

AUTHOR INDEX

Abragam, A., 5, 172
Allen, L. C., 66, 88, 92
Aller, L. H., 165
Altick, P. L., 90, 91
Amemiya, A., 69
Amos, A. T., 66
Anderson, H. L., 112
Ando, T., 185
Andrew, E. R., 107, 108
Anex, B. G., 76
Appel, K., 56
Arai, T., 141
Araki, G., 164
Armstrong, L., Jr., 117

Bacher, R. F., 116
Back, E., 116
Bader, R. F. W., 77, 130
Bagus, P. S., 56, 57
Baird, J. C., 171
Baker, J., 117
Baker, M. R., 100
Banyard, K. E., 98, 102
Bardeen, J., 74
Barnes, R. G., 136, 156
Barnett, G. P., 76
Bartell, L. S., 175, 185
Bates, D. R., 89
Baudet, J., 97
Beams, J. W., 96
Beck, J., 117
Benesch, R., 180, 183, 185
Berencz, F., 91, 101, 112
Berghuis, J., 183
Bernheim, R. A., 125
Bernstein, H. J., 103, 107
Bersohn, R., 84, 85, 88, 91, 92, 101, 111, 112, 125, 130, 136, 139

Berthier, G., 46
Berthold, I., 139
Bessis, N., 120, 137
Bethe, H. A., 47, 48
Biedenharn, L. C., 18
Bingel, W. A., 8, 74
Birss, F. W., 43, 45, 46, 54
Bjorkstam, J. L., 139
Blatt, J. M., 74
Blinder, S. M., 116, 118
Blume, M., 155, 156, 158
Bolza, O., 55
Bonham, R. A., 98, 110, 175, 176, 177, 182, 183, 185
Bordarier, Y., 117
Born, M., 8, 90, 158
Börnstein, R., 90, 91
Bratoz, S., 74
Breit, G., 47, 116, 117, 176
Brickstock, A., 47
Bright Wilson, E., 3
Brillouin, L., 81, 141
Brindley, G. W., 183
Brown, G. E., 47
Brown, T. H., 125
Browne, J. C., 162
Buckingham, A. D., 108
Buckingham, R. A., 65, 88
Buimistrov, V. M., 81
Burke, E. A., 124
Burns, G., 88, 92, 134, 137
Byers Brown, W., 54, 61, 80

Cade, P. E., 86
Callen, H. B., 147
Carlson, D. C., 74
Carpenter, R., 54

Casimir, H. B. G., 116, 117, 125, 131, 132, 134, 135, 155, 156
Chamberlain, G. E., 89, 90, 91
Chesnut, D. B., 124, 125
Childs, W. J., 117, 121
Chiu, L. Y. C., 158, 159, 160, 161, 162
Chiu, Y. N., 171
Chong, D. P., 54, 55
Christoffersen, R. E., 147
Clementi, E., 56, 57, 98, 110, 120, 136, 137, 169, 170, 182, 185
Cohen, E. R., 187
Cohen, H. D., 57, 88, 89, 90
Cohen, M. H., 123
Cohen, V. W., 126
Cole, R. H., 89
Coleman, A. J., 76
Condon, E. U., 14, 21, 25, 28, 157, 179, 181
Coolidge, A. S., 91, 99, 101, 112
Cooper, J. R. A., 52
Cooper, J. W., 110
Cornille, M., 183
Coulson, C. A., 85, 91, 101, 112
Crawford, M. F., 117
Crozier, M. H., 154

Dailey, B. P., 136, 137, 140
Dalby, F. W., 86
Dalgarno, A., 61, 66, 80, 81, 82, 87, 88, 89, 90, 91, 92
Darwin, C. G., 143
Das, T. P., 84, 85, 88, 89, 91, 92, 97, 101, 102, 111, 112, 125, 130, 137, 139, 140
Davidson, E. R., 74
Davis, L., 135
Dearman, H. H., 125
Derbyshire, W., 124
Dickinson, W. C., 109, 110
Dirac, P. A. M., 47
Doi, S., 87
Donath, W. E., 90
Dousmanis, G. C., 140, 169
DuMond, J. W. M., 187

Ebbing, D. D., 74
Eck, T. G., 125
Eckart, C., 29, 81, 119
Edmiston, C., 77
Edmonds, A. R., 14, 18, 19, 21, 131, 158, 181
Eisenberg, D., 102
Eliason, M. A., 76
Elliott, J. P., 152, 154, 157, 168
Ellis, D. M., 139

Ellison, F. O., 110
Epstein, P. S., 87
Epstein, S. T., 61, 66, 80, 82
Eshbach, J. R., 97
Essen, L., 89
Evans, L., 117

Fabry, C., 116
Fano, U., 52
Feld, B. T., 135
Fermi, E., 116, 122, 135
Ferrell, R. A., 118
Feynman, R. P., 130
Flygare, W. H., 102, 140
Fock, V., 43
Fogel, S. J., 76, 162
Foley, H. M., 118, 137, 138
Fontana, P. R., 160, 161
Fraga, S., 9, 43, 45, 46, 54, 70, 74, 76, 82, 85, 91, 98, 101, 109, 110, 112, 120, 121, 122, 123, 126, 134, 136, 137, 138, 147, 148, 152, 154, 155, 156, 169, 170
Freeman, A. J., 57, 92, 158, 180, 183, 184
Frey, D. A., 162
Froese, C., 56, 98, 109, 110, 147, 169
Frosch, R. A., 118
Fuller, G. H., 126

Garrod, C., 74
Gavin, R. M., Jr., 175, 185
Geltman, S., 89
Ghose, T., 102, 111
Ghosh, S. K., 100, 112
Gianinetti, E., 46
Gilbert, T. L., 46
Gjonnes, J., 177
Glauber, R. J., 176
Gold, L. P., 86
Gombás, P., 46
Goodings, D. A., 123, 136
Goodisman, J., 81, 82, 86
Goodman, L. S., 117, 120
Goudsmit, S., 116, 117, 119
Graff, G., 108
Grant, I. P., 47, 50, 51, 52
Gutowsky, H. S., 172
Guy, J., 88, 97, 99, 111

Hahn, E. L., 172
Hall, G. G., 66, 81
Hall, W. D., 91
Hameka, H. F., 64, 65, 99, 100, 101, 102, 111, 112, 162

Hanson, H. P., 180, 183
Harrand, M., 88
Harris, F. E., 91, 101, 112
Hartree, D. R., 43, 46, 56, 177
Hartree, W., 46, 56
Heilbronner, E., 47
Heine, V., 123
Heisenberg, W., 90, 164
Heitler, W., 85, 91, 101, 112
Herrmann, G., 139
Herzberg, G., 158
Herzfeld, K. F., 89
Higuchi, J., 124, 125
Hijikata, K., 141
Hirschfelder, J. O., 61, 66, 76, 80, 82, 85, 91, 101, 109, 112
Horie, H., 156, 157, 158, 165, 166, 169
Hornig, J. F., 109
Howell, K. M., 18, 19
Hoyland, J. R., 91, 99, 101, 112
Hubbs, J. C., 117, 120
Huo, W., 86
Hurst, R. P., 89, 90, 91, 97, 98, 183
Huzinaga, S., 45, 46
Hylleraas, E. A., 65, 112

Ibers, J. A., 185
Iijima, T., 185
Ingalls, R., 92
Ingold, C. K., 103
Innes, F. R., 165, 166, 168
Isaacson, L. M., 79
Ishiguro, E., 69, 88, 91, 97, 99, 101, 112, 135, 137, 138, 172, 173

Jaccarino, V., 25
Jahn, H. A., 18
James, H. M., 91, 99, 101, 112
James, R. W., 177, 183
Jarrett, H. S., 125
Johnston, D. R., 89
Jucys, A., 147
Judd, B. R., 18, 19, 21, 35, 117, 146, 152, 154, 165, 168

Kahalas, S. L., 140
Kaneko, S., 88, 89, 90, 91, 92
Karo, A. M., 73
Karplus, M., 54, 65, 66, 77, 79, 84, 85, 91, 97, 99, 101, 111, 112, 134, 137, 139, 140
Karreman, G., 125
Kato, T., 8, 69

Kayama, K., 124, 137, 138, 171
Keating, D. T., 183, 184
Keller, J. M., 74
Kelly, H. P., 87, 90, 109
Kelly, P. S., 57
Kern, C. W., 77, 111, 113, 134, 139, 140
Kerwin, J., 124
Ketudat, S., 139
Khubchandani, P. G., 92
Kikuchi, C., 117
Kimura, T., 69
King, J. G., 125
Kingston, A. E., 89, 90, 91
Kirkwood, J. G., 88
Klapisch, M., 117
Klein, O., 177
Klemperer, W., 81, 82, 86
Knight, R. E., 82, 110
Koide, S., 97, 99, 101, 112
Kolker, H. J., 65, 66, 89, 91, 99, 101, 111, 112, 140
Kolos, W., 85, 147
Kopfermann, H., 116, 130, 135, 156
Koster, G. F., 122, 135
Kotani, M., 69, 137, 138
Kovacs, I., 160
Krauss, M., 124
Kuppermann, A., 79
Kusch, P., 123, 125
Kutzelnigg, W., 74

Lahiri, J., 92
Laidlaw, W. G., 43, 46
Lamb, W. E., Jr., 109, 176
Lambe, J., 117
Landolt, H. H., 90, 91
Lauterbur, P. C., 108
Lefebvre, R., 45, 125
Lefebvre-Brion, H., 120, 137, 141
Lewis, J. T., 89
Lichten, W., 162
Lide, D. R., Jr., 86
Lin, C. C., 141
Linderberg, J., 76
Linnett, W., 85, 91, 101, 112
Lipscomb, W. N., 88, 101, 111, 113
London, F., 85, 91, 100, 101, 112, 113
Loudon, R., 154
Lovering, E. G., 108
Löwdin, P. O., 46, 56, 61, 74, 81
Lowe, J. T., 140

MacDonald, J. K. L., 39
Majumdar, S. D., 14

Malli, G., 9, 46, 47, 54, 56, 57, 70, 71, 82, 98, 109, 110, 120, 121, 122, 123, 126, 134, 136, 137, 138, 147, 148, 152, 154, 155, 156, 169, 170, 180, 182, 183, 185
Mannari, I., 141
Margenau, H., 3
Marrus, R., 117, 120
Martin, J. B., 110, 124
Marvin, H. H., 144, 156, 164, 167
Massey, H. S. W., 177
Matsen, F. A., 110, 183
Maxwell, D. E., 172
Mayer, J. E., 89, 90, 91
Mayer, M. G., 89, 90, 91
Mayers, D. F., 53
McConnell, H. M., 111, 124, 125
McGarvey, B. R., 109, 111, 112
McIntyre, H. A. J., 90, 92
McLachlan, A. D., 100, 125
McLean, A. D., 100
McNamee, J., 89, 90, 92
McWeeny, R., 47, 56, 74, 76, 100, 179, 180
Menzel, D. H., 187
Messmer, R. P., 74, 76
Michels, H. H., 89
Michelson, A., 116
Miller, J., 183
Miller, R. L., 46
Mizuno, Y., 74, 137, 138
Mizushima, M., 162
Möller, C., 141
Moore, C. E., 154, 155
Moser, C. M., 120, 137, 141
Mott, N. F., 177
Mukherjee, A., 125
Mukherji, A., 54, 92
Mulliken, R. S., 72
Murphy, G. M., 3

Nakamura, K., 74
Narasimhan, P. T., 98, 110
Nesbet, R. K., 45, 46, 123, 124, 140, 141
Nethercot, A. H., 141
Newell, G. F., 85, 135
Nielson, C. W., 34
Nierenberg, W. A., 117, 120
Nordsieck, A., 85, 112, 135
Nutter, P. B., 34

Obata, Y., 107
Obi, S., 18
Ohno, K., 47
Olive, J. P., 56, 57

Oppenheimer, J. R., 8, 158
Ormand, F. T., 110
Oudemans, G. J., 89

Pacault, A., 102
Pariser, R., 47
Parkinson, D., 88, 89, 90
Parr, R. G., 47, 66, 99, 101, 112
Pascal, P., 102, 103
Pauli, W., 116
Pauling, L., 3, 104, 113
Pekeris, C., 110
Peng, H., 88
Perot, A., 116
Peterson, E. A., 57
Phelps, D. H., 86
Platas, O. R., 136, 183
Plesset, M. S., 141
Pluvinage, P., 8, 39
Pochan, J. M., 102
Pohler, R. F., 180, 183
Pople, J. A., 46, 47, 88, 91, 100, 102, 103, 104, 107, 111, 113
Posener, D. W., 139
Pound, R. V., 139
Powell, F. X., 86
Pratt, G. W., 46, 123
Proctor, W. G., 172
Prosser, F., 76
Pryce, M. H. L., 172
Purcell, E. M., 172

Rabi, I. I., 107
Racah, G., 14, 18, 21, 24, 26, 27, 34, 52, 116, 117, 118, 120, 131, 132, 133, 143, 144, 152, 153, 165, 168
Rado, G. T., 118
Rainis, A. E., 57
Rajnak, K., 146
Ramsey, N. F., 85, 101, 109, 112, 121, 123, 138, 139, 171, 172, 173
Ransil, B. J., 74, 76, 77, 85, 91, 101, 112, 140
Rasiel, Y., 54, 55
Raynes, W. T., 171
Rebane, T. K., 100, 101
Regge, T., 15, 18
Richardson, J. W., 139
Robertson, R., 125
Roothaan, C. C. J., 8, 42, 43, 44, 45, 46, 47, 56, 57, 85, 88, 98, 110
Rose, M. E., 21, 158
Rosen, N., 85, 91, 101, 112
Rosenblum, B., 141
Rosenfeld, J. L. J., 77

Rotenberg, M., 18
Roux, M., 76, 183
Ruedenberg, K., 77
Runciman, W. A., 152, 154
Rustgi, M. L., 110, 183
Rutherford, E., 176

Sachs, L. M., 46, 57, 123
Saika, A., 111
Sakamoto, M., 141
Salop, A., 89, 90, 91
Salpeter, E. E., 47, 48
Sandars, P. G. H., 117
Sanders, W. A., 82
Satten, R. A., 125
Saxena, K. M. S., 98, 110
Saxon, D., 53
Schawlow, A. L., 116
Scherr, C. W., 82, 110
Schmeising, H. N., 46
Schneider, W. G., 103, 107
Schofield, P., 47, 88, 91
Schrödinger, E., 87
Schwartz, C., 66, 87, 89, 116, 117, 126
Schwinger, J., 14
Scrocco, E., 141
Segre, E., 135
Selwood, P. W., 102
Sharma, R. D., 171
Sharma, R. R., 92
Shortley, G. H., 14, 21, 25, 28, 43, 157, 179, 181
Shull, H., 74, 76
Sidwell, T. W., 98
Silverman, J. N., 107, 183
Simincic, Z., 57
Simon, A., 18
Simonetta, M., 46
Sinai, J., 77
Sinanoglu, O., 61, 65
Sinha, S. K., 100, 112
Skavlem, S., 112
Slater, J. C., 56, 88
Slichter, C. P., 111
Smith, D. W., 74, 76
Smith, K., 19
Smith, W. V., 136, 156
Snyder, L. C., 99
Spedding, F. H., 154
Steiner, E., 8, 69
Stephen, M. J., 111, 172, 173
Sternheimer, R. M., 88, 89, 90, 91, 92, 136, 137, 138
Stevens, R. M., 88
Stevenson, J. W., 19
Stewart, A. L., 61, 66, 80, 82, 89
Strand, T. G., 98, 110, 182, 183, 185

Strandberg, M. W. P., 97, 169, 171
Stroke, H. H., 125
Stungis, G. E., 57, 98, 110
Sundbom, M., 88, 89
Swirles, B., 56
Synek, M., 47, 57, 98, 110

Talmi, I., 168
Taub, H., 123
Taylor, H. S., 90, 91, 101, 109, 112
Ter Haar, D., 74
Terhune, R. W., 117
Thomson, J. J., 176
Tillieu, J., 97, 99, 111
Tinkham, M., 169, 171
Titchmarsh, E. C., 48
Tiwari, P., 110, 183
Townes, C. H., 116, 136, 137, 140
Trees, R. E., 116, 117, 119, 120, 132, 143, 151, 164, 165, 168, 169
Tuan, D. F. T., 66, 82
Tunstall, D. P., 108
Tycko, D., 137

Uehling, E. A., 139
Ufford, C. W., 147, 165, 166
Undheim, B., 65

Valdemoro, C., 46
Van der Waerden, B. L., 14
Van Vleck, J. H., 97, 99, 158, 165
Veillard, A., 46
Vineyard, G. H., 183, 184

Wahl, A. C., 76
Waller, I., 177
Wallis, R. F., 85, 91, 101, 112
Walnut, T. H., 79
Wang, S., 85, 91, 101, 112
Watson, R. E., 57, 92, 155, 156, 158
Weber, J. P., 47
Wehner, J. H., 124
Weinbaum, S., 85, 91, 101, 112
Weinstein, D. H., 39
Weiss, A., 139
Weiss, A. W., 8, 42, 57, 100, 124
Weiss, R., 86
Weissman, S. I., 124, 125
Weltin, E., 47
Wentzel, G., 87, 177, 178
Wharton, L., 86
White, R. L., 139
Whitman, D. R., 54

Wick, G. C., 108
Wigner, E. P., 14, 15, 18, 29, 69, 119, 131
Wikner, E. G., 88, 89, 92
Wills, L. A., 116, 117
Wolf, K. L., 89
Wolniewicz, L., 147
Womack, C. M., Jr., 183
Woodgate, G. K., 117, 134
Worcester, J. L., 117, 120
Wyatt, R. E., 66
Wybourne, B. G., 134, 146, 147, 154

Yamazaki, M., 141
Yanagawa, S., 143, 144, 145, 146
Yoshimine, M., 57, 89, 90, 91, 101
Yu, F. C., 172

Zabel, C. W., 135
Zacharias, J. R., 135
Zemach, A. C., 176
Zorn, J. C., 89, 90, 91

SUBJECT INDEX

angular momentum, coupling of, 13–19, 30–32, 159

bond maps, 76
Born-Oppenheimer approximation, 8, 158

Casimir operators, 146
chemical shift, 111
Clebsch-Gordan coefficients, 14–17, 24, 30, 32, 48, 51, 144, 159, 166–167, 179
closure rule, 176
cusp condition, 8, 70

density matrix, 74–76
deuteron, quadrupole interaction of, 140
Dirac spin matrix, 48

electric field gradient, 133, 135–140, 156
electric moments, 84–87
electron density distribution, at nucleus, 10, 69–71
  atomic, 72–73
  overlap, 73

Fermi contact interaction, 6, 68, 116, 122–124, 172
fine structure, 115–117

fractional parentage, coefficients of, 32–35, 153

gauge invariance, 100, 111

hamiltonian operator, terms of, 5–7, 96, 108, 118, 122, 130, 143–144, 150–151, 156, 160, 165–167, 171–172
Hartree-Fock functions, 56–57, 81–82, 85–86, 98, 110, 120–123, 126, 136–137, 147–148, 154–155, 169–170, 182–183, 185
Hartree-Fock limit, 41, 46
Hellman-Feynman theorem, 130
hyperfine structure, 115–117
hyperfine structure constant, a_c, 123
  a_d, 120–122, 134–135
  $B(J)$, 132–135

internal diamagnetic field, 107

jj coupling, 19

magnetic moment, electronic, 118, 122–123
  nuclear, 108–109, 116, 118–119, 122–123, 135
magnetic shielding constant, 109–112

9-j symbol, 19
nuclear quadrupole moment, 131–135

nuclear spin coupling, direct interaction, 7, 171
   electron spin coupled, 172–173

octopole coupling constant, 125–126
operator, angular momentum, 4, 12–13, 26–28, 48, 150–151, 153, 156–157, 160–162, 165–166, 171–173
   hermitian, 2, 11, 26–27, 29
   shift, 13, 26–27
   tensor (see *tensor operators*)
orbit-orbit coupling, 6, 143–148

Pascal constants, 102–104
perturbation theory, 61–67, 96–99, 108–109
polarizability, 87–92
population analysis, molecular orbital, 72–74
   natural spin-function, 74–76
proton hyperfine interaction, 124–125

quadrupole coupling constant, 133–135, 137–140

Racah coefficients, 18, 30–32, 35, 131–132, 145, 153, 161, 168
radial integrals, 144, 146, 167–170
relativistic theory, 47–54
ring currents, 104
Russell-Saunders coupling, 19, 119, 151, 153

scattering factors, electron, 185
   for x-rays, 177
self-consistent field theory, for intrinsic properties, 54–56
   nonrelativistic, 41–47

self-consistent field theory (*continued*)
   perturbed, 66–67
   relativistic, 47–54
seniority number, 152, 168
singularities, 8–9, 70
6-*j* symbol, 17–18, 119, 131, 157
spherical harmonics, 24, 29, 48, 144–146, 156–157
spin-orbit coupling constant, 151–155
spin-other orbit coupling, 6, 156–158
spin-own orbit coupling, 6, 150–156
spin-spin coupling, electron dipole-dipole, 6, 164–171
   nuclear (see *nuclear spin coupling*)
susceptibility, 95–104

tensors, direct product of, 25
   irreducible, 22–24
   scalar product of, 25
tensor operators, double, 165–167
   for composite systems, 31–32
   hermitian, 26
   matrix elements of, 27–32, 157, 166
   products of, 30, 119–120, 130, 144–146, 166–167
   reduced matrix elements of, 28–32, 35, 52, 120, 131–133, 146, 151–152, 161, 166, 168
   unit, 29, 144, 146
3-*j* symbol, 15, 17–18, 31–32, 48, 131, 156–157, 166

variational principle, 37–40
variation-perturbation method, 65–66, 99, 111
vector-coupling coefficients (see *Clebsch-Gordan coefficients*)

Wigner coefficients (see *Clebsch-Gordan coefficients*)
Wigner-Eckart theorem, 29–30, 119, 165–166